The Measurement
of Engineering Services

The Measurement of Engineering Services

W. F. J. FUSSELL, F.R.I.C.S., F.I.Arb.

E. & F. N. SPON LTD.

First published 1971
by E. & F. N. Spon Ltd.,
11 New Fetter Lane, London EC4P 4EE
Printed in Great Britain by
Butler & Tanner Ltd.,
Frome and London

SBN 419 10710 X

© 1971 W. F. J. Fussell
All rights reserved. No part of this publication may be produced, stored in a retrieval system or transmitted in any form or by any means, electronic, mechanical, photocopying, recording, or otherwise, without the prior written permission of the publisher.

Distributed in the U.S.A.
by Barnes & Noble, Inc.

Contents

	Foreword	*page* vii
1.	Introduction	1
2.	Background	4
3.	Cost planning	6
4.	Tendering procedures	17
5.	Contract arrangements	22
6.	Preliminaries and preambles	27
7.	The format of the bill of quantities	42
8.	The standard method of measurement	48
9.	Sanitary installation	77
10.	Cold water installation, fire-fighting, etc.	88
11.	Hot water installation	104
12.	Low pressure hot water heating installation	111
13.	Fuel oil installation	128
14.	Gas installation	132
15.	Compressed air installation	137
16.	Mechanical ventilation	145
17.	Supports and anchors	159
18.	Pipework and fittings for internal and external installations	164
19.	Thermal insulation	171
20.	Electrical installation	175
21.	Post-contract procedures	198

CONTENTS

Appendix 1. Glossary: mechanical and electrical *page* 201

Appendix 2. British Standards: mechanical and electrical 216

Appendix 3. Codes of Practice: mechanical and electrical 223

Appendix 4. Standard symbols and notations: mechanical and electrical 225

Appendix 5. SI units and equivalent magnitudes 239

Index 240

Foreword

Lord Esher, CBE, MA, D LITT, PP RIBA, FILA DIST TP

We may still enjoy a log fire in a country cottage, but elsewhere, in our offices and factories and schools and shops and hospitals, we have grown used to the idea of a totally artificial and mechanically controlled environment in terms of heating and cooling, lighting and ventilation, not to mention the provision and evacuation of supplies by pipe or wire. On average these mechanical services account for close on a third of the cost of modern buildings and more than a third of their acceptability as sound investments; for it is increasingly by their *performance* that our buildings are judged.

It is no secret that for many years architects have been unhappy about their moral responsibility to the client for this element in their buildings, both as to design and as to cost control. This book is concerned with the second of these aspects, in particular with the logical presentation of information to those who are required to submit tenders for the heating, lighting and ventilation elements of new buildings; which will not only assist the preparation of proper tenders, but will permit the client, architect, engineer and quantity surveyor to be fully conversant with the financial implications of decisions relating to mechanical and electrical services, both before the contract is let and whilst it is in progress.

The author is a partner in a widely known firm of London quantity surveyors who have for many years been editing various price books that have done a great deal to clear our minds, and it is therefore wholly appropriate that he should now produce a textbook which is suitable for students of all ages and seeks to foster a logical approach to tendering and the collation of cost information for engineering services in building. He has done a signal service not only to the professions concerned but to the next generation for whom we build – the people who matter.

Esher

CHAPTER 1
Introduction

Over 100 years has passed since the Bill of Quantities was first introduced as the basis for tendering in the construction industry and now it is used exclusively as the primary means by which contractors calculate their tenders for all building and civil engineering work including industrialized building.

It is now universally accepted by tenderers for construction works that the bill of quantities prepared by an independent firm on behalf of all those tendering not only ensures fair competition, but also substantially reduces overheads and estimating time. The discipline invoked by having to prepare a bill of quantities often ensures that design decisions are made well in advance of the commencement of construction work on site and thereby hastens the pre-planning activities. In addition to these benefits an additional spin-off is derived by the ability to analyse a priced bill of quantities systematically and thereby provide an essential weapon in the armoury of the cost consultants and also permit the information derived from analysis to aid the construction of planning networks.

It is the lack of cost control in mechanical and electrical services – or perhaps more correctly the lack of the necessary tools – which has highlighted the fact that this is today the only major sector of the construction industry where the bill of quantities prepared by an independent firm on behalf of tenderers is the exception rather than the rule. With the ever-increasing emphasis on technology it is not surprising that engineering services are assuming an ever-increasing significance particularly from the financial point of view, and the failure to develop sophisticated tendering systems for this sophisticated and vital part of the construction industry's present and future programme can only be described as a most serious omission which it is hoped will be partly remedied by this book.

However, it is one thing to see a need and another to fulfil it adequately. There is at present a lack of experience in the preparation of bills of quantities for mechanical and electrical services. This is true not only of the quantity surveyor whose task it is to prepare the bills, but also true of the mechanical and electrical consultant who is not accustomed to preparing the necessary detailed information.

The primary purpose of this book is to fill a very real gap in the data available to the student and to encourage the engineer and the quantity surveyor to venture into this field with some confidence. The aim is not to describe how to measure a length of pipe or enumerate a lighting switch, but to give sufficient background information to permit the proper interpretation of engineers' drawings for preparing a bill of quantities and also to enable the right questions to be posed to the mechanical or electrical consultant.

It is when the fittings (and sometimes the pipes and the plant) are not shown on the drawing that this book may come into its own, by suggesting to the student that, although not shown on the engineer's drawing certain fittings are always required in connection with a particular piece of plant. It is assumed that the student has knowledge of the techniques of quantity surveying and that he is familiar with the *Standard Method of Measurement of Building Works* and in particular sections S and T.

A further assumption is that the student has a working knowledge of the various means by which liquid, gas and electricity are introduced into a building, distributed, controlled and evacuated.

After the first two introductory sections the subjects of tendering procedure, contract arrangements and preliminaries and preambles are covered in order to make this book as comprehensive a document as possible on the whole subject of mechanical and electrical contracts. Section 7 contains recommendations on a suitable format and subdivision of M & E bills.

The sections which follow comprise detailed consideration of each of the specialist subdivisions of mechanical and electrical services and contain associated reproductions of the relevant clauses of the *Standard Method of Measurement*, 5th edition.

These sections cover: Plumbing and engineering installations
Sanitary installation
Cold water installation, fire fighting etc.
Hot water installation
Low pressure hot water heating installation
Fuel oil installations
Gas installation
Compressed air installation
Mechanical ventilation
Supports and anchors
Pipework and fittings for internal and
   external installations
Thermal insulation
Electrical installation

The last section is entitled 'Post contract procedures' and covers such matters as the issue of variation orders and post contract cost control.

In order to make the book a complete work of reference it has five appendices containing a glossary of some technical terms, lists of the relevant

British Standards and Codes of Practice, Standard symbols and notations, and a list of S.I. Units and equivalent magnitudes.

No claim is made as to the originality of the contents of this book. *Engineering Services in Buildings – Report No. 1 – A guide to tendering and contract procedure based on Bills of Quantities* – produced in 1970 by the RICS Engineering Services Technical Working Party, has been followed in part, also the *Code of Procedure for Selective Tendering*, published by the National Joint Consultative Committee of Architects, Quantity Surveyors and Builders in collaboration with the then Ministry of Public Building and Works.

In addition the author would like to acknowledge the most helpful criticisms of several firms of consulting mechanical and electrical engineers, the invaluable assistance given by Mr J. R. H. Wood of a well-known firm of copper tubing and fitting manufacturers. In addition he would like to record his appreciation for the constructive contributions from the RICS Engineering Services Technical Working Party under the Chairmanship of Alfred Ovenden, FRICS, and the help given by Mr S. J. Lane, FRICS, the Principal Lecturer/Department of Surveying at the Polytechnic of the South Bank. Valuable contributions were also given by the following members of the Author's own firm – D. J. Pearce, ARICS, D. A. Mott, A. E. Clark, P. C. Green, W. G. Ollis, MIPRP, H. Yeend and J. O. Davies.

CHAPTER 2
Background

The press-button controlled environment is no longer a figment of the science fiction writer's imagination – it is with us today.

In the last four decades dramatic growth has occurred in the volume and value of engineering services. During this time, the value of pipes and wires in the average private house has increased fourfold and now represents about 20% of the total construction cost. As noise and pollution of the air increases in our cities, so will the designers rely more and more on air-conditioning together with artificial light – windows in some buildings are already obsolete. If offices are to be air-conditioned, at least a quarter of the total cost of construction will represent the value of the necessary engineering services.

It is in the medical and scientific field that the most dramatic growth has taken place in recent years; the cost of engineering services in district general hospitals is in the region of 40% of the total construction cost and considerably in excess of this for some laboratory buildings. With future technological development it is inevitable that the volume and value of engineering services in buildings will continue to grow.

Since cost is now accepted as an essential ingredient of good design it can be argued that the systematic collation of cost information is an essential prerequisite to design.

The most satisfactory method of obtaining cost information is (at present) by analysing a priced bill of quantities, which has been prepared systematically from proper information and priced intelligently.

The preparation of bills of quantities, the drafting of preliminary and preamble clauses, the establishment of proper tendering procedures and contract arrangements, the elemental analysis of the bill of quantities and its application at the post contract stage in respect of variations and payments on account are all, therefore, essential parts of the design process, as they can all affect the cost of engineering services.

It is generally accepted that the bill of quantities is the lynch pin of pre- and post-contract cost control and that it is not possible properly to cost control in the financial vacuum that can exist when tenders are called for on the basis of drawings and specification alone. Experience has shown that the provision of a schedule of rates can often be more of a hindrance than a help because of the ease by which it can be manipulated by experienced operators.

The preparation of a detailed bill of quantities measured accurately in accordance with the Standard Method of Measurement and intelligently priced, is the only method by which sufficient information can be made readily available to the building owner's professional advisors for their study of cost control. The responsibility for the preparation of the bill of quantities should rest with either the engineer or the quantity surveyor, whoever has the necessary experience in that activity.

Some argue that tenders for engineering services cannot be prepared by the methods that have been traditional in the construction industry since the turn of this century; that is by measurement and pricing. It is claimed by some that it is not possible to build up a unit rate for many mechanical or electrical operations and for this reason, tendering via the medium of a bill of quantities is not acceptable. Spon's *Mechanical and Electrical Price Book* covers the complete spectrum of engineering costs, and in addition sets out a systematic approach to the problem of building up unit rates. When the advantages of having a bill of quantities at both the pre- and post-contract stages of construction are understood and appreciated, then it can be hoped that many of the present-day archaic methods of tendering for engineering services will cease.

CHAPTER 3
Cost planning

3.1
If it is accepted that cost is an essential ingredient of design – then the establishment of a realistic budget, cost limit, cost target, or yardstick (or whatever it is called) as early as possible is an essential prerequisite of the design process. Sophisticated procedures are in existence for establishing the cost limits for buildings financed by central government departments, such as schools, hospitals, universities, naval and military establishments and housing – no such procedures exist for establishing cost limits for power-stations, local government offices, prisons, etc. – neither do they exist in the private sector. Where there is no laid-down procedure for establishing a cost limit an 'order of cost estimate' is usually prepared on a square foot (square metre) or cost per unit basis (e.g. cost per bedroom in the case of hotels).

3.2
After discussions with the building owner, architect and engineer on the general nature of the proposed building, the order of cost estimate should be broken down, a proportion of the total cost being allocated to the following major elements which coincide with the RICS publication dated February 1970 BCIS (British Cost Information Service) 'brief form of cost analysis'.

Element 1 Substructure
2 Superstructure
3 Internal finishings
4 Fittings and furnishings
5 Services
6 External works
7 Preliminaries

Elemental analysis of previous contracts will indicate that the cost of these major elements (expressed as a percentage of the total cost of the project) lie between defined limits – the following indicates these limits for engineering services which includes the services listed under Sections 7.2.2 and 7.4 but excludes special services such as lifts, pneumatic tubes, etc. The percentages given are for the total cost of both the mechanical and the electrical services – analysis shows that the value of the electrical services is generally between 20% and 33% of the total cost of all the engineering services.

Type of building	Percentage of total cost
Offices – not air-conditioned	15 to 20
Offices – air-conditioned	25 to 33
Hospitals	30 to 45
Schools	20 to 30
Universities – residential	20 to 30
Universities – laboratories	40 to 60
Theatres	20 to 25
Art centre	15 to 20
Industrial (factories etc.)	10 to 20
Domestic	10 to 20

3.3

Flexibility in the cost of each major element (within the total cost limit) should be maintained, while the outline cost plan is being considered by the professional building team, i.e. architects, engineers, quantity surveyors, etc. The object of a cost planning exercise should always be to obtain a properly balanced building, which satisfies the building owner's requirements. To overspend on one element inevitably results in one or more of the other elements being deprived. After discussion between the architect and the engineer and the other consultants it should be possible to agree in general terms whether or not the financial allocation for the major elements will permit each consultant to design within these agreed limits.

3.4

At the outline design stage the architect should consider alternatives of shape, height, interior layout, and the use of materials. The engineer should consider alternative systems of mechanical and electrical installations in the light of the building owner's brief – and the agreed cost limit for engineering services. The quantity surveyor should at the same time carry out cost exercises on the various architectural and engineering alternatives, e.g. the cost differential between an oil-fired system requiring tanker access roads and oil storage and a gas-fired installation with the boiler in a roof level plant room. At the outline design stage it should also be possible for the various members of the design team to consider the various aspects of 'cost in use', with particular reference to maintenance and running costs. The design should now be sufficiently advanced to permit the 'order of cost estimate' to be refined a stage further and an 'outline cost plan' (see Fig. 3.1) prepared – in which each sub-element is (by reference to other elemental analyses) allocated a cost that relates to the outline specification given by the architect and engineer. Previous experience, elemental analysis from previous contracts plus a knowledge of the building owner's requirements, and the design attitude of the architect and the engineer, will all aid the allocation of costs in the outline cost plan.

Outline cost plan for proposed offices at...
as architect's drawings Nos...

Floor area – 244,958 square feet (22,757 m²)

BCIS Element No.	Element	Rate per sq. ft.	Rate per m²	£
1.0	Substructure	0·40	4·31	98,000
2.0	Superstructure			
	2.1 Frame	0·50	5·38	122,500
	2.2 Upper floors	0·67	7·26	165,300
	2.3 Roof	0·44	4·71	107,200
	2.4 Stairs	0·06	0·67	15,300
	2.5 External walls	1·85	19·92	453,200
	2.6 Windows and external doors	0·16	1·75	39,800
	2.7 Internal walls and partitions	0·38	4·04	91,900
	2.8 Internal doors	0·09	0·94	21,400
3.0	Internal Finishes			
	3.1 Wall finishes	0·07	0·81	18,400
	3.2 Floor finishes	0·16	1·75	39,800
	3.3 Ceiling finishes	0·48	5·11	116,400
4.0	Fittings and Furnishings	0·48	5·11	116,400
5.0	Services			
	5.1 Mechanical (see Fig. 3.2 for list of services)	0·96	10·36	235,800
	5.2 Electrical services	0·49	5·25	119,400
	5.3 Special installations	0·36	3·90	88,800
		7·55	81·27	1,849,600
	Preliminaries	0·60	6·50	148,000
	Contingencies	0·15	1·63	37,000
	Design Reserve	0·20	2·11	48,000
		8·50	91·51	£2,082,600

N.B. 1. Element No. 6 external works excluded
2. Allowance for increased costs excluded
3. BCIS Element No. – coincides with BCIS 'brief form of cost analysis' February 1970
4. Offices have extract ventilation system only

Fig. 3.1   Outline Cost Plan

3.5

At the time of preparation of the 'outline cost plan' it should be possible for the engineer to determine in broad outline the extent of the mechanical and electrical services that are required, and with the aid of experience and previous elemental analysis to break down the engineering services budget into an estimated sum for each service.

3.6

The building owner should be given the opportunity to decide on the degree of sophistication he requires for the engineering services and time taken to explain the environmental and financial aspects of each service. In the latter category fall – costs in use (capital and running costs) – letability, re-saleability, reliability, etc. A typical exercise that might be carried out at this juncture would be to compare the capital with the running costs of various installations; e.g. electric under-floor heating – capital cost of installation is low – running costs are high.

3.7

The costing process is further refined as the building owner's brief is expanded and the architect and engineer are able to locate more precisely the centres of concentration of engineering services, such as boiler houses, internal windowless rooms, kitchens, etc.

3.8

Although detailed engineering drawings are not likely to be available at the time the preliminary cost plan is being prepared by the quantity surveyor, it should be possible to ascertain from the architect and engineer the building owner's requirements under the headings given in section 7.2 (recommended order for billing mechanical services) and section 7.4 (recommended order for billing electrical services). The information provided by the architect and engineer should cover in broad outline the various means by which all required liquids, gases and electricity arrive at the proposed building, are distributed within to achieve the desired effects and how after use they are evacuated.

3.9

Providing the engineer is able to obtain sufficient information from the building owner it should normally be possible for him, after discussion with the architect, to indicate on preliminary drawings the following:

Mechanical

3.9.1   The location of all sanitary fittings and the main pipe runs of internal drainage to these.

3.9.2   The cold water installation.
3.9.3   The fire fighting installation.
3.9.4   The heat source and the main pipe runs of domestic and heated water.
3.9.5   The fuel supplies (oil, gas or electricity).
3.9.6   The gas installation.
3.9.7   The air conditioning plant and the main distribution pipework and ductwork.
3.9.8   Other specialist services such as compressed air, medical gases etc.
3.9.9   Other specialist pieces of plant such as incinerators, kitchen equipment, laundry equipment etc.

Electrical

3.9.10 The incoming mains, switchgear, transformers and other control gear.
3.9.11 The mains distribution and controls.
3.9.12 The distribution boards.
3.9.13 The sub-mains for power, light, etc.
3.9.14 Electrical appliances such as cookers, refrigerators, fans, heaters, etc.
3.9.15 Other lighting circuits such as external, emergency etc.
3.9.16 Other circuits for bells, clocks, fire alarms, burglar alarms, etc.
3.9.17 Telephone trunking.
3.9.18 Specialist circuits for lifts, motors, boilers, etc.
3.9.19 Lightning protection and earthing.

3.10

When these services have been indicated on the architect's drawings it should normally be possible to measure approximate quantities for each service and to price these using 'all-in' rates as is usual for approximate estimating. This will establish the approximate cost of each service. Lesser services, or services for which no information exists, can be assessed from available information and a lump sum allocated for them in the cost plan.

3.11

On completion of the preliminary cost plan (see Fig. 3.2) the total cost of the engineering services can be reviewed by the professional building team in the light of the overall cost, and appropriate design and specification adjustments can be made by the engineer if the total cost of any service element is above or below the sum allocated to that element in the outline cost plan.

Floor area: 28,434 m²

Note: The cost of each section should include:

(a) A proportion of Preliminaries
(b) General contractor's profit and attendance
(c) The value of builder's work in connection.

Building: Offices

					Mechanical services		Cost check		Summary	
Service no.	Sections	Cost of section £	£/m²	%	Date: £	Date: £	Date: £	Date: £	Date: £	
1	Internal drainage	9,200	0·32	3·79						
2	Rainwater pipes	4,100	0·15	1·69						
3	Sanitary installation	10,200	0·36	4·21						
4	Cold water service	8,100	0·28	3·34						
5	Hot water service	5,400	0·19	2·23						
6	Oil installation	1,800	0·06	0·74						
7	Heating installation	90,600	3·19	37·36						
*8	Extract ventilation	67,100	2·36	27·67						
9	Supply ventilation	10,600	0·37	4·37						
10	Fire fighting	11,800	0·41	4·86						
11	Servery counter to kitchen	3,000	0·11	1·24						
12	Kitchen equipment (including cold store)	7,000	0·25	2·89						
13	Tea making equipment (1 per floor)	500	0·02	0·21						
14	Water softener for kitchen	600	0·02	0·25						
15	Air conditioning for computer suite	12,000	0·42	4·95						
16	Gas installation (kitchen)	400	0·01	0·16						
17	Mains connection for last	100	—	0·04						
		£242,500	8·53	100						
	Main contractor's discount; 1/39 say	7,500	·26							
		£250·000	8·79							

Fig. 3.2 Preliminary Cost Plan

Total cost of element : £67,108					**Building:** Offices						
Rate per m² of floor area: £2·36					**Element:** Extract ventilation						
Quantity factor : —											
All-in unit rate : —					Cost check						
					Date:		Date:		Date:		
Item and description	Quant.	Unit	Rate	£	Quant.	£	Quant:	£	Quant.	£	
Car Park											
Ductwork and fittings	16581	kg	0·49	8,125							
Grilles	50	No.	5·00	250							
Extract fan including a/vs, flexible connections and supports, and flameproof starter	1	No.	—	750							
Silencer	1	No.	—	200							
Centralized services (extract ducts as if carpark)											
Ductwork and fittings	10204	kg	0·49	5,000							
Grilles	38	No.	6·00	228							
Extract fan including a/vs, flexible connections and supports, and flameproof starter	1	No.	—	550							
Silencer	1	No.	—	175							
				continued £15,278							

Fig. 3.3 Detail of extract ventilation sub-element (Service No. 8*)

General office extract

			continued	£15,278
Ductwork and fittings	53898	kg	0·59	31,800
Fire dampers	Item		—	2,000
Dampers 610 × 457 mm	100	No.	10·00	1,000
Ditto 2438 × 914 mm	1	No.	—	65
Ditto 2489 × 914 mm	1	No.	—	65
Ditto 2896 × 914 mm	2	No.	70·00	140
Ditto 3556 × 914 mm	2	No.	75·00	150
Extra grilles	640	No.	6·00	3,840
Provision for non-standard finish	Item	—	—	1,000
Extract fans including antivibration mountings, starter, flexible connections				
10·85 m³/s	2	No.	500·00	1,000
12·98 m³/s	2	No.	550·00	1,100
15·57 m³/s	2	No.	700·00	1,400
Ductwork in plant rooms	5	No.	250·00	1,250
Silencers	Item		—	1,000
			continued	£61,088

Fig. 3.3 Detail of extract ventilation sub-element (*continued*)

Item and description	Quant.	Unit	Rate	£	Cost Check						
					Date:		Date:		Date:		
					Quant.	£	Quant.	£	Quant.	£	
				continued £61,088							
Lobby extract to cores 1, 3, 5											
Ductwork and fittings (small sizes)	816	kg	0·98	800							
Fire dampers	20	No.	5·00	100							
Dampers	12	No.	4·50	54							
Grilles	20	No.	5·00	100							
Fans, flexibles, starters	3	No.	80·00	240							
Toilet extract (5 No. cores)											
Ductwork and fittings (small sizes)	1531	kg	0·98	1,500							
Dampers	34	No.	6·00	204							
Fire dampers	34	No.	8·00	272							
Grilles	100	No.	5·00	500							
For duplicate fans, c/o starters, flexibles	5	No.	150·00	750							
Kitchen extract											
Within the general office extract cost the volume of this area has been allowed. The extra over cost for kitchen extract is for individual fans, and for special extract hoods for which we include				1,500							
			Total	67,108							

Note: To this sub-elemental total should be added the following: 1. the general contractor's profit. 2. the general contractor's attendance. 3. the value of the builder's work in connection with the installation.

Fig. 3.3 Detail of extract ventilation sub-element *(continued)*

3.12

Having established the intitial content of the cost plan (see sections 3.9 and 3.10) the architect and the engineer should continue to refine their outline proposals until the scheme design and detail design is complete. The quantity surveyor should prepare comparative cost studies of alternative solutions and 'cost checks' on revisions to the major architectural and engineering elements. Close co-operation between all members of the professional building team is essential if pre-contract cost control is to be successful. Flexibility in design and specification in each element is also essential if the cost is to be contained within the total budget.

The cost plan in Fig. 3.2 has the facility for cost checks to be recorded and compared. The first page of the example cost plan is the summary for the mechanical services element, and represents the financial outcome of detailed measurement and pricing of services 1 to 17 listed on the summary. (The total of £250,000 shown on the summary is comparable with the preliminary allocation of £235,800 (element 5.1) in the outline cost plan (Fig. 3.1).)

3.13

Fig. 3.3 gives the detail of the extract ventilation sub-element (service No. 8 in the cost plan – Fig. 3.2) plus the measured approximate quantities, the outline specification and the 'all-in' rates used for the approximate estimate. As with the cost plan a facility to record the various 'cost checks' is provided.

3.14

When the cost checking processes reveal that the total of all elemental costs is within the budget – the architect, engineer and quantity surveyor should then be able to proceed with the preparation of production information, bills of quantities and other tender documents. In some instances the cost checking process can be a continuous operation culminating in the pricing of the draft bill of quantities by the quantity surveyor – elements found to exceed the budget can in these circumstances be reduced in cost by specification or quantity amendment.

3.15

The benefits of proper cost planning of engineering services, may therefore be summarized as follows:

3.15.1 Cost planning stimulates thought and may speed up decision making.
3.15.2 If proper techniques are used it can help prevent tenders differing substantially from the budget (i.e. too much above or below).
3.15.3 It helps avoid abortive work by architects and engineers occasioned by tenders exceeding the budget.

3.15.4 It stimulates co-operation between the various members of the professional building team and develops a financial consciousness that helps create a satisfactory elemental cost balance.

3.15.5 It should enable the building owner to know precisely what is included in the total budget for engineering services.

3.15.6 It forms a basis of comparison with other projects that have been properly cost planned, or for which there is an elemental analysis.

3.15.7 Cost planning is a logical prerequisite to the preparation of bills of quantities; both activities can assist in reducing the volume of design work that would normally be carried out by the engineer at the post-contract stage.

CHAPTER 4

Tendering procedures

4.1

The principles of the *Code of Procedure for Selective Tendering 1969*, prepared by the National Joint Consultative Committee (NJCC) in collaboration with the then Ministry of Public Building and Works are equally applicable for general building work and engineering services.

4.2

A precis of the code is given below:

Section 1 Foreword
- 1:1 Building owner is not obliged to accept the lowest or any tender.

Section 2 Introduction
- 2:1 Assumes that in the contract which will follow tendering, the use of a standard form of building contract.
- 2:2 Introduces the alternative methods of adjusting errors in bills of quantities, dealt with in Section 9 of the Code.

Section 3 The list of tenderers
- 3:1 The establishment of a short list of tenderers in accordance with the following scale:

	Size of contract	*Max. number of tenders*
1	Up to £10,000	5
2	£10,000 to £100,000	6
3	£100,000 to £1 million	8
4	£1 million plus	6

to this list should be added one or two names as reserves.
- 3:2 Short list prepared from
    - (a) Building owner's approved list
    - or (b) An *ad hoc* list of contractors of established skill, integrity, responsibility and proven competence, for work of the character and size contemplated.
- 3:3 Recommends that generally the firm offering the lowest tender should be awarded the contract.

	3:4 The tender documents should state the contract period – tenderers can offer alternative prices and time.
Section 4	Preliminary enquiries for invitation to tender – to give potential tenderers information about the project and to establish at an early date those firms who are prepared to submit a tender.
Section 5	Tender documents
	5:1 These should consist of
	(a) A formal invitation to tender covering the list of documents provided (bills, specification, drawings, etc.) and inspection of site.
	(b) A form of tender (2 copies) and envelope for return – tender forms should state clearly which alternative in Section 9 will apply in respect of pricing errors, and also the number of weeks that tender should remain open prior to acceptance.
Section 6	Time for tendering
	6:1 Four weeks for major projects.
	6:2 If bills of quantities are issued to tenderers in sections, the time for tendering should be calculated from the date of issue of the last section.
Section 7	Submission of priced bills of quantities
	7:1 The lowest tenderer should be expected to submit his priced bill(s) of quantities as soon as possible, but in any case within four working days of being asked to do so.
Section 8	Opening tenders and notifying results
	8:1 Only the bill of quantities for the lowest tender received should be examined – if for any reason this tender is withdrawn then the next lowest tenderer's bill should be examined. Unsuccessful tenderers should be informed immediately.
	8:2 An alphabetical list of tenders received should be circulated to all tenderers as soon as one has been accepted.
Section 9	Examination and correction of the priced bill(s)
	9:1 Priced bills under consideration are confidential.
	9:2 Two alternative methods of adjusting pricing errors in bills of quantities
	Alternative 1 – Tenderer informed of his errors and given the opportunity of withdrawing his tender.
	Alternative 2 – Tenderer informed of his errors and given the opportunity of altering his tender figure and correcting genuine errors and risking whether or not his tender is still lowest.
Section 10	Negotiated reduction of tender

TENDERING PROCEDURES

10:1 If tender exceeds building owner's budget, then an attempt should be made to negotiate with the lowest tenderer on the basis of revised drawings, specification, etc.

10:2 If these negotiations fail then similar negotiations should take place with the next lowest tenderer.

10:3 If these negotiations fail new tenders should be called for, using redrafted documents.

4.3

General comments on the above Code of Procedure for selective tendering in relation to tendering for engineering services.

Generally – The main points of procedure contained in the code are confirmation of recognized good practice applicable to both general building work and engineering services.

Section 3:1 Number of tenderers. It may be argued that the number of tenderers for category 2 and 3 could be reduced to 4 and 6 respectively for engineering services tenders.

Section 3:4 Competitive in price only. It is important that the tender time should be the same for each tenderer and that competition is on price alone – a base for comparison is thus established.

Section 5 Tender documents. Although the code only requires tenderers to receive general arrangement drawings indicating the general character and shape and disposition of the works, it is sensible and desirable for tenderers to be given as much information as possible by way of additional drawings and specifications (if these are available) to help the tenderer obtain quotations for plant and materials, and thereby ensuring that the tender is based on fact rather than surmise.

Formal invitation to tender. If the name of the main contractor is known then it is desirable that the engineering services tenderers should be informed. In addition it is recommended that tenders by services sub-contractors should be obtained on the *Standard Form of Estimate for Nominated Sub-Contractors* (published by the RIBA) for use in connection with the *Standard Form of Building Contract* produced by the Joint Contracts Tribunal.

Section 6 Time for tendering. It is generally desirable for engineering services tenders to be returned in advance of the main tender so that they can be checked, errors (if any) dealt with, and the contract sum related to the PC sums in the main bill of quantities.

Section 9 Examination and correction of the priced bills. Alternative 1 (commonly known as 'stick or bust') is the most usual alternative to adopt.

Alternative 2 is almost entirely the monopoly of central government.

4.4

Generally engineering services are covered by a PC sum in the bills of quantities for the main contract and in practice the architect and/or engineering consultant selects the firms who are to be invited to tender. Separate bills of quantities are then sent to the mechanical engineering and electrical engineering sub-contractors. Combined mechanical and electrical tenders are rarely called for. Once the main contractor has been instructed to accept (and has agreed to accept) the respective tenders and the sub-contractor has entered into a sub-contract with the main contractor, the respective mechanical and/or electrical firms become nominated sub-contractors under the terms of the Standard Form of Building Contract.

An alternative method of obtaining tenders for engineering services (thereby avoiding the contractual problems that result from nomination) is to include the quantities relating to mechanical and electrical services in the bills of quantities issued to the tenderers for the main contract. These tenderers would then obtain tenders for the engineering services from firms of their (or the consulting engineers) choice.

4.5

Two-stage tendering procedures can be used for engineering services. The primary object of this method of obtaining tenders is to establish, by means of a limited competition amongst three or four carefully selected firms, a basis for subsequent negotiation. The main advantage is that by adopting this procedure, time is saved at the pre-contract stage.

The mechanics of two-stage tendering are, briefly, as follows:

4.5.1   From the final cost plan an approximate bill of quantities is prepared, this bill should include conditions of contract, preliminaries and approximate quantities for all major items.

4.5.2   The approximate bill of quantities is priced by the three or four selected firms and the quantity surveyor generally recommends the firm that submits the most satisfactory tender (usually the lowest).

4.5.3   At the post-contract stage the engineer would develop his design – the quantity surveyor would produce a firm bill of quantities, price this at the rates included in the approximate bill referred to in section 4.5.1, and negotiate with the sub-contractor those items which did not appear in the original approximate bill, and at the same time (if need be) reductions would be introduced if it was found that the cost plan figure was likely to be exceeded.

4.6

The necessity to consider at a very early date the various aspects of tendering procedure outlined above cannot be over-emphasized.

4.7

It should be emphasized that the accuracy of the bill of quantities both from the point of view of quantity and description, is the responsibility of the professional engineer or quantity surveyor.

4.8

Quantities or descriptions should never be altered by tenderers, as this undermines the whole basis of competitive selective tendering – where all compete on the same basis. When inaccuracies in the bills are discovered before tenders are submitted, the engineer or quantity surveyor should be informed and he will then (if need be) notify all tenderers. Inaccuracies discovered (and proved) after a tender has been accepted will be the subject of an architect's instruction and will be adjusted (if need be) financially and included in the final account.

CHAPTER 5
Contract arrangements

5.1
Types of contract. The following are the usual engineering services contracts

5.1.1 A direct contract, in which the services contractor is employed direct by the building owner.

5.1.2 A direct contract, in which the installation of services is carried out by the main contractor with his own employees, as part of the construction works.

5.1.3 A nominated sub-contract between a main contractor and a services sub-contractor, originating from a nomination of the services sub-contractor by the architect or engineer. In this case the services are covered in the main contract bills of quantities by prime cost or provisional sums.

5.1.4 A sub-contract between a main contractor and a services sub-contractor of the main contractor's own choice, the services being measured in detail in the main bills of quantities.

5.2
Available forms of contract. The forms of contract at present in use are:

	Form of contract	*Purpose*
5.2.1	*Agreement and Schedule of Conditions of Building Contract* (private edition with quantities) issued by the Joint Contracts Tribunal (known as the *Standard Form of Building Contract*).	(*a*) Main contract between an employer (building owner) and a contractor for construction works consisting mainly of buildings, and usually under the supervision of an architect. (*b*) Main contract between an employer and an engineering services contractor for installation of services only, usually under the supervision of an architect.
5.2.2	As above but for use by local authorities.	As (5.2.1) (*a*) and (5.2.1) (*b*), but for local authority works.

5.2.3	*General conditions of contract and forms of tender, agreement and bond for use in connection with works of civil engineering construction* (known as the *ICE general conditions of contract*).	Main contract between an employer and a contractor for the construction of works of a civil engineering nature and usually under the supervision of a consulting engineer.
5.2.4	Model form A of general conditions recommended by the Institution of Mechanical Engineers, the Institution of Electrical Engineers and the Association of Consulting Engineers for use in connection with home contracts.	Main contract between an employer and an engineering services contractor for installation of services only, usually under the supervision of a consulting engineer. (This contract does not call for bills of quantities.)
5.2.5	*General Conditions of Government Contracts for Building and Civil Engineering Works, Form* CCC/Wks/1.	As (5.2.1) (*a*) and (5.2.1) (*b*) above, but for works sponsored by Central Government.
5.2.6	Sub-contract for use in conjunction with the *Standard Form of Building Contract* and issued by the National Federation of Building Trades Employers (NFBTE) and the Federation of Associations of Specialists and Sub-Contractors (FASS).	Sub-contract between a main contractor for the construction works and a nominated sub-contractor or sub-trader, usually under the supervision of an architect.
5.2.7	(Normal sub-contract for use with nominated sub-contractor) sub-contract for use in conjunction with the *ICE general conditions of contract*.	Sub-contract between a contractor for the construction works and a nominated sub-contractor or sub-trader, usually under the supervision of a consulting engineer.

5.3

Basic ingredients of good contract arrangements. Whether the contract be main or sub, the following must be clearly stated:

5.3.1 The conditions of contract.
5.3.2 The requirements for carrying out the works.
5.3.3 The conditions likely to be encountered on site.
5.3.4 The respective rights and obligations of the parties.
5.3.5 The description and measurement of the works.

5.4

Form of Agreement. The RIBA *form of agreement* between Employer and nominated Sub-Contractor should always be used in connection with the appointment of sub-contractors (nominated or otherwise) where the possibility of faulty design, delays or latent defects exist. The properly completed and signed form of agreement helps to protect the employer against these events.

5.5
The Sub-Contract.

5.5.1 Although the selection of a suitable form of sub-contract is the prerogative of the main contractor the NFBTE/FASS Sub-Contract (detailed in 5.2.6 above) is the form most commonly used for the appointment of a nominated sub-contractor under the terms of the standard form of building contract. The following points are relevant to this form of sub-contract when it is used on contracts where tenders were called for on the basis of bills of quantities. Suggested amendments to the standard form of sub-contract are given below with explanations, the amendments should be given in full in the tender documents under a heading of 'amendments to form of sub-contract'. If the form of sub-contract is incorporated in the sub-contract tender documents (this is recommended), the amendments could follow. Clauses in the standard form which are subject to amendment should, for clarity, be rubber-stamped 'see later amendments', and initialled by both parties. By adopting this method rather than manuscript alterations to the form of sub-contract, a neater and more professional looking document is produced and initialling each amendment by both parties is avoided.

5.5.2 Clause 2. (Execution of the sub-contract works.) This clause requires supplementing to coincide with the main contract clause number 1 which covers discrepancies between architect's drawings and the bills of quantities. A suitable clause might read:

'If the sub-contractor shall find any discrepancy in, or divergence between, the sub-contract drawings and/or specification of the works and/or bills of quantities, or if the foregoing documents and/or directions to the sub-contractor contain anything which the sub-contractor considers inconsistent with his contractual responsibilities and/or guarantees, he shall inform the contractor in writing immediately. The contractor shall obtain the architect's instructions and inform the sub-contractor in writing of these instructions.'

5.5.3 Clause 7. (Variations, etc.) This clause coincides with main contract clause number 2 and states the respective rights of main contractor and sub-contractor regarding instructions issued by the architect.

5.5.4 Clause 8(c). (Completion.) This clause coincides with main contract clause number 24 and covers loss or expenses by the sub-contractor.

5.5.5 Clause 10. (Sub-contract sum – valuation of variations.) In order to make this clause coincide with the main contract the following amendments are recommended:

Delete the sentence commencing 'The valuation of all variations authorized under Clause 7' continuing to the end of the clause, and to substitute the following additional paragraph:

'No variation required by the architect or subsequently sanctioned by him in writing shall vitiate this sub-contract. All variations authorized in accordance with Clause 7 hereof shall be measured and valued by the quantity surveyor who shall give to the sub-contractor and main contractor an opportunity of being present at the time of such measurement, and of taking such notes and measurements as they may require. The sub-contractor shall be supplied with a copy of the priced bills of variation not later than the end of the period of final measurement and valuation stated in the appendix to the main contract conditions, and the valuation thereof, unless previously or otherwise agreed, shall be made in accordance with the following rules:

(a) The prices in the sub-contract bills of quantities shall determine the valuation of extra work of similar character executed under similar conditions as work priced therein;

(b) The said prices, where extra work is not of a similar character or executed under similar conditions as aforesaid, shall be the basis of prices for the same so far as may be reasonable, failing which a fair valuation thereof shall be made;

(c) Where extra work cannot properly be measured and valued, the sub-contractor shall be allowed daywork prices at the rates, if any, inserted by the sub-contractor in the bills of quantities above-mentioned, or where none, at rates considered fair and reasonable by the architect, engineer and/or quantity surveyor. Provided that in any case vouchers specifying the time spent daily upon the work (and if required by the architect the workmen's names) and the materials employed shall be delivered for verification to the architect or his authorized representative not later than the end of the week following that in which the work has been executed;

(d) The prices in the above-mentioned bills of quantities shall determine the valuation of items omitted; provided that if omissions substantially vary, the conditions under which any remaining items of work are carried out the prices for such remaining items shall be valued under rule (b) of this clause.'

Effect shall be given to the measurement and valuation of variations by adjustment of the 'sub-contract sum'. These amendments qualify, but are not at variance with condition 5 of the *Standard Form of Tender*.

5.5.6 Clause 11. (Sub-contractor to apply for certificates of payment.) It is considered advisable that where the supply of as-fitted or record drawings, and of operating and maintenance manuals, forms part of the sub-contract, the sub-contract works shall not be considered complete and retention monies released until all such documents have been handed over to the architect (this requirement may require varying where the completion of the works are phased). A suitable amendment stipulating this requirement would be as follows:

Insert additional sub-clause:

'(j) Notwithstanding the foregoing, the sub-contractor shall not be entitled to any portion of the retention money above-mentioned until he has provided the architect with all as-fitted or record drawings, operating and maintenance manuals, and other particulars of the completed sub-contract works as stated in the bills of quantities.'

5.5.7 Clause 23. (Fluctuations.) This clause requires the selection of available alternatives in accordance with the *Joint Contracts Tribunal Practice Note No. 15*. It should be noted that the main contract and sub-contract may differ in this respect.

5.5.8 Sub-contractor's supervision. In sub-contract works of any magnitude it is recommended that the sub-contractor should be required to keep a qualified supervisor on the works. Additional clause should be inserted as follows:

'Clause 25. (Sub-contractor's supervision.) The sub-contractor shall keep upon the works at all times whilst the sub-contract works are in progress a suitably qualified resident engineer/foreman/working charge hand.'

CHAPTER 6

Preliminaries and preambles

6.1

Preliminaries

Order of billing preliminary clauses. There is no standard order for billing of preliminaries – the primary object is to make certain that the tenderer pricing the bill of quantities for engineering services is given the opportunity to price all items that have a financial implication. Preliminary clauses are sometimes given in full in the specification and sometimes in full in the bill of quantities – whichever method is adopted the following is a suitable bill layout in respect of the priceable headings.

Allow for any costs in connection with the following clauses in the sub-contract as issued by the NFBTE and FASS (see section 5.2.6)

Clause	
1	Notice of the main contract to the sub-contractor.
2	Execution of the sub-contract works.
3	Sub-contractor's liability under incorporated provisions of the main contract.
4	Insurance against injury to persons and property.
5	Damage by fire.
6	Policies of insurance.
7	Variations, etc.
8	Completion.
9	Defects, shrinkages, etc.
10	Sub-contract sum – valuation of variations.
11(*a*)	Contractor to apply for certificates of payment.
11(*b*)	Interim payments to the sub-contractor.
11(*c*)	Retention money.
11(*d*)	Dispute as to certificate.
11(*e*)	Right of sub-contractor to suspend execution of sub-contract works.
11(*f*)	Special interim payment.
11(*g*)	Final payment to the sub-contractor.
12	Sub-contractor's claim to rights and benefits under the main contract.

13	Contractor's right to deduction or set-off.
14	Right of access of contractor and architect.
15	Sub-letting of sub-contract works.
16(a)	Provision of water etc. for sub-contract works.
16(b)	Temporary workshops, etc.
17	Sub-contractor's use of scaffolding of contractor.
18	Contractor and sub-contractor not to make wrongful use of, or interference with, the property of the other.
19	Plant, tools etc. of sub-contractor.
20	Determination of this sub-contract by the contractor.
21	Determination of the main contract.
22	Wages and conditions.
23	Fluctuations.
24	Arbitration.

Note:
References to amendments and supplementary clauses (see sections 5.5.8) should follow here. In addition a list of the contract headings in the main bill of quantities should be given – preferably a copy of the conditions of main contract and appendix should accompany tender documents sent to tenderers.

It should be remembered that amendments to sub-contract (or contract) conditions must be incorporated with the conditions themselves, and should not be limited solely to references within bills of quantities as this would be contrary to Clause 12 of the standard form of building contract.

6.2

Preliminary clauses

6.2.1 Introduction. Preliminary clauses should describe the names of the parties to the contract, the names of the consulting engineers, the availability of the site, site conditions, access, restrictions on use of and access to site, the works and any special requirements for carrying them out, the tendering procedure to be adopted (i.e. normal or two-stage), the scope of the contract, the programme and all other general relevant information necessary to afford the sub-contractor a clear indication of the works and his obligations. As these clauses form part of the bills, they also form part of the sub-contract. A list of preliminary items applicable to main contracts is given in Standard Method of Measurement, section B.

6.2.2 Definitions. The following words and expressions used in the bill of quantities and in the documents relating to the contract should be defined:

Engineer
Main contractor

Contractor
Site
Works
Main contract
Contract
Bill of quantities
Approved
Directed
As described
A nominated sub-contractor
A nominated supplier
Plural
B.S. or B.S.S.
Tender drawings
Fix and fixing

6.2.3 Format. The preliminary clauses may be presented in several ways:
(a) written on plain paper at the front of the bills (i.e. immediately following the heading 'Bills of Quantities'), subsequent to which the clause headings only are repeated on single cash column bill paper for pricing purposes, or
(b) as a complete preliminaries bill, in which the full text of the clauses is written directly onto single-cash column bill paper.
The sample clauses given below (see section 6.3) are in the style of (a) above; they comprise a series of headings with a brief guide as to what should be described under each, and are not intended to be typical clauses suitable for copying. They are given in what is considered to be a good general order, but this may be re-arranged as required.

6.2.4 Establishment charges and profit. Establishment charges and profit may be (a) included in the prices for measured work (as Standard Method of Measurement, Clause A3(b)), (b) included as a lump sum preliminaries item, or (c) included as a percentage addition at the end of collections or summaries, and before any addition for cash discount (see section 6.2.5). The option is usually left to the estimator.

6.2.5 Main contractor's discount. Under the Standard form of building sub-contract, the main contractor is entitled to $2\frac{1}{2}\%$ cash discount if he pays the sub-contractor within fourteen days of his receiving an appropriate certificate from the architect. This discount may be (a) allowed for (in so far as any extra allowance is required) in the prices for the measured work, or (b) included by adding $\frac{1}{39}$ as the penultimate item in the summary (the discount thus applying to all other items contributing to the sub-contract sum). The choice is usually left to the estimator.

6.2.6 Identification of sub-contract documents. In order to identify the sub-contract properly it is suggested that the following should be printed on the fly-leaf of the bill of quantities: 'this is the bill of quantities referred to in the sub-contract dated . . .' This should be signed by both parties to the contract.

6.3
Typical preliminary clauses

6.3.1 Site. The precise location of the site of the works shall be given and described with special emphasis on any limitations of the working area, means of access, traffic restrictions, police regulations and the like. The sub-contractor requires all information concerning the site which affects his freedom of movement to and from the works, and the execution of the work.

6.3.2 Works. The sub-contractor should be given a broad outline description of the main contract and sub-contract works to be undertaken. Descriptions of main contract works may be quite brief, and descriptions of sub-contract works confined to single references to the individual services, e.g. rainwater installation, sanitary installation, cold and treated water installation, fire-fighting installation, etc. in the order recommended in sections 7.2 and 7.4 mentioning the situation of boiler house and plant rooms, and whether the service runs are concealed, in ducts or exposed.

The sub-contractor's attention may also be drawn in this clause to the need to comply with the requirements of various authorities (e.g. the gas, water and electricity authorities) and of the *British Standard Codes of Practice* etc. (see also section 6.3.32).

6.3.3 Other works. The sub-contractor's attention should be drawn to current or proposed works on adjoining sites. Reference should also be made to the necessity for co-operation with other contractors and sub-contractors. This is particularly necessary where access and facility of movement about the site may be affected. The sub-contractor may also be required to provide facilities to the employer's insurance company in their testing of materials and completed work during the currency of the sub-contract.

6.3.4 Definition of parties. It is desirable to inform the sub-contractor of the names and addresses of the interested parties in the main contract. These are usually the employer, the architect, various consulting engineers and the quantity surveyor. In the event of the main contractor not having been selected during the preparation of tenders for sub-contract works, the main contract may be defined as 'the contract, yet to be entered into, between the employer and the contractor for the construction works'.

It should be borne in mind that the engineers are not mentioned in the Standard Form of Building Contract or in its allied sub-contract, and that all engineer's instructions and drawings should be issued to the main contractor by the architect. Consequently, the term 'engineer' must be explained as meaning the architect or his authorized representative.

6.3.5 Sub-contract conditions. The sub-contractor's attention should be drawn to any particular form of sub-contract into which he will be required to enter with the main contractor (see section 5.2). If a copy of the document is attached, this should be stated. All other documents forming part of the sub-contract should also be mentioned. These would normally be the bills of quantities and the engineer's drawings listed therein. The engineer's specification may also be named as forming part of the sub-contract, but this is not essential, provided that all necessary contract information is fully covered by the other documents. These should incorporate or cross-refer to the specification information accordingly, including priceable items in the preliminaries and elsewhere in the bills of quantities as appropriate (see section 6.3.43). Where the specification is not a contract document, it may nevertheless be appended to tender documents to provide additional information. It should be noted that the exclusion of specifications as contract documents in the Standard Form of Building Contract does not necessarily exclude the specification from forming a legal part of a sub-contract. The procedure to be adopted in the case of a fluctuating contract should be clearly defined, including the compilation of the list of basic prices.

6.3.6 Main contract conditions – (generally required in both the main and the sub-contract). The sub-contractor should be given all relevant particulars of the main contract between the main contractor and the employer, as both the main contract and the sub-contract require the sub-contractor to observe, perform and comply therewith. The sub-contractor should be told where he may examine a full copy of the main contract, the details of the appendix to the main contract conditions relevant to the sub-contract being included in the *Standard Form of Estimate for Nominated Sub-Contracts* and incorporated at the beginning of the tender documents. It is recommended that for all mechanical and electrical services installations which include heating and cooling systems, the defects liability period in the main contract should be twelve months. The sub-contractor's obligations during the defects liability period should also be made clear – including remedying defects, indemnifying employer and main contractor and failure to remedy defects.

6.3.7 Insurances. The sub-contractor should be reminded of his insurance responsibilities in the sub-contract clauses (NFBTE/FASS sub-contract 4, 5 and 6) and told that the following insurances in the

Standard Form of Building Contract will have to be allowed for in his tender:

(a) For insuring, as Clause 19(1)(a) of the Conditions of the Main Contract against all risk of injury to persons as defined in Clause 18(1) of the main contract.

(b) For insuring, as Clause 19(1)(b) of the Conditions of the Main Contract against all risk of injury or damage to property as defined in Clause 18(2) of the main contract, including subsidence or collapse of adjoining property.

(c) For any other insurances that he may require.

6.3.8 Certificate valuation. The sub-contractor should be informed that a detailed approximate priced statement of work executed and materials supplied (supported by invoices) will be required by the main contractor at agreed times to enable interim payments to be made under Clause 11(b) of the sub-contract. It should also be made clear to the sub-contractor the method proposed by the quantity surveyor for inclusion of preliminaries etc. in interim valuations (normally on a percentage basis).

6.3.9 Labour on – costs. The sub-contractor should include all costs in respect of the following:

(a) National insurance contributions.
(b) Pensions.
(c) Annual and public holidays.
(d) Travelling time, expenses, fares and transport.
(e) Importing labour from other districts.
(f) Guaranteed time.
(g) Non-productive time and all other expenses in connection with overtime.
(h) Incentive and bonus payments.
(j) Selective employment tax (to be abolished April 1973).
(k) Any other disbursements arising from the employment and determination of the employment of labour.

6.3.10 Obligations of main contractor. All facilities and items of attendance to be provided by the main contractor free of charge to the sub-contractor should be described. These may include the provision of the following free of charge to the sub-contractor:

(a) General attendance on nominated sub-contractors as defined in Clause B30(b) of the Standard Method of Measurement of Building Work including allowance for the use of standing scaffolding, messrooms, sanitary accommodation and welfare facilities, providing space for office accommodation and for storage of plant and materials, providing light and water for the work.

PRELIMINARIES AND PREAMBLES 33

(*b*) Use of erected hoisting facilities.
(*c*) Protecting completed work.
(*d*) Use of three phase and single phase electric power for work essentially required to be carried out on site (cost of power consumed will be paid by main contractor).

Mention should also be made of the main contractor's responsibility for builder's work in connection, the sub-contractor's obligations with regard to setting out and the procedure by which the installation of all services (including internal drainage and electrical installation) will be co-ordinated should also be clearly defined.

Provision for these items is also given in the Standard Form of Estimate for Nominated Sub-Contractors.

6.3.11 Cleanliness of site and works. It should be stated that the sub-contractor shall (*i*) collect together all rubbish and debris as it arises for removal by the main contractor, (*ii*) remove all surplus materials and temporary works when no longer required, and (*iii*) thoroughly clean the whole of the sub-contract works at completion.

6.3.12 Taking over date. Engineering services sub-contracts are invariably completed before or at the same time as main contracts and it is therefore necessary to lay down precisely the respective parties' responsibilities under these circumstances. It is important that (unless he so wishes) the employer to the main contract should not be handed the responsibility of the services in advance of the remainder of the works. The sub-contractor should be told of this, and also that before the date of practical completion is established, the sub-contractor and the engineer shall together examine the works to ensure that these have been executed in accordance with the sub-contract.

It should also be stated that up to the date of completion of the sub-contract, the sub-contractor should supply such protection and supervision, either continuous or intermittent as may be necessary, to maintain the sub-contract works and materials in good condition, and that any loss or damage, other than risks covered by insurance Clauses 19 and 20 of the main contract, shall be made good by the sub-contractor at his own expense. After completion of the sub-contract works the main contractor assumes responsibilities for their protection.

Any requirements for operating the services or equipment before or after the date of completion of the sub-contract shall also be described under this heading together with the method of payment, or shall be cross referenced to sections 6.3.41.

6.3.13 Bills of quantities. The sub-contractor should be advised upon what basis the bills have been prepared, normally the latest edition of the Standard Method of Measurement, any departures from this should be specifically mentioned.

6.3.14 Overtime working. Where it is known in advance that certain work is to be executed wholly at overtime rates, the work should be given separately in the measured sections of the bills, and so described. Otherwise the extra cost of any overtime working which may be specifically required should be covered by a provisional sum, or allowed as an extra, in the final account. In either case the conditions of payment should be prescribed here.

6.3.15 Procedure. The sub-contractor should be informed (*a*) of any special requirements concerning set procedures for carrying out the works; or (*b*) that the works are to be carried out in accordance with a programme to be arranged between the sub-contractor and the main contractor; (*c*) of any specific period to be allowed between the notice to start and the actual start on site of the sub-contract works; (*d*) of his responsibilities for adjusting his labour force, ceasing and recommencing works, paying incentives and arranging for overtime to be worked if necessary to comply with the requirements of the main contractor's programme, all at the sub-contractor's expense.

6.3.16 Programme and progress chart. The sub-contractor should be informed of the main contract provisions in this respect. Progress charts may either be in accordance with the principles set out in the Ministry of Public Building and Works (now the Department of the Environment) pamphlet entitled *Programme and Progress* (published by HM Stationery Office), or by means of a critical path network. The period for their preparation and submission should be stated.

It should also be emphasized that the sub-contractor shall cooperate with the main contractor in the preparation of the programme and progress chart, and that after its submission and acceptance it should be adhered to and not varied without proper authority.

6.3.17 Employer's restrictions. The sub-contractor should be informed of any restrictions imposed by the employer on the main contractor under the main contract. Likely restrictions cover noise and various methods of its abatement, dust and its prevention and disposal, and access to existing or adjoining premises.

6.3.18 Sub-letting. The sub-contractor should be informed that subletting of any of the work will not be permitted without the architect's or engineer's permission. The sub-contractor should be asked to state at the time of tendering the percentage required to cover establishment charges and profit in respect of any sub-contract that is not part of a prime cost sum.

6.3.19 Notice boards and advertisements. Any special requirements of the main contract should be mentioned under this heading. If no such requirements are known, it is usual to state that notice boards and advertisements shall not be exhibited on the site without the written consent of the architect, subject to such conditions as he may prescribe.

6.3.20 Time and wage sheets. Reference to these is required only if the sub-contract is to be on a fluctuations basis, in which case the sub-contractor should be asked to keep sheets in the standard form set out in BS 1151, or in such other form as may be approved in advance by the quantity surveyor. The method to be adopted in preparing accounts for fluctuations in labour costs should be described. Method A (procedure 1) as described in the BS is usual.

6.3.21 Samples of materials. The sub-contractor should be informed that he may be required to submit for prior approval and without extra charge samples of certain materials proposed to be used in the sub-contract works.

6.3.22 Delivery of materials. As a safeguard against damage, the sub-contractor should be informed that materials should not be delivered to the site unreasonably in advance of the requirements of the programme. Any materials obtained prematurely should be stored off the site until such time as they are required for installation, any extra storage expenses being met by the sub-contractor. It should also be stated that the sub-contractor should give reasonable notice to the main contractor of his intention to deliver materials and plant to the site, so that the main contractor may fulfil any obligations which he may have in respect of unloading and storing.

6.3.23 Specific manufacturers. It should be stated that for parity of tendering, the sub-contractor should price the particular items of plant and equipment described in the bills or specification.

An appendix may be attached to the bills in which the sub-contractor may quote alternative proposals, together with their proposed effect on price.

It may be added that similar alternative proposals may also be submitted at any time during the sub-contract. In either case, any agreed changes would be subject to negotiation with the quantity surveyor, and treated as variations.

6.3.24 Purchase Tax,
6.3.25 National Insurances, Pensions, HWP, Redundancy payments, SET

It shall be stated that all these and similar items shall be deemed to have been included in the tender. For fluctuations in the rates, see the Joint Contracts Tribunal's Practice Note No. 15.

6.3.26 Sub-contractor's staff. It should be stated that all necessary surveying and office staff for measuring and keeping records should be provided by the sub-contractor.

6.3.27 Temporary offices for sub-contractor's staff. It should be stated if this is a sub-contract requirement, or at the sub-contractor's option. In either case it should be added that all necessary rates, taxes, heating, lighting, furniture, sanitary installations and attendance should be included, and that the office should be maintained and finally cleared away by the sub-contractor who should make good any associated damage. It should also be stated that the position of temporary offices shall be agreed with the main contractor and the architect before they are erected.

6.3.28 Temporary telephone. It should be stated if this is a sub-contract requirement, or at the sub-contractor's option. It should be stated that the cost of installation and charges for calls are to be met by the sub-contractor.

6.3.29 General plant and facilities. An item shall be given for the provision of all general plant including tools, mechanized plant, vehicles, fuel, attendance, protective clothing, consumable stores and the like, and for subsequently clearing away and making good on completion. Attention shall also be drawn to any facilities (e.g. storage and scaffolding) listed under the heading of 'Attendance' in Standard Method of Measurement Clause B20, and which are to be provided by the sub-contractor.

6.3.30 Local authority's requirements. Attention should be drawn to any such requirements, including the prior submission of any component for approval, testing, stamping or certifying. All costs in connection therewith and with collecting and returning to the site shall be met by the sub-contractor. (See also section 6.3.2.)

6.3.31 Notice prior to cover. It should be stated that the sub-contractor must give reasonable notice to the engineer/architect, whenever any works or materials are to be covered with earth, insulation etc. In default of so doing the sub-contractor shall if required uncover and afterwards recover such work and materials at his own expense.

6.3.32 British Standards and Codes of Practice. It shall be stated if copies of British Standards and Codes of Practice are required to be kept on the site.

6.3.33 Terms. The meanings of any special terms requiring definition and occurring frequently throughout the document should be given under this heading. For example, the term 'provisional' could be defined as 'subject to remeasurement or omission if not required', and the term 'approved' as 'approved in writing by the engineer/architect'.

6.3.34 Abbreviations. It should be stated that all abbreviations used in the tender documents are in accordance with BS 1991. No other abbreviations should be used, apart from recognized manufacturers' abbreviations.

6.3.35 Descriptions. If (as is common practice) items in the bills are described in the singular this should be stated, adding that the plural shall apply equally, where appropriate.

6.3.36 Percentage additions or deductions. It should be stated that if any percentage additions or deductions have been made to any items or collection of items in the bills, the same shall be similarly applied to the corresponding items or collection of items in the bill of variations.

6.3.37 Builder's work. It should be stated that all builder's work associated with the sub-contract will be carried out by the main contractor free of cost to the sub-contractor. To avoid ambiguity a comprehensive list of items comprising builder's work should be given. This would normally comprise excavation and reinstatement of earth, forming structural ducts, plinths, bases, manholes, sumps and pits; forming holes, slots or recesses in the fabric of the building and making good finishings in all trades; cutting and pinning or building in holderbats, pipe clips, hangers, brackets and supports and making good finishings in all trades; and all painting work other than manufacturers' priming or other protective coats. However, it should be noted that certain site painting is frequently made the responsibility of the mechanical engineering and insulation trades.

6.3.38 Sub-contractor's drawings. Whilst it is most unusual for the main contractor to be called on to provide drawings of any kind, in the case of services it is customary for consultants to produce schematic or outline drawings (usually referred to as 'tender drawings') only, and to require the sub-contractor to produce some or all of the following:

(*a*) Working (or detailed) drawings.
(*b*) Co-ordinated drawings.
(*c*) Manufacturers' drawings.
(*d*) Builder's work drawings.
(*e*) Variation drawings.
(*f*) As-fitted (or record) drawings.

In every case the availability of 'master' drawings or negatives prepared by the architect or consulting engineer should be made clear, likewise the required amount of detail, scale, size, method of execution, and the number and type of prints. Sub-contractors are usually required to submit their drawings to the architect or engineer for approval before the requisite prints are sent to the architect for distribution, and the associated materials ordered and work executed. Consequently the sub-contractor must allow time for this, and be responsible for ensuring that his drawings programme is fully in accordance with the main contract programme. The approval of the architect or engineer does not relieve the sub-contractor of his responsibility for the accuracy of his drawings, unless any such inaccuracies are due to inaccurate information provided by the employer, architect or engineer. The sub-contractor should allow both for the time and cost of revising his drawings as necessary as the work proceeds.

It is recommended that item (*f*) above be included here, rather than in the measured bills as might be implied by Standard Method of Measurement, Clauses S108 and T30.

It is advisable to clarify any division of responsibility for drawings concerning the work of further specialists (e.g. for sheet metal ductwork) employed in turn by the sub-contractor. This is particularly important when any such specialists' work is covered by PC or provisional sums (see section 6.3.42).

A typical preliminaries clause could read:

Drawings necessary for accurately and properly carrying out the works shall be prepared by the sub-contractor for the engineer's/architect's approval. The sub-contractor shall amend these drawings from time to time as necessary and shall be responsible for their accuracy.

Sufficient numbers of copies of the drawings shall be prepared for the engineer, architect, structural consultant, quantity surveyor, clerk of works, contractor and other sub-contractors whose work may be affected. All drawings shall be issued to the architect for distribution by him to those concerned and not issued direct by the sub-contractor.

All drawings shall be prepared in sufficient time to be approved and issued to suit the contractor's phasing and programme of work. Any delay in preparing these drawings resulting in extra costs for cutting away or reinstatement will be the responsibility of the sub-contractor.

The engineer's/architect's approval of these drawings does not relieve the sub-contractor from his responsibility in respect of the accuracy of these drawings providing any discrepancies, errors and omissions are not due to inaccurate information given in writing by the employer or engineer/architect.

The following drawings shall be prepared by the sub-contractor:

(*a*) Working or detailed drawings – in particularly congested areas such as plant rooms the sub-contractor shall submit detailed dimensioned layouts of plant, equipment and pipework (state number of copies required) and such other matters that the engineer/architect considers should be in greater detail than shown on his drawings.

(*b*) Manufacturers' drawings – before orders are placed for machinery, plant or equipment the sub-contractor shall submit to the engineer/architect for approval drawings (state number of copies required) showing construction and dimensions. No orders shall be placed before these drawings are approved.

(*c*) Builder's work drawings – drawings shall be prepared from gold-

PRELIMINARIES AND PREAMBLES

backed negatives which will be provided by the engineer to the sub-contractor at the time the sub-contract is placed. The sub-contractor shall add his requirements to these negatives and submit drawings (state number of copies required) for the engineer's/architect's approval.

(d) Variation drawings – the sub-contractor shall prepare all necessary variation drawings as (a) above, in addition to which he shall keep on site a full set of drawings altered in red ink as a running record indicating the variations authorized by the engineer/architect. These drawings shall be made available for inspection by the architect, engineer and quantity surveyor.

(e) As-fitted or record drawings – the sub-contractor shall prepare within 28 days of completion of tests one complete set of negatives on linen (state number of further copies required) showing the installation as fitted, together with any further information necessary for the efficient maintenance of the installation. (Add any particular information which should be included on these drawings.)

6.3.39 Sub-contractor's specifications, diagrams and schedules. Any requirement for the sub-contractor to produce specifications, diagrams and schedules shall be described, in which case the foregoing clauses governing sub-contractors' drawings apply similarly hereto.

6.3.40 Operating and maintenance instructions. The sub-contractor may be required to provide written and fully detailed instructions for operating and maintaining the plant and equipment fitted, in which case the foregoing clauses governing sub-contractor's drawings apply similarly hereto. The sub-contractor may also be required to supplement these instructions by demonstration and verbal explanation, in which case any specific requirement for the provision of sub-contractor's staff should be described, and due allowance made in the contract programme.

6.3.41 Drying out the building. If the sub-contract works are required to be completed in time for drying out the building this shall be described so that due allowance may be made in the contract programme. The cost shall be allowed for in accordance with Standard Method of Measurement, Clauses S105 and T28, as appropriate (see cross-reference in clause B23). It is recommended that this item be included here rather than in the measured bills, as might be implied by Standard Method of Measurement, Clauses S105 and T28.

An alternative to the above is to include a clause permitting the use of the central heating plant for the purpose of drying out the buildings by the main contractor and for testing, etc., by the sub-contractor.

A typical clause might be as follows:

The permanent central heating installation will be subject to a test programme and warm-up period some weeks prior to hand-over. This will be accepted as being the measures necessary to dry out and control the humidity of the works immediately prior to hand-over. The sub-contractor should allow for operating the plant during the test programme and warm-up period to pay all costs, excluding fuel, the cost of which will be met by the main contractor.

6.3.42 Prime cost sums within prime cost sums. The standard form of sub-contract does not provide for nominated suppliers or for further nominated sub-contractors to be employed in turn by the sub-contractor, and this procedure is not recommended (all such firms being employed direct by the main contractor). However, where employment by the sub-contractor happens to be advantageous, it is advisable to obtain and to adjust the 'second level' PC quotations on a net basis, in order to avoid the complication of discounts on discounts. All tenderers should be advised accordingly, and the sub-contract conditions duly endorsed. The customary items for profit and attendance apply as usual.

6.3.43 Engineer's specification. The engineer's specification should be appended to the tender documents, and the sub-contractor's attention drawn to this in order that all items of a preliminaries nature not otherwise provided for may be duly priced. For other aspects of the engineer's specification, see section 6.3.5.

6.3.44 Daywork. Daywork is not a true preliminaries item, but may be included here as a matter of convenience, in order to avoid a separate bill section. The conditions of payment should be prescribed and/or tendered for in one of the alternative forms laid down in the Standard Form of Building Contract, and it is open to choice whether:

(a) The daywork rates and percentages are monied out and extended into the cash column.
(b) Daywork is covered by provisional sums.

Alternative (a) is to be recommended as it establishes a precise basis for calculating the cost of dayworks.

It should be noted that certain standard daywork rules direct that rates and percentages are to include the main contractor's cash discount referred to in section 6.2.4. Where these rules are adopted daywork should be priced after any addition of the $\frac{1}{39}$ referred to.

6.3.45 Contingencies. It is recommended that engineering services sub-contracts should include their own contingency sums. Where the entire contingency sum for a contract is included in the main contract bills, this shall be stated.

6.3.46 Bill ending items. The following general items are classed as 'bill-

PRELIMINARIES AND PREAMBLES   41

ending' items for inclusion in the measured sections of the bills of quantities in accordance with Standard Method of Measurement, Clauses S100–S104, S106, S109, S122, T22–T25, T29, T31 and T43, and consequently should not be included in preliminaries bills (see chapter 7).

(a) Marking the position of holes, mortices, chases and the like. (*Note:* This is for physical marking out; for builder's work drawings, see section 6.3.38.)
(b) Drainage and refilling.
(c) Identification plates.
(d) Loose keys, tools and spares.
(e) Disconnecting and re-fixing equipment.
(f) Testing and commissioning.
(g) Protection and risk of damage.

However, it should be noted from Standard Method of Measurement, Clause S109, that the provision of fuel and electricity for testing mechanical engineering installations shall be given as a provisional or prime cost sum. Rather than enter a whole series of such sums (after each and every testing item), it may be preferable to include a single sum in the preliminaries bill. If preferred, this sum may include due allowance for fuel and electricity in connection with drying out the building, and temporarily operating the installation (see sections 6.3.41.)

6.4

Preambles

6.4.1   Specification-type descriptions. Preambles representing full descriptions of materials and workmanship follow the preliminaries. These same descriptions are frequently included mainly or wholly in the engineer's specification, in which case the necessary specification clauses should be repeated or referred to, as appropriate (see section 6.3.5). Where preambles include unqualified alternatives in the selection of materials and methods of working, the choice is at the sole discretion of the sub-contractor.

6.4.2   Supplementary rules of measurement. Trade preambles frequently include in addition supplementary rules of measurement, making clear the extent of work which is to be priced in individual unit (measured) rates. It may be preferable to list any departures from recognized methods of measurement referred to in section 6.3.13.

6.4.3   Presentation. Trade preambles may be grouped together before the measured sections of the bills, or interspersed with the measured work, as best suits the overall presentation.

CHAPTER 7
The format of the bill of quantities

7.1
Mechanical engineering services

The following are general recommendations on billing that will aid both tendering and cost analysis procedures.

7.1.1 Double cash columns. Traditionally, mechanical engineering estimators price labour and materials separately on double-cash column paper. Consequently it is recommended that mechanical engineering bills are printed accordingly with unheaded columns, the estimator being invited to use one or both columns as best suits his customary system of estimating. Where two cash columns are used, sub-traders' work and any items of plant are usually priced with the materials. Establishment charges, profit and cash discounts may be allowed for in the unit rates, or priced separately on summaries, as preferred. However, this double-cash column technique is not feasible where multi-cash columns are used for the separate pricing of different blocks (see section 7.2).

7.1.2 Colour coding. In order that mechanical engineering documents may be readily distinguished, it is recommended that covers and binding be colour-coded in red throughout the industry.

7.1.3 Plant rooms. In interpreting Standard Method of Measurement Clause S1(j) (i.e. the separate measurement of work in boiler house and plant rooms), it is considered that:
  (*a*) The term 'plant rooms' shall be deemed to include boiler houses, boiler rooms, plant rooms, tank rooms, and the like.
  (*b*) If this rule is to apply, it is logical that it should govern all mechanical engineering installations, not merely 'heating, ventilating and air-conditioning work'.

7.1.4 Explanatory notes. The inclusion of explanatory notes are recommended wherever bill items might be expected, but do not appear. Typical instances are as follows:
  (*a*) In insulation bills, where certain insulation has already been

described with items of equipment (e.g. on the grounds that this is factory-applied).
(b) Wherever appliances or items of equipment are either outside the contract, or billed elsewhere for greater convenience.
(c) Wherever cold-water supplies to hosereel systems cannot be divorced from the cold-water installation.
(d) To emphasize that pipework serving air-handling installations is given separately in the appropriate pipework installations.
(e) Following items for 'commissioning and testing', where certain items of equipment have already been described as commissioned and tested by the manufacturer or supplier.
(f) Wherever prime cost and provisional sums are collected together into another part of the bill.

7.1.5 Pre-fabricated work. Pre-fabricated assemblies should be measured in detail under descriptive headings. Alternatively (and notwithstanding the specific requirements of the Standard Method of Measurement), smaller assemblies might be enumerated complete.

7.1.6 Extra over items. It is recommended that:
(a) Extra over items in connection with piping are billed immediately following the particular type and size of piping in which they occur (i.e. written short).
(b) Extra over items in connection with ducting are billed following complete groups of associated ducts, so that similar extra over items are grouped together in ascending order of size (i.e. written long).

This difference in procedure reflects the likelihood of longer descriptions for purpose-made ducting fittings, a difference which may gradually disappear with the introduction of standard sizes, sections and fittings.

7.1.7 Protection. With reference to Standard Method of Measurement, Clause S122, it is considered that protection and risk of damage to engineering installations should be included as a priceable 'sundries' item. In the case of nominated sub-contracts and the like, a similar item should also appear in the main contract bills, the extent of responsibility being made clear in both cases. Attention is drawn to condition 9 of the RIBA and RICS Standard Form of Estimate for Nominated Sub-Contractors which reads as follows: 'Casing and Protection. The sub-contractor should be responsible for his work during execution but the main contractor shall be responsible for necessary casing and protection after the sub-contractor's work has been executed.'

7.1.8 Page signposting; list of contents. It is recommended that bills are preceded by lists of contents, and that the top right-hand corner of

44   THE MEASUREMENT OF ENGINEERING SERVICES

each page bears an abbreviated reference to the appropriate bill section. Although this point may be regarded as fundamental to quantity surveying in general, it is particularly important in engineering bills, in which it may be more difficult to locate particular items in the bills of quantities.

7.2

Recommended order for billing mechanical services

7.2.1 Sectionalization. Separate bills of quantities should be prepared for each building block (if this is practicable) followed by a separate bill of quantities for external works applicable to the whole scheme. An alternative is to bill each block separately using multi-cash column techniques.

7.2.2 Recommended order of installations. (*Note:* this order does not coincide with Standard Method of Measurement Clause S1 (*a*).)

Rainwater installation (plumbing service)
Internal drainage (separate section for each material)
Soil and ventilation pipes
Wastes and anti-syphonage pipes
Overflows
Sanitary fittings

Cold or treated water installation (may be classed as plumbing service)

(*a*) Mains
(*b*) Supplies to sanitary appliances, to special equipment, and to general purpose outlets.
(*c*) Supplies to heat source, to domestic hot water, and to space heating and cooling.

Fire-fighting installation

(*a*) Hosereel system
(*b*) Dry riser system
(*c*) Wet riser system
(*d*) Sprinkler system (dry or wet – alternate wet and dry)
(*e*) CO_2 system
(*f*) Foam inlets
(*g*) Hand appliances

Heated-water installation

(*a*) Heat source and mains
(*b*) Domestic hot water
(*c*) Space heating without fresh air
(*d*) Supplies to space heating with fresh air
(*e*) Supplies to elements in special equipment

THE FORMAT OF THE BILL OF QUANTITIES

Steam and condensate installation

(a) Heat source and mains
(b) Space heating without fresh air
(c) Supplies to space heating and cooling with fresh air
(d) Supplies to elements in special equipment

Fuel oil installation

Fuel gas installation

(a) Mains
(b) Supplies to heat source
(c) Domestic hot water (all-gas, i.e. using gas-operated terminal appliances)
(d) Space heating (all-gas, *i.e.* using gas-operated terminal appliances)
(e) Supplies to special equipment and to general purpose outlets

Refrigeration installation

(a) Supplies to air handling plant
(b) Domestic chilled water
(c) Cold rooms

Compressed air installation
Hydraulic installation
Chemical installation (stating the type)
Medical gas installation
Medical suction installation
Pneumatic tube installation
Vacuum cleaning installation
Refuse disposal installation
Air handling installation

(a) Ventilating
(b) Space heating without fresh air
(c) Space heating with fresh air – air heated locally
(d) Space heating with fresh air – air heated centrally
(e) Space heating and cooling with fresh air – air treated locally
(f) Space heating and cooling with fresh air – air treated centrally

Automatic control installation

Special equipment

(a) Incinerators and flues
(b) Kitchen equipment
(c) Laundry equipment
(d) Occupational equipment (i.e. associated with the occupation of the building occupier)

Supports and anchors common to more than one installation.

7.2.3 General notes applicable to paragraph 7.2.2.

(a) 'Mains' should include all work serving and common to the further sub-classifications listed below, but in practice no separate mains section is required where only one further sub-classification follows.

(b) Cold water feeds to domestic hot water systems should normally be billed with cold water installations, but similar feeds to heating shall normally be billed with the appropriate heating systems.

(c) Where closely inter-related, cold water supplies to hosereel systems may be given (if possible under a sub-heading) with cold water installations, in which case explanatory cross-reference notes should be included.

(d) Where final connections of blended and domestic hot water services to sanitary appliances and the like are executed by the plumbing trade, these should be given under a further sub-heading with cold water installations, in which case explanatory cross-reference notes should be included.

(e) Calorifiers and the like should be given with secondary installations wherever primary and secondary installations are billed separately.

(f) Any compressed air and hydraulic installations which are an integral part of fire-fighting or automatic control installations should be given therewith.

(g) Automatic controls should be given as a separate installation only where the items cannot with convenience be given with the various installations controlled.

7.3

Electrical engineering services

The following are general recommendations on billing that will aid both tendering and cost analysis procedures.

7.3.1 Double cash columns. The remarks made in paragraph 7.1.1 apply equally to electrical engineering.

7.3.2 Colour coding. In order that electrical engineering documents may be readily distinguished, it is recommended that covers and binding be colour coded in blue throughout the industry.

7.4

Recommended order for billing electrical services. (*Note*: This order does not coincide with *Standard Method of Measurement* Clause T1(a), but is based on the *Model Bill* produced by the Electrical Contractors' Association.)

Incoming services including high voltage switchgear, high voltage cables, transformers, sub-station equipment and control gear, and medium voltage cables up to but excluding main medium voltage switchgear.

Mains, all as shown on mains diagram including main medium voltage switchgear, sub-mains and distribution boards, but excluding final sub-circuits.

Power (*a*) Multi-phase (e.g. three phase busbar distribution and the like).
       (*b*) Single phase (e.g. low voltage socket outlets, spur units and the like).

Electrical appliances and apparatus including cookers, refrigerators, incinerators, fans, water heaters and the like.
General lighting and external lighting (each kept separately).
Emergency lighting.
Electric heating.
Trunking, ducting and cable trays.
Motive power and controls and other electrical work associated with mechanical and lift engineering services.
Telephones.
Clocks.
Sound distribution, bells, signals and the like installations (each kept separate).
Fire alarms.
Burglar alarms.
Earthing systems.
Lightning protection.
Special services including direct current installations, extra-low voltage installations, pressurized lighting and the like shall be so described and kept separate under appropriate headings.

CHAPTER 8

The standard method of measurement

Extract from *Standard Method of Measurement of Building Works* – fifth edition – metric – July 1968, which is produced by kind permission of the SMM standing joint committee.

The comments in italics that follow the extracts from the Standard Method of Measurement are by the author and do not form part of the official text of the SMM.

Various bodies have suggested that improvements could possibly be made to the SMM in the light of experience gained in both pre and post contract activities where engineering bills of quantities have been used. The author's comments in italics are (it is hoped) constructive and may possibly be relevant to future revisions to the SMM.

It should be noted that all deviations from the SMM must be stated in the tender documents if the Standard Form of Building Contract is to be used – if none are stated then the tenderers can rightly assume that the bill of quantities have been prepared strictly in accordance with the SMM.

SECTION S

PLUMBING AND ENGINEERING INSTALLATIONS

For General Rules see Section A

THE UNIT OF BILLING SHALL BE THE METRE

Generally to Section S

S1 (*a*) Work shall be grouped as follows and each group shall be given under an appropriate heading:

    (*i*)   Rainwater installation.
    (*ii*) Sanitary installation.
    (*iii*) Cold water installation.
    (*iv*) Hot water installation.
    (*v*)   Heating installation stating the type.
    (*vi*) Ventilating and air-conditioning installation stating the type.
    (*vii*) Fire-fighting installation.
    (*viii*) Hydraulic installation.

THE STANDARD METHOD OF MEASUREMENT 49

- (*ix*) Compressed air installation.
- (*x*) Gas installation stating the type.

See Section 7.2 and note minor additions to be the suggested grouping.

(*b*) Particulars of the following shall be given:

- (*i*) Any regulations, rules, byelaws and the like with which the installation is required to comply.
- (*ii*) Kind of material (e.g. iron; steel; asbestos-cement; lead; aluminium; zinc; copper; polythene; glazed stoneware; glazed fireclay).
- (*iii*) Quality of material.
- (*iv*) Gauge, thickness or substance of material.
- (*v*) Any tests with which materials, plant and equipment are required to comply.

(*c*) Assembling and jointing together the component parts of composite units and providing any necessary mating flanges and jointing materials shall be deemed to be included with the items concerned. Where composite units are supplied by the employer, particulars of the assembly work involved shall be given.

Mating flanges should be enumerated separately, flanged pieces of plant are often bolted directly together. To include mating flanges within the description would unnecessarily increase the unit cost.

(*d*) Patterns, moulds, templets and the like shall be deemed to be included with the items.

(*e*) Work required to be primed or painted before delivery to the site shall be so described.

(*f*) Work required to be galvanized, chromium-plated, stove-enamelled, porcelain-enamelled, anodized or otherwise specially finished shall be appropriately described stating whether treated before or after manufacture or assembly.

(*g*) The method of fixing and the provision of nails, bolts, nuts, holes, screws, plugs, shot-fired pins and the like shall be given in the description of the work. For bedding and pointing see Clause S116 hereof. For cutting and pinning see Clause S117 hereof.

(*h*) The nature of the background to which work is fixed shall be given in the description of the work. Backgrounds shall be grouped and described as follows:

- (*i*) Building-board (which shall be deemed to include hardboard, asbestos-cement sheet, plasterboard, fibreboard and similar materials which do not grip a wood screw).
- (*ii*) Timber (which shall be deemed to include softwood, hardwood, blockboard, plywood and similar materials which will grip a wood-screw when a lead-hole has been drilled).
- (*iii*) Metal-faced or composition-faced timber (which shall be deemed to include faced blockboard, faced plywood and similar materials which will grip a wood-screw when a lead-hole and a shank-clearance hole have been drilled.
- (*iv*) Brickwork, concrete or stonework (which shall be deemed to include reinforced concrete, blockwork and similar materials which require

50 THE MEASUREMENT OF ENGINEERING SERVICES

   plugging) irrespective of any plaster, glazed tiles, composition or other finish (excluding glass) to the surface.
   (v) Plain metal (which shall be deemed to include any metal which requires drilling).
   (vi) Glass (which shall be deemed to include any material resembling glass).
(j) Heating, ventilating and air-conditioning work within boiler-houses and plant rooms and such work external to buildings shall be so described in each case.

   All work within 'plant rooms' (and not just heating, ventilating and air conditioning work) and other work external to the building should be described. (See section 7.1.3.)

(k) Temporary work shall be so described. Removing temporary work and making good after shall be deemed to be included with the items.
(m) Adequate drawings and specifications of engineering installations shall be provided with the bill.
(n) For sheet metal roofing, flashings and linings to gutters see section M hereof.
(o) For sheet metal coverings to doors, bench-tops and counter-tops and linings to safes, cisterns and sinks see section R hereof.

Gutterwork

Gutterwork generally S2 (a) For rules relating to section S generally see Clause S1 hereof.
   (b) For steel gutters in conjunction with structural steelwork see section Q hereof.
   (c) Purpose-made gutters and purpose-made gutter-fittings shall be so described. Curved gutters shall be so described stating the mean radius.

Gutters S3 (a) Rainwater gutters (measured over all gutter-fittings, short running lengths and branches) shall be given in linear metres stating the type and the size.
   (b) Isolated lengths of gutter not exceeding 2 metres shall be enumerated stating the length, the grade, the type and the size.

Gutter-joints S4 (a) Providing materials, bolts, nuts, washers and everything else necessary for jointing shall be deemed to be included with the items of gutterwork.
   (b) Joints in the running length shall be given in the description of the gutter stating the method of jointing.
   (c) Joints of a special or ornamental character in the running length shall be enumerated as extra over the gutter in which they occur.

Gutter-fittings S5 Gutter-fittings (e.g. bends; elbows; junctions; stopped ends; nozzle outlets) shall each be enumerated separately as extra over the gutter in which they occur. Cutting and jointing the gutters to gutter-fittings shall be deemed to be included with the gutters.

   Bends and elbows, state if these are internal or external angles. Check that the degree of angles are standard

THE STANDARD METHOD OF MEASUREMENT 51

and if not, measure purpose-made. Note a drop end is available which is a nozzle outlet with a stopped end.

Gutter-supports   S6 (*a*) Lugs cast on to gutters, standard brackets and standard straps shall be given in the description of the gutter.
(*b*) Brackets and straps of a special or ornamental character shall each be enumerated separately.

Pipework

Pipework generally   S7 (*a*) For rules relating to section S generally see Clause S1 hereof.
(*b*) Purpose-made pipes and purpose-made pipe-fittings shall each be so described. Purpose-made curved pipes shall be so described stating the mean radius.
(*c*) Pipes and pipe-fittings which are wrapped, coated or lined by the manufacturer shall be so described stating the type of treatment.
(*d*) Pipework required to be temporarily fixed in position, dismantled for chromium-plating or other special finishing and subsequently refixed shall be so described.

Pipes   S8 (*a*) Pipes (measured over all pipe-fittings, short running lengths and branches) shall be given in linear metres stating the type and the nominal size. Classification shall be according to the purpose for which the pipes are installed (e.g. rainwater; overflow; waste; soil and vent; cold-water service; high-pressure cold-water supply; water main; cooling-water; condense-water; hot-water service; low-pressure hot-water heating; high-pressure hot-water heating; steam heating stating the pressure and the temperature; low-pressure hydraulic; high-pressure hydraulic; gas; compressed-gas; compressed-air; oil; smoke-flue; gas-flue).
(*b*) Flexible pipes and extensible pipes (measured as fully extended) shall each be so described.

Unnecessary to state 'classification according to the purpose for which the pipes are installed' as under S1(a), pipework is grouped under appropriate heading. (See 7.2.2.)

(*c*) Pipes laid or fixed in ducts, trenches and chases shall be so described in each case.
(*d*) Pipes embedded in floor screed shall be so described.
(*e*) Flow-and-return header pipes (except those forming an integral part of plant or equipment) shall be enumerated stating the length, type and nominal size of the main pipe, the number, length, type and size of each branch pipe, the method of construction and the method of jointing the ends.

Flow-and-return header pipe descriptions should also include for necessary supports. (See also comments on S12.)

Pipe-joints

S9 (a) Providing materials, heat, bolts, nuts, washers and everything else necessary for making joints in pipes shall be deemed to be included with the items.

(b) Joints and couplers normally necessary in the running length shall be given in the description of the pipe stating the method of jointing.

> *Where pipework is flanged throughout and all fittings are flanged, it is often more realistic to measure all flanges separately. This frequently occurs when there are a number of flanged fittings adjoining each other – these can be bolted together – thus considerably reducing the number of flanges required.*

(c) Ornamental joints, extra couplers (i.e. couplers required in addition to those normally necessary) and demountable couplers in the running lengths shall each be enumerated separately as extra over the pipe in which they occur.

(d) Reducing joints between pipes of different sizes shall be enumerated as extra over the main pipe in which they occur. Classification shall be as follows:

  (i) Soldered reducing joints.
  (ii) Welded reducing joints.

> *Soldered joints should state whether tafted, underhand or rolled. The classification should also include brazed joints.*

(e) Branch joints shall be enumerated as extra over the main pipe in which they occur. Perforating the pipe shall be deemed to be included with the items. Classification shall be as follows:

  (i) Soldered branch joints.
  (ii) Welded branch joints stating the type of branch (e.g. square; angle; sweep).

> *Soldered joints should state whether tafted or underhand. The classification should also include brazed joints. The size of the branch should also be stated.*

(f) Screwed sockets, tappings, bosses and welding-necks welded to pipes or flanges shall each be enumerated separately stating the size and kind of pipe or flange concerned. Perforating the pipe or flange shall be deemed to be included with the items.

(g) Special connections and special joints in pipes shall each be enumerated separately (except where given in the description of another enumerated item) stating the size and kind of pipe concerned and the method of jointing. Classification shall be as follows:

  (i) Connections between pipes of differing materials.
  (ii) Connections between pipes and appliances or equip-

THE STANDARD METHOD OF MEASUREMENT 53

ment stating the nature of the appliance or equipment.

(*iii*) Isolated joints which differ from those given in the description of the pipe (e.g. flanged joints in pipes having welded joints generally).

The specification sometimes requires flanged joints at 12 m intervals. To achieve this joints are alternately welded and flanged. In such a case it is advisable for welded joints to be included in the pipe description noting that flanges (at 12 m intervals) are enumerated separately.

(*iv*) Expansion joints stating the type of joint (e.g. bellows; sliding) and the amount of the expansion to be accommodated.

(*h*) Connecting ends of flue pipes to boilers, brick chimneys and the like shall each be enumerated separately stating the size and kind of pipe concerned, the method of jointing and the type of packing required.

Labours on pipes   S10   Labours on pipes (e.g. made bends; made springs; made offsets; beaded ends; ornamental ends) shall each be enumerated separately as extra over the pipe on which they occur.

The following 'sets' are found in practice:

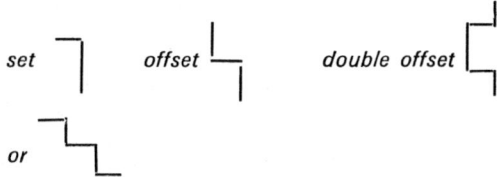

Pipe-fittings   S11 (*a*) Pipe-fittings (e.g. bends; springs; swannecks; offsets; Y-junctions; double Y-junctions; shoes; blank flanges; puddle flanges; bushes; reducers; elbows; twin elbows; tees; crosses; unions) shall each be enumerated separately as extra over the pipes in which they occur. Cutting and jointing the pipes to such fittings shall be deemed to be included with the items.

All fittings should be kept separate and described fully in order that they can be properly priced. e.g.
(i) *45° and 90° welding bends.*
(ii) *Eccentric and concentric reducers, the sizes of both ends should be stated.*
(iii) *Tees should be described as swept, angle, pitcher, square, etc. and give the size of all three ends in order that the necessary reducers can be included when pricing. Alternatively measure the tee and enumerate the reducers required.*

(iv) *Unions should state the type of seatings, etc., i.e. Navy pattern union with bronze seats.*
(v) *Blank flanges should state the table of BS10 to which they are flanged.*
(vi) *Hexagonal nipples should be enumerated; a barrel nipple is deemed to be a joint in the running length.*

(b) Expansion loops shall be enumerated stating the limiting dimensions and the amount of the expansion to be accommodated.

Pipe-supports S12 (a) Particulars of the method of fixing shall be given in the description of pipe-supports as Clause S1(g) hereof. Cutting and pinning ends of pipe-supports shall be given as Clause S117 hereof.

(b) Ears cast, soldered or welded on to pipes shall be given in the description of the pipe.

Ears can also be brazed on.

(c) Standard pipe-supports (e.g. clips; saddles; pipehooks; holderbats) shall be given in the description of pipes not exceeding 55 mm bore.
(d) Components for supporting pipes (e.g. clips; saddles; pipehooks; holderbats; brackets; rollers; chairs and hangers; back-plates and girder-lugs; anchors; guides) shall each be enumerated separately (except as provided in paragraph (c) of this clause) stating the size of the component and the size and kind of pipe. Spring-compensated components shall be so described stating the loading and the movement to be accommodated.
(e) Pipe-stays and collars shall be enumerated stating the size and kind of pipe and the length of the stay.
(f) Pylons and other pipe-supports shall be given as Clause S119 hereof.

These clauses are exceedingly difficult to comply with when measuring, as the engineer usually produces separate drawings for each service. It is therefore difficult to establish exactly which pipes and which ventilation ducts are together horizontally or vertically. For this reason it is sometimes nearly impossible to establish whether a multiple pipe bracket should be used or if each service should be independently supported. Assuming it was possible to determine which pipes and ducts did require multiple supports, it would be difficult from the engineer's drawings to establish whether they were to be supported side by side or one above the other. It would also be difficult to ascertain the size of the various pipes, whether they were copper, iron, steel or plastic, etc., or the intervals at which they were required (by the engineer) to be supported. When pipes are run beneath ventilation ducts they are often attached to the underside of the duct supports. For these reasons it is recommended that all pipe and ventilation duct

THE STANDARD METHOD OF MEASUREMENT

supports should be included in the description of the pipe or duct and priced accordingly. Pipe anchors and RSJ supports should be enumerated separately.

Pipe-sleeves and plates   S13 (*a*) Supplying pipe-sleeves (e.g. short lengths of metal or stoneware pipe) for fixing by other trades through walls, floors and ceilings shall be enumerated stating the length thereof, the size and kind of pipe passing through and the type of packing required.

The materials of the sleeve should be stated. It is suggested that sleeves could be grouped as follows, not exceeding 150 mm, exceeding 150 mm, not exceeding 300 mm and so on. Telescopic pipe sleeves should be described.

(*b*) Wall-plates, floor-plates and ceiling-plates shall each be enumerated separately stating the size thereof and the size and kind of pipe passing through. Where plates are fitted to pipe-sleeves they shall be given in the description of the sleeve stating whether to one or both ends.

Cleaning caps and plugs   S14   Cleaning caps, plugs and the like shall each be enumerated separately stating the size of the item, the kind of pipe to which it is attached and the method of jointing thereto. Perforating the pipe shall be deemed to be included with the item.

Inspection doors   S15   Inspection doors in pipes shall be enumerated as extra over the pipe in which they occur stating the method of sealing the door. Where such doors occur in pipe-fittings they shall be given in the description of the fitting concerned.

Access doors should state whether to end or side of pipe.

Dampers   S16   Dampers in pipes shall be enumerated as extra over the pipe in which they occur stating the method of operation.

The construction of the damper should be described.

Traps, thimbles, ferrules and cones   S17   Traps, thimbles, ferrules, cones and the like shall each be enumerated stating the size thereof, the kind of pipe and appliances to which it is attached and the method of jointing thereto.

Rainwater-heads and roof-outlets   S18   Rainwater-heads, roof-outlets and the like shall each be enumerated separately stating the type, the size and the method of jointing. Wire gratings and cast gratings shall be given in the description.

The method of fixing rainwater-heads should be described.

Hopper-heads	S19	Hopper-heads and the like shall be enumerated stating the type and size thereof, the kind of pipe to which it is attached and the method of jointing thereto. Wire gratings shall be given in the description.

The method of fixing hopper-heads should be described.

Balloon-gratings	S20	Balloon-gratings shall be enumerated stating the size of pipe or outlet to which it is attached.
Cowls, terminals, flaps and cross-wires	S21 (*a*)	Cowls, terminals, hinged flaps, cross-wired ends and the like shall each be enumerated separately stating the size and kind of pipe to which it is attached and the method of jointing thereto.
	(*b*)	Flashing-plates, weathering-aprons, cravats and the like shall each be enumerated separately stating the size thereof and the size and kind of pipe passing through.

The method of construction should be described and also the means of ensuring watertightness.

Exhaust heads	S22	Exhaust heads shall be enumerated stating the number, type and size of the connections.
Drip-trays and tundishes	S23	Drip-trays and tundishes shall each be enumerated separately stating the number, type and size and the connections.

Describe method of construction.

Independent chimneys	S24 (*a*)	Independent vertical steel chimneys shall be enumerated stating the internal diameter and the method of jointing. Base-plates, linings, claddings, anchor-bolts, guy-ropes, ladders, guard-rails, painter's hooks, cleaning-doors, cowls, terminals and the like shall be given in the description stating the number, the type and the size.
	(*b*)	Connections to boilers and connections to brick chimneys shall each be enumerated separately stating the method of jointing and the type of packing required.
Connections to mains	S25	Connecting the ends of pipes to public mains (e.g. water mains; gas mains; district-heating mains), making good public highways and any other work which may only be carried out by a public undertaking or local authority shall be given as a provisional or prime cost sum as Clause A7 hereof.

Ductwork

Ductwork generally	S26	For rules relating to section S generally see Clause S1 hereof.
Ducting	S27 (*a*)	Ducting (measured over all ducting-fittings, short running lengths and branches) shall be given in linear metres stating the size. Stiffeners shall be given in the description.

THE STANDARD METHOD OF MEASUREMENT

(b) Flexible ducting and extensible ducting (measured as fully extended) shall each be so described.

(c) Curved ducting shall be so described stating the mean radius.

(d) Lining ducting internally with acoustic or protective material shall be given in the description of the ducting.

Ducting-joints S28 (a) Providing materials, heat, bolts, nuts, washers and everything else necessary for making joints in ducting shall be deemed to be included with the items.

(b) Joints in the running length shall be given in the description of the ducting stating the method of jointing.

(c) Special connections and special joints in ducting shall each be enumerated separately (except where given in the description of another enumerated item) stating the size and kind of ducting concerned and the method of jointing. Classification shall be as follows:

(i) Connections between ducting of differing materials.
(ii) Connections between ducting and equipment stating the nature of the equipment.
(iii) Isolated joints which differ from those given in the description of the ducting (e.g. flanged joints in ducts having spigot and socket joints generally).
(iv) Flexible connections between ducting and plant.

Ducting-fittings S29 Ducting-fittings (e.g. stop-ends; bends; offsets; diminishing pieces; change-of-section pieces; junction pieces; nozzle outlets) shall each be enumerated separately as extra over the ducting in which they occur. Where there is a preponderance of fittings (e.g. in plant rooms), they shall each be enumerated separately as individual items. Cutting and jointing ducting to the fittings and forming openings in ducting for branches shall be deemed to be included with the ducting.

Where there is a preponderance of fittings, e.g. in plant rooms, these may be enumerated separately as individual items and described 'full value'.

Note: Items described as 'full value' are not 'extra over'.

Ducting-supports S30 (a) Particulars of the method of fixing shall be given in the description of ducting supports as Clause S1(g) hereof. Cutting and pinning ends of ducting supports shall be given as Clause S117 hereof.

(b) Components for supporting ducting (e.g. brackets; hangers) shall be enumerated stating the size of the component and the size of the ducting. Spring-compensated components shall be so described stating the loading and the movement to be accommodated.

The comments made against S12 for pipework supports apply to ducting supports.

58 THE MEASUREMENT OF ENGINEERING SERVICES

Dampers, ducting-turns, access-doors and openings S31 Manually operated regulating dampers and louvres in ducts, ducting-turns and mid-feathers, test-holes and covers, access-doors and openings in ducting (other than for branches) shall each be enumerated separately as extra over the ducting in which they occur. Forming and stiffening openings in ducting shall be given in the description.

The construction of dampers should be described, i.e. multi-leaf, butterfly, opposed blade, etc. Non-return dampers should be described. Where duct-turns and mid-feathers are an integral part of a fitting, i.e. a bend, they shall be included in the description of the fitting.

Shutters, grilles, diffusers and equalizers S32 Louvre-and-butterfly back-draught shutters, grilles, diffusers, diffusers with special dampers, deflectors, equalizers and anti-smudge rings shall each be enumerated separately stating the method of jointing. Forming and stiffening openings in ducting shall be given in the description.

The description of grilles, diffusers, etc., should include the type of finish; means of fixing, with or without dampers stating the type.

Cowls and terminals S33 (a) Cowls, terminals and the like shall each be enumerated separately stating the size and type thereof, the size of ducting to which it is attached and the method of jointing thereto.
(b) Flashing-plates, weathering-aprons, cravats and the like shall each be enumerated separately stating the size thereof and the size of the ducting passing through.

The method of construction should be stated together with any work in connection in making them water and/ or airtight.

Roof-ventilators S34 (a) Roof-ventilators shall be enumerated stating the type, the rated output of air, the temperature, the minimum static resistance, the maximum outlet velocity, the minimum efficiency and the number, type and size of the connections for ducts. Prime-movers, drives and guards shall be given in the description stating the number, the type and the size.
(b) Weathering-aprons, flashing-plates and the like where not forming an integral part of the unit shall each be enumerated separately stating the type and the size.

When prime-movers are electric motors, describe the type and rev./min. of the motor, i.e. totally enclosed squirrel cage, and details of the electric supply. Starters should be described stating type, i.e. direct or line, star-delta, etc., and the wattage of the motor that it controls.

Fire dampers	S35	Fire dampers shall be enumerated stating the type and the size. Fusible links and integral operating-gear shall be given in the description.

Description of fire dampers should state the number of hours resistance that is required.

Special dampers	S36	Damper units other than fire dampers shall be enumerated stating the type and the size. Operating-motors with linkage shall be given in the description.
Extract hoods	S37	Extract hoods shall be enumerated stating the type and the size.

Description of extract hood should include detail of any fittings to be installed in the hood, i.e. grease filters, light fittings, together with the method of support and details of condense channels, and the required finish.

Equipment

Equipment generally	S38	(a) For rules relating to section S generally see Clause S1 hereof.
		(b) Electrically-operated equipment shall be so described stating the type and voltage of the main electricity supply.

Most manufacturers provide detailed literature relating to equipment etc. that they manufacture – it is advisable to include as much information as is available – when describing equipment. It should be stated in the description when boilers and other equipment are required to be 'witness inspected' or inspected and/or tested by insurance companies, etc. If it is essential to control noise levels – this should also be stated.

Boilers	S39	(a) Boilers shall be enumerated stating the rated output, the method of firing, the type of fuel to be used, the working and test pressures of the boiler and the number, type and size of the connections for pipes and mountings. Firebrick linings, insulating jackets forming an essential part of the boiler, automatic damper and draught regulators and any steel or other strips fitted under the edges of a boiler-base shall be given in the description stating the number, the type and size. For flow and return connecting headers see Clause S8(e) hereof.
		(b) Soot-doors, dampers, damper-operating gear and other ironwork for a brick-set boiler shall be given in the description stating the number, the type and the size.
		(c) Packaged boilers (complete with automatic firing equipment, controls, gauges and other mountings normally forming part of the assembly) shall be given in accordance with paragraph (a) of this clause.

Where supports or anti-vibration pads are required for equipment they should be included in the description or alternatively enumerated separately (see S80). Details of the fire outlet should be given, along with flow and return temperatures. Access doors and explosion doors, where an integral part of the boiler, should be described.

Steam generators	S40	Steam generators shall be enumerated stating the rated evaporation of water, the nature of the heating medium, the working pressures of the battery and body and the number, type and size of the connections for pipes and mountings. Access-holes and covers shall be given in the description stating the number, the type and the size.

Test pressures should be stated.

Gas-firing equipment	S41	Gas-firing equipment (except where forming an integral part of other plant) shall be enumerated stating the rated output and the calorific value and pressure of the gas to be used. Draught-divertors, baffles, front-plates, fire-brick linings, safety devices, gas-regulators, gas-governors and automatic controls shall be given in the description stating the number, the type and the size.
Oil burners	S42 (*a*)	Oil burners (except where forming an integral part of other plant) shall be enumerated stating the rated output and the grade of fuel to be used. Oil heaters, firebrick linings to form combustion chambers, front-plates to boiler and holes in boiler to accommodate the burner shall each be given in the description stating the number, the type and the size.
	(*b*)	Electric tracer equipment shall be given in accordance with Section T hereof.
De-superheater	S43	De-superheater units shall be enumerated stating the type of unit, the initial and final conditions of the steam and the number, type and size of the connections for pipes and mountings. Control equipment shall be given in the description.
Water-treatment plant	S44 (*a*)	Water-treatment plant shall be enumerated stating the rated output of water and the number, type and size of the connections for pipes and mountings.
	(*b*)	The quantities of chemicals required shall be enumerated stating the nature thereof.
Pressurizing units	S45 (*a*)	Pressurizing units for medium-pressure and high-pressure hot-water heating systems shall be enumerated stating the water-content of the system, the temperature rise and the working pressure of the system. Air compressors, nitrogen equipment, pumps, valves and interconnecting pipework where they form an integral part of the pressurization unit shall be given in the description stating the particulars required by the appropriate Clauses hereof.
	(*b*)	Standard gas bottles shall be enumerated.

(c) Pressurizing cylinders (except those attached to boilers) shall be enumerated stating the working and test pressure of the cylinder and the number, type and size of the connections for pipes and mountings. Access-holes and covers shall be given in the description stating the number, the type and the size.

Soot-blowing equipment	S46	Soot-blowing equipment shall be enumerated stating the type, the size and the relevant boiler details. Flexible tubes and lances shall be given in the description. Air compressors which form an integral part of the soot-blowing equipment shall be given in the description stating the particulars required by Clause S58 hereof.
Automatic stokers	S47 (a)	Automatic stokers shall be enumerated stating the rated output, the nature of the fuel to be handled and the capacity of the hopper. Prime movers, slide-rails, drives, guards and fire-brick linings shall be given in the description stating the number, the type and the size.
	(b)	Bunker-to-boiler automatic stokers shall be so described stating also the distance between bunker and boiler. Platework shall be given in accordance with the rules in Section R hereof.
Fuel conveyors and hoppers	S48	Fuel conveyors shall be enumerated stating the length and rate of travel of the conveyor and the nature of the fuel to be conveyed. Fuel hoppers shall be given in accordance with the rules in Section R hereof. Prime movers, slide-rails, drives, guards and quantity-measuring equipment shall be given in the description stating the number, the type and the size.
Ash-removal plant	S49	Ash-removal plant shall be enumerated stating the rated output. Prime movers, slide-rails, drives and guards shall be given in the description stating the number, the type and the size.
Draught stabilizers and explosion doors	S50	Draught stabilizers and explosion doors shall each be enumerated separately stating the type and the size.
Water tanks	S51 (a)	Expansion tanks, water-storage tanks and condensed-water tanks shall each be enumerated separately stating the type, the nominal or actual capacity and the number, type and size of the connections for pipes and mountings. Standing overflows, access-holes and covers shall be given in the description stating the number, the type and the size.

Descriptions of tanks should include details of any accessories and mountings required, i.e. internal and external access ladders, vent cowls. Special finishes to tanks should be described. Where tanks have division plates they should be described. The description of sectional tanks should include whether they are internally or externally flanged.

(b) Heating coils in tanks shall be enumerated stating the area of heating surface and the number, type and size of the connections to pipes. Brackets to support coils shall be given in the description.

(c) Electric immersion-heaters shall be enumerated stating the loading. For electrical connections see Section T hereof.

Description of immersion-heaters should include type, size, etc.

Hot-water and thermal storage cylinders

S52 (a) Hot-water cylinders and thermal-storage cylinders shall each be enumerated separately stating the nominal or actual capacity, the working and test pressures, the maximum operating temperature and the number, type and size of the connections for pipes and mountings. Access-holes, covers and internal fittings shall be given in the description stating the number, the type and the size.

State whether fixed vertically or horizontally, detail of construction and type of support, i.e. cradles or legs and if site welded or prefabricated.

(b) Electric immersion-heaters shall be given in the description of the cylinders stating the loading. For electrical connections see Section T hereof.

See comment S51(c).

Calorifiers

S53 (a) Calorifiers shall be enumerated stating the rated output, the pattern (e.g. horizontal; vertical), the area of the heating surface, the nature of the primary and secondary mediums, the test and working pressures of the battery and shell and the number, type and size of the connections for pipes and mountings.

(b) Storage-type calorifiers shall be so described stating also the capacity of the shell, the arrangements for removing the battery and the number, type and size of the connections for pipes and mountings. Access-holes and covers shall be given in the description stating the number, the type and the size.

The area of the heating surface for a hot-water storage calorifier should normally be determined by the manufacture. Part of the description of the calorifier should be: . . . to raise contents from 4°C to 66°C in one hour when fed with primary low pressure hot water at 82°C/71°C flow and return . . .

(c) Electric immersion-heaters shall be given in the description of the calorifiers stating the loading. For electrical connections see Section T hereof.

Oil tanks

S54 (a) Tanks for oil storage shall be enumerated stating the nominal or actual capacity, the type and limiting dimen-

THE STANDARD METHOD OF MEASUREMENT 63

sions of the tank, and the number, type and size of the connections for pipes and mountings. Anti-convection shields, dip-sticks, cradles, lead or other strips under tanks, access-holes and covers shall be given in the description stating the number, the type and the size.

Tanks and cylinders are used for oil storage – descriptions should state whether they are to be horizontal or vertical mounted. Describe whether site welded or prefabricated.

(b) Heating-coils in tanks shall be enumerated stating the area of heating surface and the number, type and size of the connections for pipes. Brackets to support coils shall be given in the description.

(c) Electric immersion-heaters shall be enumerated stating the loading. For electrical connections see Section T hereof.

See comment S51(c).

(d) Filler-caps and chains, wall-boxes, drip-trays and other accessories for tank-filling pipes shall each be enumerated separately stating the size and kind of pipe to which they are attached and the method of jointing thereto.

Oil-heaters S55 Oil-heaters (except where forming an integral part of other plant) shall be enumerated stating the rated output, the nature of the heating medium and the number, type and size of the connections for pipes and mountings.

Pumps S56 (a) Pumps (except where forming an integral part of other plant) shall be enumerated stating the rated output, the kind of liquid to be handled (e.g. oil; water), the temperature, the method of operating, the inlet pressure, the outlet pressure, the static head and the number, type and size of the connections for pipes and mountings. Prime-movers, slide-rails, drives, guards, air-vessels and water-collecting receivers shall be given in the description stating the number, the type and the size.

(b) Oil pumps complete with heaters shall be so described stating the nature of the heating medium.

(c) Sump pumps and other pumps with vertical spindles shall each be so described stating the depth of the sump or spindle and particulars of any cover or bearing plates.

(d) Boiler-feed pumps shall be so described stating the type (e.g. horizontal; vertical). Twin sets complete with interconnecting pipework and valves shall be so described.

Pump descriptions should include type of pump, i.e. centrifugal, type of drive, i.e. 'V' belt. Prime-movers such as motors should be described in full including W, rev./min. of motor, type of motor and electric supply, the description of starters should include type and W of motor it controls. Full details of pump construction including type of bearings and seals should be given.

Where pumps require cooling jackets (normally where handling temperature over 121°C) it should be stated.

Pumping traps	S57	Pumping traps shall be enumerated stating the rated output, the pressure of the operating medium, the discharge head and the number, type and size of the connections for pipes and mountings. Water-collecting receivers shall be given in the description stating the number, the type and the size.
Air compressors	S58	Air compressors (except where forming an integral part of other plant) shall be enumerated stating the rated output, the outlet pressure and the number, type and size of the connections for pipes and mountings. Prime-movers, slide-rails, drives, guards, air receivers and after-cooling equipment shall be given in the description stating the number, the type and the size.

See comments regarding prime-movers and starters in S56.

Nitrogen equipment	S59	Nitrogen equipment (except where forming an integral part of other plant) shall be enumerated stating the number of standard gas bottles and the number, type and size of the connections for pipes and mountings.
High-velocity air units	S60	High-velocity air units shall be enumerated stating the type (e.g. single-duct; dual-duct; induction), the rated capacity, the inlet air pressure and temperature, the nature of the heating or cooling medium, the limiting dimensions, the maximum sound level and the number, type and size of the connections for pipes and ducts.
Air silencer units	S61	Air silencer units shall be enumerated stating the rated quantity of air handled, the maximum permissible resistance, the required sound reduction, the limiting dimensions and the number, type and size of the connections for pipes and ducts.
Unit coolers	S62	Unit coolers shall be enumerated stating the rated quantity of air handled, the initial and final conditions of the air, the nature of the cooling medium, the maximum sound level, the speed of the motors in revolutions per minute, the height of the unit above floor-level, and the number, type and size of the connections for pipes and ducts.

Give details of prime-movers and starters as S56.

Fans	S63	Fans shall be enumerated stating the type, the rated output of air, the temperature, the minimum static resistance, the maximum outlet velocity, the maximum sound level, the minimum efficiency, the type and arrangement of the bearings and the number, type and size of the connections. Prime-movers, slide-rails, drives and guards shall be given in the description.

Access-doors, drain points, etc., should be described. Details of drives, prime-movers and starters as before.

Air-filters and dust separators

S64 (a) Air-cleaning filters and dust separators shall each be enumerated separately stating the rated quantity of air handled, the maximum permissible resistance when clean and dirty, the limiting dimensions, the minimum efficiency for a specified dust-particle size and the number, type and size of the connections. Cleaning tanks, cleaning agents and oils for viscous types shall be given in the description stating the number, the type and the size. Supporting structures shall be given in accordance with the rules in other sections hereof.

(b) Oil pumps forming an integral part of the air-cleaning equipment shall be given in the description stating the particulars required by Clause S56 hereof.

The description of roll filters, etc., should include full details of motors, starters, electric supply, etc., and provision should be made for replacing after testing and commissioning have been carried out. It should also be stated that all filters should be left with clear media after all testing, etc., has been done.

Air purification equipment

S65 Air purification and sterilization equipment shall be enumerated stating the rated quantity of air handled, the maximum permissible resistance, the limiting dimensions, the minimum efficiency and the number, type and size of the connections for pipes and ducts.

Air heating or cooling batteries

S66 (a) Air heating or cooling batteries shall be enumerated stating the rated quantity of air handled, the nature of the heating or cooling medium, the working and test pressures, the entering and leaving conditions of the air, the maximum permissible air resistance, the limiting dimensions and the number, type and size of the connections.

(b) Water-operating tanks and air-compressor sets shall each be enumerated separately stating the particulars required by Clauses S51 and S58 hereof.

The construction of coils should be stated, and also the type of fins, i.e. aluminium or copper.

Air washers

S67 (a) Air washers shall be enumerated stating the rated quantity of air handled, the maximum permissible air resistance, the limiting dimensions, the minimum efficiency, the quantity of water and the number, type and size of the connections for pipes and ducts. In the case of spray-type washers, the number of spray banks and nozzles shall also be stated. Inspection doors, internal electric light, heating coils, overflows, strainers, ball valves, quick-fill connections and internal platforms shall be given in the description stating the number, the type and the size.

(b) Water pumps forming an integral part of the washer shall be given in the description stating the particulars required by Clause S56 hereof.

The description should include full details of pump, motor and starter, etc., as before.

Air humidifiers	S68	Air humidifiers shall be enumerated stating the type, the duties, the method of operation (e.g. centrifugal water; steam jet) and the number, type and size of the connections for pipes and ducts.
Refrigerating apparatus	S69	Refrigerating apparatus shall be enumerated stating the type of machine, the heat-extraction capacity, the temperature of extraction, the nature of the refrigerant, the method of cooling (e.g. direct expansion; indirect cooling), the type of condenser and the temperature and quantity of the medium for dissipating heat. Automatic controls, gas lines and initial charges of refrigerant and oil shall be given in the description.
Self-contained air-conditioning units	S70	Self-contained air-conditioning units (complete with integral refrigerating equipment) shall be enumerated stating the rated quantity of air handled, the initial and final conditions of the air, the limiting dimensions and the maximum sound level. Automatic controls, electrical switchgear and controls, gas lines and initial charges of refrigerant and oil shall be given in the description.
Water cooling towers	S71	Water cooling towers shall be enumerated stating the type of draught (e.g. natural; mechanical), the quantity of water to be cooled, the initial and final temperatures of the water, the maximum external wet-bulb temperature, the limiting dimensions and the number, type and size of the connections for pipes and ducts.
Radiators	S72	(a) Radiators shall be enumerated stating the area of the heating surface, the type and the number of columns or the width and height. Curved radiators and angle radiators shall each be so described.

Details of connections including sizes, bushes, air cocks, etc., should be given.

(b) Loose feet, integral feet, extended feet, baffle-plates, top-shields and air-gratings with registers and controls shall each be enumerated separately stating the number, the type and the size.

Convectors	S73	Convectors shall be enumerated stating the rated output, the type, the size, the heating medium, the ambient temperature and the number, type and size of the connections for pipes and mountings. Concealed-type fan-operated convectors shall be so described stating the method of connecting to the duct. Control dampers, hinged covers and front plates for recessed non-mechanical convectors shall be given in the description stating the

THE STANDARD METHOD OF MEASUREMENT

number, the type and the size. For backing insulation see Clause S78 hereof.

See sections 12.34 and 12.35 for description of convector.

Skirting-heaters — S74 (a) Skirting-heaters shall be given in linear metres stating the output and the number, type and size of the connections for pipes. Alternatively, they may be enumerated in sections or in units stating the length and the output. Edge-sealing strips shall be given in the description. For backing insulation, see Clause S78 hereof.

(b) Angle-sections, matching plates and valve-access covers shall each be enumerated separately stating the type and the size.

Unit heaters — S75 Unit heaters shall be enumerated stating the rated output of heated air, the nature of the heating medium, the inlet and outlet air temperatures, the speed of the motors, the height of the unit above floor level and the number, type and size of the connections to pipes and ducts.

See section 12.36 for full description of a unit heater.

Radiant panels — S76 (a) Radiant panels shall be enumerated stating the type and size of the panel and the number, type and size of the connections for pipes and mountings. Edge-sealing strips shall be given in the description stating the number and the size. For backing insulation see Clause S78 hereof.

(b) Access-plates and closing plates between panels shall each be enumerated separately stating the type and the size.

Embedded panels — S77 Embedded panels shall be enumerated stating the bore of the tube, the overall size of the panel, the length of the loops, the centre-to-centre spacing of the tubes, the number, type and size of the connections for pipes, the test pressures at works and on site and the duration of the tests. Hanger-brackets, wires and clips shall be given in the description but temporary supports during concreting shall be deemed to be included with the items. For backing insulation see Clause S78 hereof.

Backing insulation — S78 Backing insulation to convectors, skirting-heaters, radiant panels and embedded panels shall be given in square metres stating the nature of the material and the thickness.

Prime movers — S79 Prime movers for plant shall be enumerated stating the type (e.g. electric motor) and the rated output. Slide-rails, drives and guards shall each be enumerated separately.

The description should include full details of type of motors, starters, etc., all as before.

Anti-vibration and sound-insulation — S80 (a) Anti-vibration mountings for plant shall be enumerated stating the type and the size.

(b) Anti-vibration material and sound-insulating material in plant bases shall be given in square metres stating the nature of the material (e.g. cork) and the thickness.

(c) Flexible pipe connections or articulators shall be enumerated stating the type, the size and the method of jointing.

See S39(a).

Water- and gas-meters   S81   Water-meters and gas-meters shall each be enumerated separately stating the capacity and type thereof and the number, type and size of the connections for pipes. Meters designed for by-pass fixing shall be so described and the reduction counters, by-passes, isolating valves and orifice plates shall be given in the description stating the number, the type and the size.

Appliances

Appliances generally   S82 (a) For rules relating to section S generally see Clause S1 hereof.

(b) Providing mating flanges, couplings and everything necessary for jointing shall be deemed to be included with the appliance items.

Descriptions of appliances should include details o. materials, etc. See comment against S1(c) and S9(b).

Sanitary appliances   S83   Baths, lavatory-basins, wash-tubs, showers, W.C. pans, W.C. suites, sinks, urinals, flushing cisterns, drinking fountains and the like shall each be enumerated separately stating the type and the size. Cantilever brackets shall be given in the description.

Include in description for sanitary appliances whether they are coloured or have a special finish.

Fire-fighting appliances   S84   Fire-fighting appliances, foam-inlets, hydrants and the like shall each be enumerated separately stating the type and the size.

Ancillaries

Ancillaries generally   S85 (a) For rules relating to section S generally see Clause S1 hereof.

(b) Providing mating flanges, couplings and everything necessary for jointing shall be deemed to be included with the ancillary items.

See comment against S1(c) and S9(b).

(c) Notwithstanding the following provisions for the enumeration of ancillaries, where such items form an integral part of the equipment to which they relate, or where they are required to be supplied by the manufacturer of the

THE STANDARD METHOD OF MEASUREMENT

equipment to which they relate, they shall be given in the description of the equipment concerned.

Valves and cocks   S86   Valves and cocks shall each be enumerated separately stating the type and the size. Those with extended spindles shall be so described stating the length of the spindle and details of integral locking devices and remote operating gear. Those with hose-unions shall be so described. Connecting ends of valves and cocks to pipes and appliances shall be given in the description stating the kind and type of pipework and appliance and the method of jointing thereto. Classification shall be as follows:

    (*i*)   Draw-off taps.
    (*ii*)   Stop-valves.
    (*iii*)   Ball-valves.
    (*iv*)   Control valves.
    (*v*)   Regulating valves.
    (*vi*)   Radiator valves.
    (*vii*)   Convector valves.
    (*viii*)   Safety valves stating the type and the loading.
    (*ix*)   Reducing valves.
    (*x*)   Automatic control valves and thermostats.
    (*xi*)   Non-return valves.
    (*xii*)   Blow-down valves.
    (*xiii*)   Drain cocks.
    (*xiv*)   Stopcocks.
    (*xv*)   Air cocks.
    (*xvi*)   Automatic air-relief valves and air-bottles.

Descriptions of valves should state the form and operation of parallel slide, diaphragm, etc., and also the materials used in manufacture. It is important to distinguish between bronze, steel and cast iron, etc., there being a considerable price differential. Angle valves should be described stating type of valve, i.e. gate, lockshield, or wheelhead. If the specification is not absolutely clear, the engineer should be asked to confirm (prior to measurement) the type of valves required and that they are suitable for the fluids, pressure, temperature, etc., for which they are required.

Mixing valves and blenders   S87   Mixing valves and blenders shall each be enumerated separately stating the size of inlet and outlet and the method of operation. Connecting the inlets and outlets to pipes shall be given in the description stating the kind and type of pipework and the method of jointing thereto.

Fire-valves and fusible links   S88 (*a*)   Fire-valves shall be enumerated stating the type and the size.

    (*b*)   Fusible links systems (complete with controlling wires, guiding pulleys and manually-operated emergency levers) shall be enumerated stating the length of the wires.

Reducing-valve sets	S89	Reducing-valve sets for steam, water or air systems shall each be enumerated separately stating the maximum and minimum rate of flow of steam, water or air, the inlet pressure, the outlet pressure and the number, type and size of the connections for pipes and mountings.
Steam traps	S90	Steam traps shall be enumerated stating the size or capacity, the type (e.g. thermostatic; float; bucket), the pattern (e.g. angle; straight) and the working pressure. Combined trap and strainer units shall be so described. Connections to pipes shall be given in the description stating the kind and type of pipework and the method of jointing thereto.
Strainers	S91	Strainers shall be enumerated stating the type and the size. Connections to pipes shall be given in the description stating the kind and type of pipework and the method of jointing thereto.
Gauges and thermometers	S92	(a) Altitude gauges and pressure gauges shall each be enumerated separately stating the type and the size. Those with syphons and cocks shall be so described. (b) Liquid-level gauges and glasses shall each be enumerated separately stating the type and the size. (c) Thermometers shall be enumerated stating the type and the scale range. Those with pockets shall be so described. (d) Gauges and thermometers having remote-reading indicators shall each be so described stating the type and the length of the capillary or other tubing. (e) Hardwood boards and the like for gauges shall be enumerated stating the type and the size.
Automatic controls	S93	(a) Automatic liquid-level control units and alarm units shall each be enumerated separately stating the type and the method of operation. (b) Automatic valve and control units shall be enumerated stating the type and the operational purpose. Those with direct-acting thermostats shall be so described stating the length of the capillary tubes. (c) Separate pockets for thermostats shall be enumerated.
Indicating, measuring and recording equipment	S94	(a) Indicating, measuring and recording instruments (e.g. distance-thermometers; CO_2-indicators or recorders; smoke-indicators) shall each be enumerated separately. Panel-mounted instruments shall be so described. (b) Compensating leads and connecting tubing shall each be given separately in linear metres. Clips for fixing shall be given in the description. Supporting trays shall be given in linear metres. (c) Panels for mounting the instruments and switchgear shall be enumerated stating the type and the size. (d) Panel and instrument assemblies (complete with internal wiring, tubing and terminal points) shall be enumerated stating the relevant particulars.

Thermal insulation

Thermal insulation generally

S95 (a) For rules relating to section S generally see Clause S1 hereof.
(b) Particulars of the following shall be given:
  (i) Kind of insulating material.
  (ii) Thickness.
  (iii) Finish.
  (iv) Method of fixing.
(c) Smoothing the insulation material and working around supports (e.g. hangers; brackets) shall be deemed to be included with the insulation items.

Insulation to plant

S96 (a) Insulation to plant (e.g. boilers; calorifiers; cylinders; tanks; pumping equipment; fans; heating or cooling batteries; water and steam humidifiers; refrigerating apparatus) shall be enumerated stating the overall size of the unit. Particulars shall be given of any protection to the insulation. Where units of plant are contained in casings of specified dimensions, the insulation may alternatively be given in square metres (measured on the surface of the insulation).

The insulation to dampers should be enumerated describing the arrangement of the insulation around the operating gear.

(b) Providing detachable mattresses and working insulation around hole covers, access-doors, gauges, thermostats, thermometers and the like shall each be enumerated separately as extra over the insulation in which they occur or they may be given in the description of enumerated items of insulation.

Insulation to pipework and fittings

S97 (a) Insulation to pipework shall be given in linear metres stating the type and bore of the pipe. Insulation to flanged pipework, to the traced oil pipework and to smoke or flue pipework shall each be described. Particulars shall be given of any protection to the insulation and of any air space between flue pipes and their insulation.
(b) Working insulation around ancillaries (e.g. valves; access-doors; gauges; thermostats; thermometers) shall each be enumerated separately as extra over the insulation in which they occur. Particulars shall be given of any boxes for valves.
(c) Working insulation over flanges and pipe-fittings (e.g. elbows; bends; reducers; twin elbows; crosses; branch joints) shall each be enumerated separately as extra over the insulation to pipework over 50 mm bore, but shall be given in the description of insulation to pipework not exceeding 50 mm bore.
(d) Sectional insulating coverings to pipework shall be so described and given in accordance with paragraphs (a) and (b) of this clause.

(e) Fitting sectional coverings around pipe-fittings shall each be enumerated separately as extra over the sectional coverings in which they occur.

(f) Flanged joints in sectional coverings shall each be given in the description stating whether boxes are required. Isolated flanged joints (i.e. where not consistent with the general method of jointing described) shall be enumerated as extra over the sectional coverings in which they occur.

Experience has shown that most insulation contractors are content to price insulation as described in S97(a) (i.e. measured over all fittings, irrespective of size). Only valves and flanges require to be enumerated and in the description of these it should be stated how they are insulated, i.e. boxes, mattresses, etc.

Insulation to ductwork

S98 (a) Insulation to ductwork shall be given in linear metres stating the size of the ducting.

(b) Working insulation around ducting-fittings (e.g. stop-ends; bends; offsets; diminishing pieces; change-of-section pieces; junction pieces; nozzle outlets) shall each be enumerated separately as extra over the insulation in which they occur. Alternatively, insulation around such fittings may each be enumerated separately as individual units.

(c) Working insulation around test-holes and covers, access-doors, openings, grilles and the like shall each be enumerated separately as extra over the insulation in which they occur.

See comments under S97.

Loose insulation and cellular concrete

S99 (a) Loose insulation in trenches, ducts, tank casings and the like shall each be given separately in cubic metres stating the nature of the material (e.g. slag wool).

(b) Cellular concrete insulation in trenches and ducts (grouped together) shall be given in cubic metres stating the mix of the concrete.

(c) Special protection or finish at openings through walls, valve chambers and the like shall each be enumerated separately, stating the relevant particulars.

Sundries

Sundries generally

S100 For rules relating to section S generally see Clause S1 hereof.

Marking positions

S101 Marking the position of holes, mortices, chases and the like in the structure shall be given as an item for each installation. Where the nature of the work necessitates any of these to be formed during construction, the relevant particulars shall be given.

Draining and refilling	S102	Draining and refilling an existing system shall be given as a provisional or prime cost sum as Clause A7 hereof.
Identification plates	S103	Plates, discs and labels for the identification of plant, equipment, appliances, pipes, valves and the like shall each be enumerated separately. Charts giving the key thereto shall be enumerated.
Loose keys, tools and spares	S104	Loose keys, tools, spares (e.g. parts; fittings; apparatus; chemicals other than for initial commissioning) and the like shall each be enumerated separately stating the type and the quantity. Racks for holding tools and the like shall be enumerated stating the size.
Temporarily operating the installation	S105	Temporarily operating the installation (except for testing) shall be given as an item stating any required qualifications of the attendant, the duration of the operating period in hours, the purpose (e.g. drying the lagging; drying the building; reducing the ambient humidity) and particulars of any special insurance cover required by the employer. Providing solid fuel, liquid fuel, gas and electricity for power and lighting shall be given as a provisional or prime cost sum as Clause A7 hereof.
Disconnecting and refixing equipment	S106	Disconnecting, setting aside and refixing appliances (e.g. radiators; convectors) for the convenience of other trades shall be given as an item stating the relevant particulars.
Refractory linings to flues	S107	Refractory linings and precast concrete linings to flues shall be given in accordance with the rules in section G hereof.
Plans of the installation	S108	Preparing plans or diagrams of the installation as fitted shall be given as an item stating the kind of information required to be shown and the number of copies of each drawing required to be provided.
Testing the installation	S109	Testing each installation shall be given as an item stating any required qualifications of the attendant, the number of stage tests in addition to the final, the purpose of the tests (e.g. water-pressure; weld-soundness; air-tightness; performance) the instruments and appliances required to be provided and particulars of any special insurance cover required by the employer. Providing solid fuel, liquid fuel, gas and electricity for power and lighting shall be given as a provisional or prime cost sum as Clause A7 hereof.

A separate item should be given together with a full description for any of the following: flushing out, sterilizing, chlorinating, degreasing, etc. (See also section 6.3.46.)

Electrical work

Electrical work	S110	Electrical work in connection with plumbing and engineering installations shall be given in accordance with section T hereof and where required to be executed by the plumber or engineer it shall be so described and billed with the installation concerned.

Builder's work

Builder's work generally	S111	Builder's work in connection with plumbing and engineering installations shall be grouped together under an appropriate heading and where required to be executed by the plumber or engineer it shall be so described and billed with the installation concerned.
General attendance	S112	For general attendance on nominated plumbing and engineering sub-contractors, see Clause B20(*b*) hereof.
Special attendance	S113	For special attendance on nominated plumbing and engineering sub-contractors, see Clause B20(*c*) hereof.

See section 6.3.10(d). It should be remembered that all welding operations require a three phase electrical supply and this should be provided by the main contractor and described as 'special attendance' in the appropriate section of the bill of quantities for the main contract.

Pipe-trenches	S114	Excavating trenches for pipes not exceeding 55 mm bore shall be given as Clause D12 hereof. Excavating trenches for pipes over 55 mm bore shall be given in accordance with Clause X3 hereof.
Inspection chambers	S115	Inspection chambers shall be given in accordance with the rules for drainage in Clause X7 hereof.
Bedding and pointing	S116	Bedding and pointing components or units of plant, sanitary appliances and the like shall be enumerated stating the size thereof and the composition and mix of the bedding material.
Cutting and pinning	S117 (*a*)	Cutting and pinning ends of supports for equipment, appliances, fittings and the like shall be enumerated stating the size of the support and the nature of the structure (e.g. concrete; brickwork; blockwork; stonework).
	(*b*)	Cutting and pinning ends of supports for pipes over 55 mm bore shall be enumerated stating the size and kind of pipe and the nature of the structure.
	(*c*)	Cutting and pinning ends of supports for pipes not exceeding 55 mm bore (grouped together) shall be given in linear metres (measured over pipework) stating the nature of the structure.
Cutting away and making good	S118	Cutting away for and making good after the plumbers and engineers shall be given as follows:
		(*i*) Holes for pipes and the like shall be given in

THE STANDARD METHOD OF MEASUREMENT 75

           accordance with the rules in the appropriate section hereof.

(ii) Mortices, sinkings and the like shall each be enumerated separately stating the size thereof and the nature of the structure.

(iii) Lifting and replacing old chequer-plates and the like shall be given in linear metres.

(iv) Lifting and replacing old floorboards (measured along the route of the pipe or ducting) shall be given in linear metres stating the number and size of pipes or ducts. No distinction shall be made between routes parallel to or at an angle to the floorboards. Cutting floorboards and notching joists shall be deemed to be included with the items.

(v) Cutting chases shall be given in linear metres stating the size of the pipe and the nature of the structure.

(vi) Cutting out old plasterwork, old brickwork, old plain concrete, old reinforced concrete and the like not exceeding 300 mm in width and making good after shall each be given separately in linear metres.

Pylons and poles   S119 (a) Pylons, poles, wall-brackets, pole-brackets, pole-stays and the like for supporting pipework shall each be enumerated separately stating the size, the method of fixing and the nature of the structure.

(b) Boring or excavating holes in ground for poles and stays shall be enumerated stating the depth, the nature of the filling (e.g. excavated material; concrete) and the treatment of surplus spoil.

(c) Excavating pits and forming concrete bases for pylons shall be given in accordance with the rules in sections D and F hereof.

(d) Catenary cables shall be given in linear metres stating the type and the size. Eye-bolts, shackles and straining screws shall be given in the description stating the method of fixing.

Metalwork   S120   Metalwork in connection with plumbing and engineering installations (e.g. frameworks for supporting plant, control-gear, equipment and the like; metal ladders and gantries for access to plant; metal duct-covers) shall be given in accordance with the rules in section R hereof.

Painting   S121   Painting shall be given in accordance with the rules in section W hereof.

Protection

Protection   S122   Protecting the work in this section shall be given as an item.

See section 6.3.46.

(End of extract from the standard method of measurement)

Bill descriptions – basic ingredients

The primary object of 'measuring and describing' is to give the tenderer the maximum number of facts in order to permit him to estimate the unit cost of the particular component properly.

The following should assist in the building up of a complete description for either plant or equipment:

	The piece of plant and/or equipment	*Its joints*	*Its fixings*
(a) Supply only or	(a) General size or size and duty	Types of joints and joint components	How it is fixed to the building e.g. Type of fixing and fixing component and background. (See S1H.)
(b) Fix only or	(b) If purpose made		
(c) Supply and Fix	(c) Method of fabrication		
Note:	(d) Finish		
(c) is normally implied unless stated to the contrary.	(e) Material		
	(f) (Trade name)/ item number		
	(g) Reference to British standards and tests		
	(h) Manufacturer's name and address		
	(i) Detailed size and duty		
	(j) Use or function		
	(k) Components		
	(l) Insulation		
	(m) Ancillaries		
	(n) Labours		
	(o) Treatments		
	(p) Suitability i.e. for single- or 3-phase electric supply.		

CHAPTER 9

Sanitary installation

9.1

Soil and Waste (see Figs. 9.1 and 9.2)

9.1.1 Soil and waste pipes carry foul water and solids from the various sanitary appliances within the building to the external drainage installation. In order to prevent destruction of the water seal in the trap of sanitary appliances, the trap should be ventilated by a ventilating pipe positioned in order to prevent nuisance, injury, or danger to health arising from the emission of foul air, the open end of the ventilating pipe should be fitted with a balloon guard. Alternatively the pipe may be connected to the main soil or waste ventilating pipe at a point above the highest sanitary appliance. The ventilating pipe should be extended above roof level to the height required by the By-Laws.

9.1.2 Where practicable all appliances should be connected to one main stack, the diameter of which is calculated from the number and type of fittings against the frequency of use, from which the number of 'discharge units' can be established (*BS Code of Practice* 304:1968 tables 2, 3 and 4) by the use of design graphs the minimum diameter of pipe to accommodate the number of fittings may be calculated. The diameter of the ventilation pipework required may also be established by reference to *BS Code of Practice* 304:1968 table 7.

9.1.3 Sufficient access points should be provided to enable all pipework to be tested and maintained properly. Access points should be sited to permit the insertion of testing apparatus and clearing apparatus. One such access point should be at the base of the soil or waste stack where it connects to the drainage system.

Bends and offsets in the vertical stack give rise to pressure fluctuations in the stack and should be avoided if possible. If it is not possible to avoid offsets then short projection offsets should be used – the 914 mm overall length being suitable. Longer offsets should be made up with two 135° bends with a short length of connecting pipe to make up the required projection.

9.1.4 To prevent discharge from a W.C. branch backing up the bath waste, the latter should be connected to the stack so that the centre line of the bath waste meets that of the stack at or above the level at which the centre line of the W.C. branch meets that of the soil stack, or a minimum of 203 mm below it.

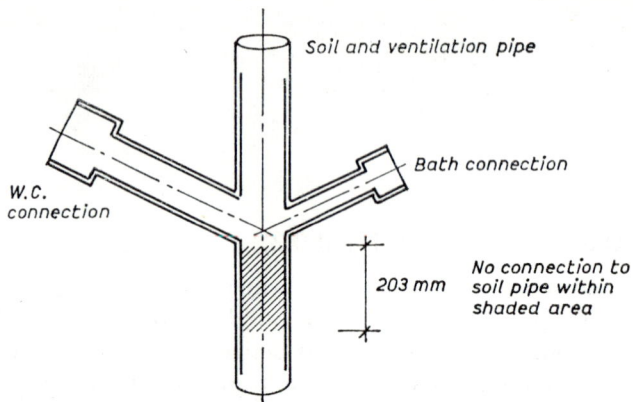

Fig. 9.1 W.C. connection to soil stack.

9.1.5 Branch connections on cast iron or PVC stacks may be made by utilizing single or double arm junctions (with or without access doors), or composite multi-arm junctions manufactured to specific requirements and referred to as 'boss pipes' which have normal socket arms for W.C. connections and bosses drilled and tapped BSPT (in the case of cast iron) or prepared for PVC or copper tube (in the case of PVC).

9.1.6 Stacks may also be prefabricated off site in copper, galvanized mild steel or PVC. When there is a possibility of corrosive effluent being discharged into a stack the pipework should be a chemical resistant type such as special glass pipework (QVF), vulcathene, glass lined cast iron or chemical lead pipes.

9.2
Soil pipe materials, in general use

9.2.1 Asbestos-cement. Light in weight. Fragile. Not normally used in multi-storey installations. Required to be treated with bitumen by dipping at works. Jointed with tarred hemp gasket and cement mortar or by means of proprietary neoprene ring. Boss pipes can be formed on site by use of 'Fixacon' connectors which will accommodate copper waste pipes – fixed with holderbats.

9.2.2 Cast iron. In most common use. Jointed with yarn gasket and caulked lead or proprietary mastic joint.

SANITARY INSTALLATION

A wide range of fittings is available. Boss pipes may be manufactured to order to suit individual site requirements and fixed by means of ears cast on to socket and pipe nails or holderbats.

9.2.3 Copper. Vertical stacks may be fabricated on site or manufactured by specialist firms. If the latter the supply may be covered by a PC sum in the bill of quantities and the fixing of the pipework measured as fix only including the supply of all necessary jointing materials, brackets and holderbats. Horizontal branches to ranges of fittings are normally fabricated on site utilizing tube to BS 659 which may be formed into made bends (up to 51 mm) by the use of bending springs or machines. Over this size BS 3931 tube should be used as bending by machine is impractical, manufactured fittings should be used. These can be compression or capillary to BS 864, or, alternatively the pipework may be brazed with oxy-acetylene equipment with

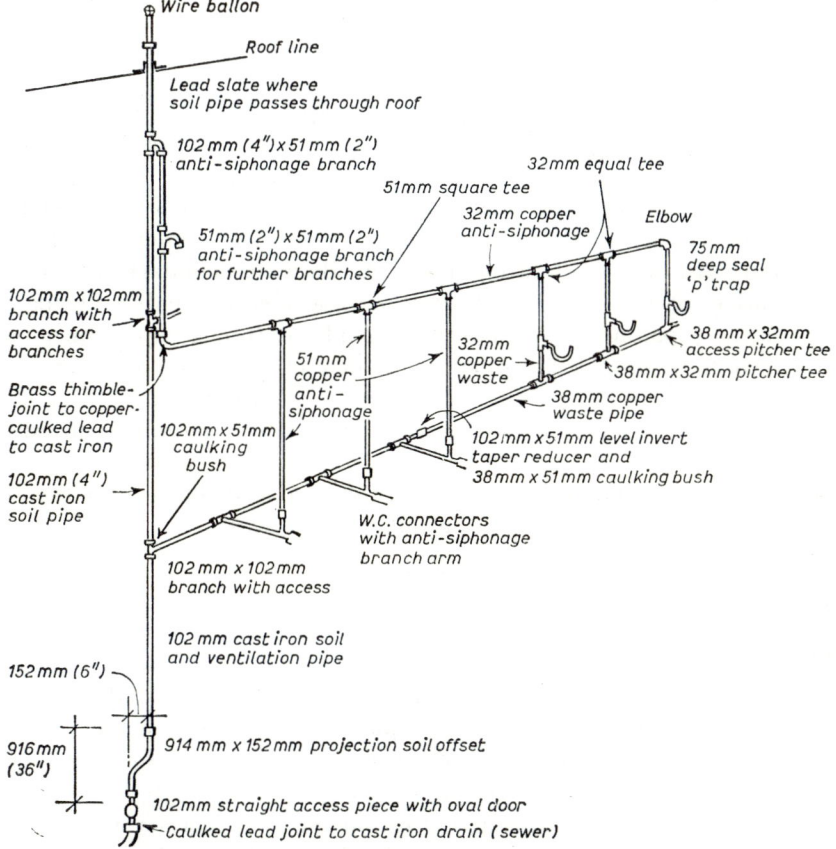

Fig. 9.2 Typical soil, waste and ventilation arrangement.

sif-bronze rods and flux or Silbralloy rods (which do not require flux when brazing copper to copper joints).

9.2.4 Galvanized steel. Vertical stacks normally manufactured off site by specialist. Horizontal branches fabricated on site from tube to BS 1387 with screwed and socketed joints.

9.2.5 Lead. Not normally used in vertical stacks, but frequently used in W.C. connections in confined spaces (jointed with wiped soldered joints). Requires more supports in the running length than other more rigid pipework.

9.2.6 Pitch impregnated fibre. Light and easy to joint by means of tapered sockets driven on with hammer blows or alternatively by using polypropylene fittings. Boss connections may be fitted where desired on stacks.

9.2.7 Plastic. Manufactured from a variety of thermoplastic materials such as:

(*i*) Unplasticized polyvinylchloride (UPVC)
(*ii*) Polyethylene.
(*iii*) Polypropylene.
(*iv*) Acrylonitrile butadiene styrene (ABS).
(*v*) Vulcathene.

Joints in plastic pipes may be made with a neoprene ring, solvent cement or in the case of Vulcathene by means of heat application which fuses the pipe and fitting together. Because manufacturers use a variety of wall thickness, fittings are not interchangeable. Owing to linear expansion that takes place in plastic tubing expansion joints have to be provided in pipe runs to take up thermal movement.

Vulcathene has a high chemical resistance to many corrosive substances and is normally used in chemical plumbing installations.

9.2.8 Special glass. Glass lined cast iron, chemical lead. These are normally used in chemical plumbing installations.

9.3

Traps, connectors, overflows

9.3.1 Traps to individual sanitary fittings (baths, basins, bidets, sinks) should be 76 mm deep seal two piece drawn copper or PVC which permit flexibility for connections to waste pipework and allow the base section to be removed for cleaning.

9.3.2 Public health inspectors do not favour the use of bottle traps on bowl urinals as this type of trap is easily blocked. If bottle traps are used they are usually chromium plated or PVC.

9.3.3 Branch connections to washdown W.C. suites are 102 mm diameter but syphonic W.C. suite outlets vary from 76 mm–89 mm–102 mm.

9.3.4 On W.C. flushing cistern overflows most manufacturers provide a compression outlet for copper overflow pipes, it is not therefore necessary to measure a connector with backnut, merely a labour item for making the compression joint.

9.4
Jointing W.C. pans

When a W.C. pan is fitted on a solid floor a mastic or cement joint should be measured connecting the outlet to the soil pipe (with the exception of PVC pipework). On a wooden floor a mastic joint to pipework is normally required unless the W.C. connector incorporates a patent PVC self-sealing unit.

9.5
Testing

Testing of the installation should normally be by means of an air test. A section of the pipework is sealed off and pressure tested as required by the local authority Public Health Inspector (normally 3·7 mbar water gauge to remain constant for a minimum of 3 minutes).

It is considered unreasonable for a water test to be applied to the whole of the plumbing system, as the only section at risk is the section below the lowest sanitary appliance and this can easily be tested by plugging off the lower end of the pipe and filling the pipe with water up to the flood level of the lowest sanitary appliance. The maximum permitted static head for a water test is 6 m.

9.6
Sanitary fittings

9.6.1 Generally.

Unless the architect (or the client) has chosen a specific make of sanitary fitting, it is more economical to quote the appropriate British Standard Specification for each fitting, or alternatively a particular merchant's catalogue reference followed by the qualifications 'or other equal and approved'. Many of the larger sanitary fittings merchants market fitments under a trade name, these fittings are manufactured for them by one of the numerous pottery firms who may supply identical items to other merchants who in turn market them under their own trade name.

9.6.2 Sinks.

Fireclay sinks to BS 1206 – usually referred to as 'Belfast' sinks supported on build-in cantilever brackets or strap brackets and tubular leg supports. Taps are fitted above the sink.

Stainless steel sinks for domestic purposes to BS 1244. A wide variety is obtainable from single bowl, single drainer units to double drainer units with several bowls which sometimes incorporate waste disposal units. Taps are mounted on perforations through the rear top edge of the unit.

An alternative to a stainless steel unit top is the inset bowl which can be fitted in a worktop. Sink tops and inset bowls are also obtainable in vitreous enamelled cast iron or pressed steel, the latter are easily damaged.

Cleaners' sinks are manufactured from glazed fireclay with a hardwood pad on the leading edge, a hinged metal bucket grating, and are fixed on cantilever brackets or strap brackets and legs. Taps are mounted over the top of the sink.

9.6.3 Lavatory basins.

Ceramic lavatory basins to BS 1188. Sizes vary considerably, usual sizes are 559 × 406 mm or 635 × 457 mm. Fixed on cantilever brackets, build-in or screw-on towel rail brackets, strap brackets and tubular legs or pedestals. Either separate taps or mixer fittings fitted to perforations on side or rear edge of fitting. They are obtainable in white or coloured. The range of colours available varies between different manufacturers.

Basins are also available in vitreous enamelled cast iron or pressed steel, stainless steel or polypropylene.

Basins may be fitted individually or in ranges with overlap joints. A further refinement is the vanitory unit comprising an inset basin on a marble or formica covered worktop.

9.6.4 W.C. suites.

W.C. pans to BS 1213, plastic seats BS 1254, wooden seats BS 2089, flushing cisterns and pipes BS 1125, ball valves to BS 1212, copper ball valve floats BS 1968 or plastic floats BS 2456.

Suites may be high or low level. The high level suite does not take up as much space as the low level suite whilst the latter may generally be fitted below the level of window sills which is sometimes a design advantage.

Low level suites may be the wash-down type with a single trap outlet and flushing cistern fitted to the wall above the pan and connected with a short flush pipe, alternatively the suite may be close-coupled with the cistern fitted directly on to the pan.

A better quality fitting is the double trapped syphonic suite.

High and low level suites are obtainable in white or coloured.

Where floor areas are required to be kept clear for cleaning, pans can be corbel pattern, mounted on a cast iron chair which is built into the wall.

SANITARY INSTALLATION

When a range of W.C. suites is required, a combined flushing cistern should be fitted (preferably in a duct behind the range).

Stainless steel W.C. pans can also be obtained.

9.6.5 Baths.

Vitreous enamelled cast iron baths to BS 1189 with rectangular top are available in various lengths 1524 mm–1676 mm–1829 mm. Similar baths are available in vitreous enamelled, pressed steel, acrylic plastic or fibreglass obtainable in white or coloured.

Taps may be fixed in a variety of positions around the rim of the bath. They may be separate taps, mixer or a mixer incorporating a shower fitting.

Baths are normally supplied with an overflow outlet and pipework which is connected to the side of the bath waste outlet, which incorporates a special connector for this purpose. As an alternative, a combined waste and overflow fitting is available which permits the use of a normal deep seal trap (see Fig. 9.3). Another type of combined

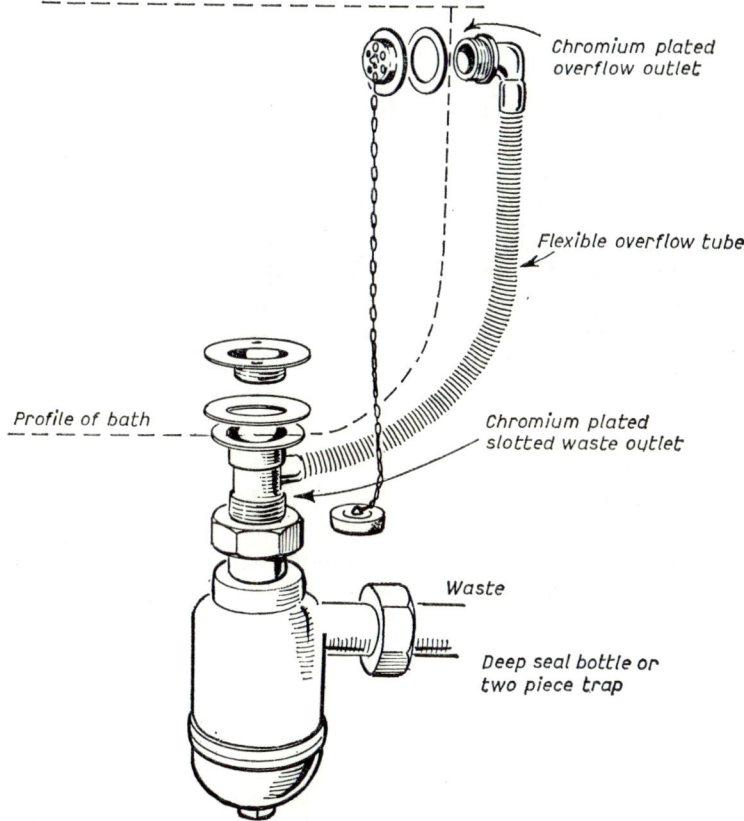

Fig. 9.3 Combined waste and overflow fitting.

waste and overflow permits the connection of the adjacent W.C. flushing cistern's overflow.

9.6.6 Urinals.

White glazed fireclay slab urinals (with or without division pieces) require a raised step or chase in floor to accommodate the channel. The waste trap and pipe are suspended at high level over the floor below, except on ground floor where the outlet may be connected direct to drainage system.

Slab urinals may also be obtained in stainless steel or fibreglass. The size of automatic flushing cisterns is calculated on the basis of 4·546 litre per 610 mm length of slab or per division.

Bowl urinals in vitreous china, stainless steel or fibreglass are normally screwed to wall and provided with individual traps. Waste pipes are fixed at low level below bowls. Separate division pieces may be screwed to walls between bowls.

Automatic flushing cisterns are fitted with a syphon box and a valve by the Water Board to regulate the flushing operation at set intervals, the cisterns do not require overflow pipes.

9.6.7 Bidets.

Bidets are normally fitted with a mixer fitting and pop-up waste together with a selector which feeds the mixed water via an upward jet when the fitting is in use or around the rim as a flushing action on completion of use. Waste fittings for bidets are similar to lavatory basins. They are obtainable in white or coloured.

9.6.8 Drinking fountains.

Glazed fireclay, porcelain enamelled cast iron, stainless steel or chromium-plated brass, wall-mounted or pedestal drinking fountains are available. The jet nozzle should be so placed as to prevent contamination and the water supply controlled by a self-closing, non-concussive valve to the approval of the local Water Board.

9.6.9 Showers.

Shower trays can be constructed *in situ* and lined with tiles, or be manufactured in terrazzo, glazed fireclay, fibreglass or plastic. Mixer fittings should be the thermostatic anti-scald type. If several showers are fitted in a range, then one mixing valve can be fitted to supply water at a pre-selected temperature to each shower outlet, a strainer should also be incorporated in the distribution pipework.

SANITARY INSTALLATION 85

9.7
Measurement

The following points may assist measurement.

Standard Method of Measurement Clause

9.7.1 Joints to drain.   S9(*g*)(*i*)

9.7.2 Pipework is measured over all fittings with the following exceptions:

    (*a*) W.C. connectors and vent pipe roof connectors   S9(*g*)(*ii*)
    (*b*) Traps.
    (*c*) Thimbles, ferrules and caulking bushes.   S.17

9.7.3 Fittings are enumerated as extra over the pipes in which they occur with the exception of those listed in 9.7.2.   S.11(*a*)

9.7.4 Branch joints are described by the diameter of the main pipe, then the diameter of the branch (see Fig. 9.4).

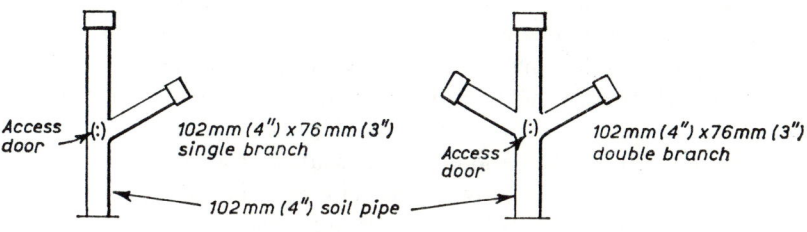

Fig. 9.4 Typical branch joints.

9.7.5 Branches are manufactured to the following degrees $92\tfrac{1}{2}°$, $95°$, $100°$, $112\tfrac{1}{2}°$, $120°$, $135°$, $145°$ and $157\tfrac{1}{2}°$, in order to arrive at alternative angles to suit the requirements of individual installations a bend is usually fitted into the branch arm with angles varying from $92\tfrac{1}{2}°$–$157\tfrac{1}{2}°$. It is not necessary to state when measuring the degrees of the respective angles.

9.7.6 Branches or tees used in soil or waste pipes should always sweep into the direction of the flow.

9.7.7 Where a swept branch joint is measured on a welded copper waste or soil pipe the description should include the made bend necessary to sweep the branch into the direction of the flow.   S9(*e*)(*ii*)

9.7.8 Made bends on copper waste and vent pipes may be

	Standard Method of Measurement Clause
fabricated on site up to and including 51 mm diameter. Bends on pipes over this diameter are usually made by means of manufactured fittings, bending machines capable of bending pipes in excess of 51 mm diameter are cumbersome and expensive to install on site.	S.10

9.7.9 A number of manufacturers supply copper bends to the angles listed in BS 659 with ends flared for welding.

9.7.10 Copper pipework up to 51 mm diameter should be BS 659 in order that made bends may be fabricated on site. Pipework exceeding 51 mm diameter should be as BS 3931 which is cheaper than copper tube to BS 659.

9.7.11 Where a cast iron pipe terminates as a ventilating pipe above roof level a beaded end should be measured. This is the spigot end cut off a length of pipe. The cut end is caulked into the socket of the topmost pipe leaving the beaded end of pipe at the top of the stack; this helps to prevent corrosion.	S.10

9.7.12 Where pipes project through a sloping roof a sheet metal flashing slate should be measured (lead or copper). The space between the slate and the pipe should be pointed with a non-setting mastic. Preformed manufactured flashing plates for various pipe sizes are available.

9.7.13 Galvanized wire balloons are available from 51 mm diameter upwards and may be used on cast iron pipes. If copper stack pipes have been used copper wire balloons should be fitted. Copper or lead pipework with an internal diameter less than 51 mm should have cross wired ends in lieu of wire balloons.

9.7.14 PVC balloon guards are available to suit different diameters of pipes.

9.7.15 Jointing W.C. outlet to soil pipe – where a pan is fixed on a solid floor a mastic or cement joint should be measured, when the pan is fixed to a wooden floor the joint should be in non-hardening mastic.	S.9(g)(i)

9.7.16 Sanitary fittings should be fully described including the material from which they are manufactured (e.g. porcelain enamelled cast iron, stainless steel, white glazed fireclay or vitreous china, etc.), waste outlet and valves, the method of fixing brackets or other supports. Traps to basins, baths and sinks, etc. should not generally be included in the description of the sanitary fitting, but should be enumerated separately.

CHAPTER 10

Cold water installation, fire-fighting, etc.

General

A cold water installation normally consists of the following:

10.1

A communication pipe from the water mains to the water authorities stopcock, usually positioned just inside the site boundary – this pipe service is normally provided and installed by the local water authority.

10.2

Service pipes, which are subject to mains pressure, can be sub-divided into two groups, those below ground and those above ground.

10.3

For service pipes below the ground the most common pipework used is copper tube to BS 1386. This tube is flexible and is supplied in rolls and laid continuously, thus limiting the number of joints below ground. Other tubes used for underground service pipes include heavy gauge copper to BS 61, polythene to BS 1972 and 3284, PVC to BS 3505, lead to BS 602 Table 1 and to BS 1085 Table 1, galvanized steel to BS 1387, spun-iron to BS 1211, asbestos to BS 486.

10.4

For the services above ground copper tubing to BS 659 and 3931 is most commonly used. It should be noted that the difference between copper tubes to BS 659 and 3931 is that the bendability factor has been omitted from tubes manufactured to BS 3931, thus making it impracticable to 'pull' bends (sometimes called 'made' bends) in the tube on site. All fittings used in conjunction with tubes to BS 3931 should be manufactured fittings. The most economic system from the cost point of view is where the main cold water runs are in copper tube to BS 3931 and where the connections to fittings in copper tube are to BS 659 – the latter being suitable for pulled bends.

COLD WATER INSTALLATION, FIRE-FIGHTING, ETC.

10.5

Other tubes used for service pipes above ground are lead to BS 602 and to BS 1085, galvanized steel to BS 1387, spun iron to BS 1211 and polythene to BS 1972.

10.6

At the point of entry into a building a stop valve and drain off cock should be provided on the water main. The stop valve should be of the loose jumper type to prevent reverse flow.

10.7

The two most common types of cold water installation are:

10.7.1 Direct – where all sanitary and other fittings are directly connected to the rising main.

10.7.2 Indirect – using a cold water storage tank, where only drinking water points and the tank are fed from the main.

10.8

The indirect cold water installation is the more common of the two systems. Its main advantages are:

10.8.1 That a reserve of water is available in the event of mains failure.

10.8.2 Peak demand on the mains is reduced.

10.8.3 Smaller diameter service pipes can be used and these give a more even demand than the larger pipes required for direct supply, making main installation more economical and reducing pressure fluctuations in the main.

10.8.4 The noise factor is usually reduced due to lower pressure than that in the direct system – the lower pressure enables cylinders and other fittings to be of lighter construction.

10.8.5 The risk of back-syphonage to the mains is reduced.

Its main disadvantages are:

10.8.6 Additional space is required to house the storage tank.

10.8.7 The additional cost of tank, its supports and insulation etc.

10.8.8 The possibility of water pollution due to the protective cover being misplaced.

10.9

Boosted systems

Where the mains pressure is inadequate boosting equipment should be installed on the service pipe to force the water up to the storage tanks. There are basically two forms of boosting equipment: (*a*) Duplicate pump sets and (*b*) pneumatic booster sets. Whichever system is used it may be necessary to install a break tank prior to the pumps as some water boards will not permit pumping direct off the main.

90   THE MEASUREMENT OF ENGINEERING SERVICES

Fig. 10.1 shows a duplicate pump set boosted water supply system which operates as described below.

(*a*) The break tank, the drinking water and those floors within mains pressure are fed directly from the main. (*Note:* mains pressure water varies throughout the country – in parts of London it is about 30 psi (206,850 N/m² or 2·0685 bar). One foot head is equivalent to 0·434 psi

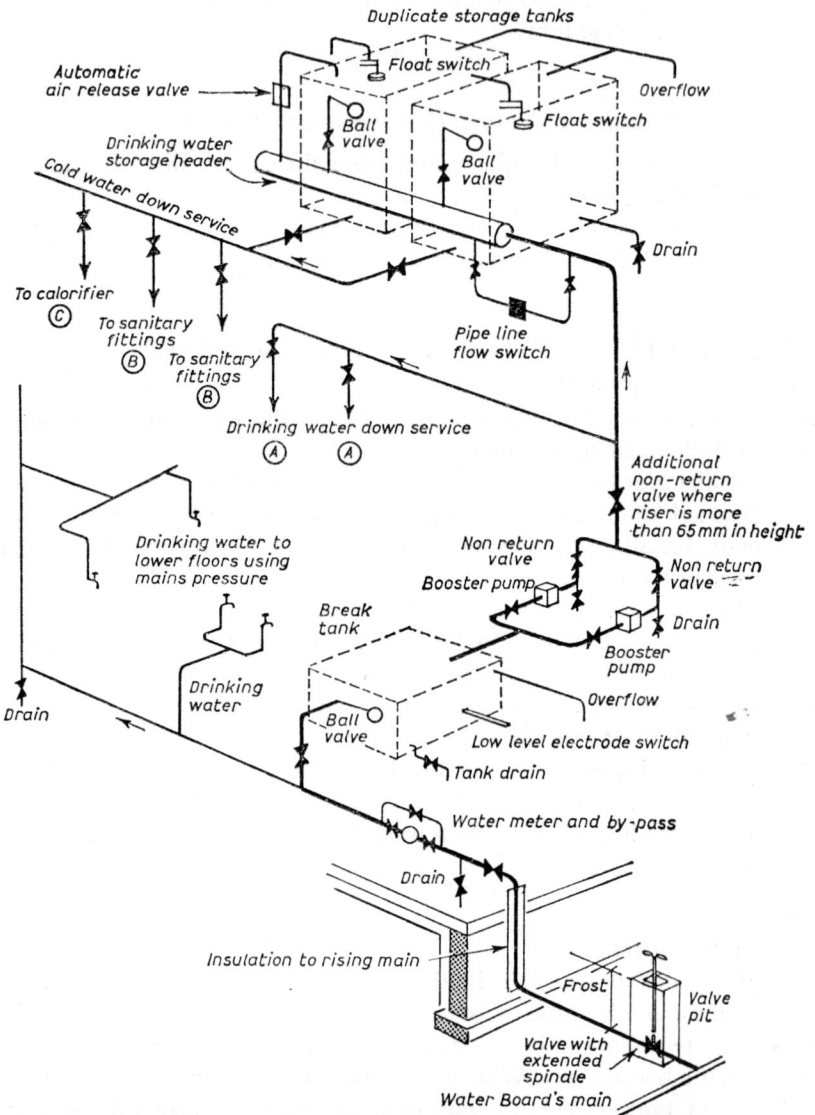

Fig. 10.1   Cold water boosted system – duplicate pumps and break tank.

COLD WATER INSTALLATION, FIRE-FIGHTING, ETC. 91

– on this basis water pressure in those areas could serve fittings up to 21·336 m above mains level (30)/(·434).

(*b*) From the break tank the water is pumped to the drinking water storage header normally a 102 mm diameter tube fitted with an air release valve, which allows air to be vented from or to enter the pipework. From this header the drinking water supplies (lines A) serve the upper floors by gravity. The level of water in the header is controlled by a float switch which operates the pumps.

(*c*) The pump is operated by a time delay unit in order to refill the header and to replace water as it is used.

(*d*) The storage tanks are fed from the rising main and the water level of the tanks is controlled by float switches which cut the pumps 'in' and 'out' as required, the float switches override the time delay unit. Down-service (lines B) are connected to the sanitary fittings and (line C) the calorifiers.

(*e*) The break tank is fitted with a low level electrode switch – this turns off the pumps in case of water mains failure.

The booster pumps controls are mounted on a control panel which contains duplicate starters each having hand auto switch, pilot lights (to show pump

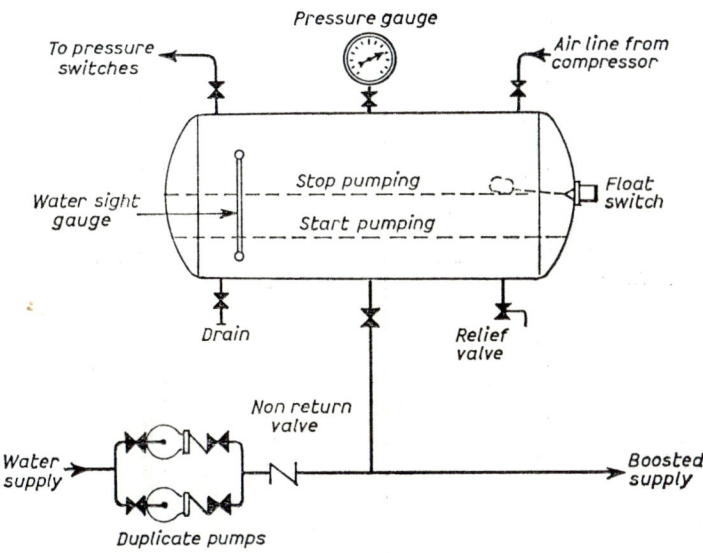

Fig. 10.2 Cold water boosted system – pneumatic booster set.

running) and tripped current delay unit, etc. This panel can be purchased as a composite item from the pump manufacturer.

The second form of boosting equipment, the pneumatic booster set, basically comprises two or three pumps, a control panel, a pressure vessel and

92   THE MEASUREMENT OF ENGINEERING SERVICES

an air compressor. The system includes a pneumatic pressure vessel which contains both air and water under pressure. The pump cycle is controlled by the air pressures which occur when water is drawn off and subsequently replaced. Generally the pressure at the highest point should not fall below 10 psi and gauge pressure (·8 bar) nor exceed 25 psi gauge pressure (2 bar). For this reason the settings of the pressure switches controlling the pumps should switch the pumps on at the lower pressure and off at the higher. Fig. 10.2 shows the diagrammatic layout of this system of controls.

10.10
Cold water installations to buildings of 15 storeys or more

The main problem with buildings above 15 storeys is excessive static water pressure and the limited amount of roof storage permissible due to the weight of water. For instance the water pressure at the lowest point in a

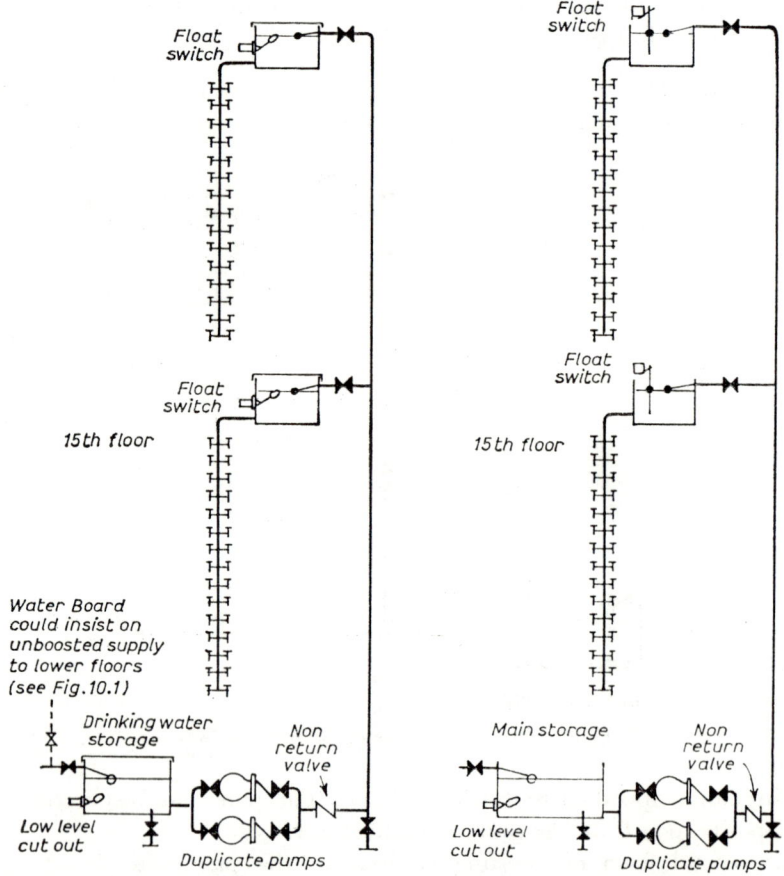

Fig. 10.3   Cold water boosted system – duplicate pumps.

COLD WATER INSTALLATION, FIRE-FIGHTING, ETC.

20-storey building could be in the region of 5·99 bars above normal mains pressure (20 × 3·048 m × 0·098 bars).

This problem is overcome by the use of zones. Each zone supplies about 15 floors each, thus limiting the static pressure possible in each to about 448,160 N/m² or 4·4816 bars (15 × 3·048 m × 0·098 bars).

Water storage is divided between two or more tanks. In some cases the uppermost floors are supplied from roof level and the lower zone from tanks placed about half way up. It may be preferable to have the majority of the storage at ground level with smaller break tanks supplying a number of intermediate zones. These smaller break tanks are supplied direct from the pump riser. Some water authorities require the drinking water storage to be separated from the water required for general purposes. About one hour's storage is sufficient for each of the tanks. The main storage break tank is fixed at ground level.

Fig. 10.3 shows a 30-storey block of flats, the water supply is divided into two zones, the pressure at the lowest outlet in any zone will then not exceed 65 psi (448,160 N/m² or 4·4816 bar). When ball valves at different levels are fed from the same pumped riser, regulation (by means of valves or orifice plates) should be provided for the lower ball valves so that they do not rob the upper ones. A float switch should be fitted in each tank for pump control and another in the main storage tank supplying the pumps to prevent them operating should the tanks become dry.

10.11

Measurement – boosted systems (see Fig. 10.1). When measuring note the following:

10.11.1 The stop cock at the site boundary should be provided with a suitable operating key.
10.11.2 The builder's work in connection with the stop cock pit should be measured in detail.
10.11.3 All valves should comply with the water board's requirements.
10.11.4 Supports may be required for the water meter – which is provided with a line size by-pass and should be suitably isolated.
10.11.5 The break tank may be required to have an air tight and rust proof lid with vent pipe incorporating filter, etc., if the water in this tank is to be used for drinking purposes.
10.11.6 Pumps may require pressure gauges, flexible connections on the suction and discharge side to avoid noise vibration on pipe-work. Strainers may be required on the suction side.
10.11.7 A cork pad should be provided to the concrete base for the pumps or alternatively suitable anti-vibration mountings.
10.11.8 Connections to pumps are usually a different size to the line in which the pumps are mounted, reducers must therefore be measured

on these connections. The engineer will state whether it is permitted to reduce the pipe size prior to the isolating valves.

10.11.9 Certain non-return valves are suitable only for horizontal or vertical mountings.

10.11.10 Where flanged valves are installed next to each other (see Fig. 10.1, non-return valve and isolating valve), they are usually bolted together. It is advisable to check that the flanges are from the same table in BS 10 (table D is the most common).

10.11.11 The type of ball valve should be stated, i.e. Portsmouth or equilibrium, high or low pressure etc. with copper or plastic float, with silencer tube.

10.11.12 In addition to normal overflow pipes the water board may require warning pipes.

10.11.13 The description of tanks should give details of all connections, the cover and the perforations in the cover, access to ball valves, vent cowl etc., internal and external access ladders and any other special features.

10.11.14 With pressed steel or fibreglass section tanks ascertain whether these are to be internally or externally flanged, also ascertain the details of the tank supports and by whom these are to be provided.

10.11.15 Ascertain whether any linings are required between tank supports and tanks.

10.11.16 Ascertain if the tanks are to be painted internally and externally and if any special finishes are required.

10.11.17 Ascertain that the electrical connections to apparatus are included in the electrical bill of quantities and that starters for motors are not measured twice. Also ascertain that all electrode float switches have been included.

10.11.18 Ascertain whether pipework is to be fixed with holderbats or screw-on brackets. Where the specification states that either may be used, ensure that when 'screw to wall' is measured that cutting and pinning is not included in the main bill of quantities under builder's work in connection.

10.11.19 Isolating valves should generally be allowed in the following positions, (*a*) around all plant and equipment, (*b*) to all main branches and (*c*) to a branch serving a range of fittings.

10.11.20 Drain off cocks should be allowed on (*a*) the dead side of isolating valves and (*b*) the suction connections of pumps. Provision should be made when measuring cold water storage tanks for a drain line.

10.12

Storage cisterns

Cisterns are usually open-topped rectangular containers used to store cold water – and may be fitted with a loose fitting cover to exclude impurities. Cisterns are available in the following materials:

10.12.1 Galvanized mild steel to BS 417.
10.12.2 Asbestos cement to BS 2777.
10.12.3 Polythene and polypropylene to BS 4213.
10.12.4 Sectional cast iron or pressed steel to BS 1563 and 1564 respectively.

10.13

Galvanized cisterns are inexpensive and robust, but are liable to rust if the galvanized coating is damaged. They are obtainable either welded or riveted and are available in two grades – (A) or (B), Grade A being the heavier gauge. Sizes vary from 18 litres actual capacity to 3364 litres actual capacity.

10.14

Asbestos cement cisterns are also inexpensive, rustless and rot proof, but are subject to damage by frost. Care should be taken to ensure that the cisterns are thoroughly cleaned before use to remove any asbestos particles. Sizes are from 17 litres actual capacity to 709 litres actual capacity.

10.15

Polythene and polypropylene cisterns are rot proof, resistant to frost and chemical damage and are available in sizes from 18 litres actual capacity to 455 litres actual capacity.

10.16

Cast iron and fibreglass sectional cisterns are made up of a series of flanged square plates which are bolted together and jointed with gaskets. The plates on the cast iron tanks are 610 mm, 914 mm or 1219 mm square, 10 mm to 13 mm thick. Cisterns are available in sizes up to 12 m square and 3·6 m deep. Pressed steel sectional tanks are available in m^2 plates, and cisterns can be made up to 16 m square, 4·9 m deep.

10.17

Fire-fighting installations include:

10.17.1 Fire brigade hydrants – when the use of hydrants in the roadway would entail extensive runs of fire hose – hydrants are placed in strategic points in the building. They consist of a valve controlled mains water outlet (normally 63 mm diameter) into which can be screwed a stand pipe with a hose coupling at its head. The

96   THE MEASUREMENT OF ENGINEERING SERVICES

hydrant point may be contained in a brick or concrete chamber with a cast iron lid.

10.17.2 Dry or wet risers installation are usually required by the local authority for large buildings – (the fire officer would decide if they are required).

Dry riser installation comprises an inlet box in which an inlet breaching piece is housed from which a large diameter (usually 102 mm) pipe is run vertically from basement to highest floor (this may be the roof). At each floor level a 63 mm landing valve is connected to the riser. At the highest point of the riser an air release valve (usually 25 mm) is installed in order to release air when water is pumped through the riser and also a landing valve to permit testing without inconveniencing the occupants of the building – see Fig. 10.4. The dry rise is usually galvanized heavy weight mild steel tube to BS 1387.

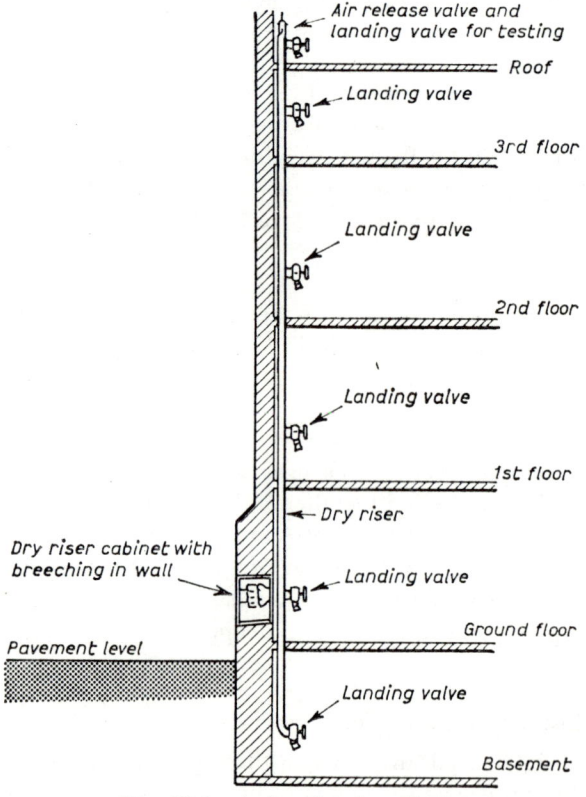

Fig. 10.4   A dry-riser installation.

Wet riser installation. A local authority usually requires wet risers to be installed in tall buildings in lieu of dry risers, the height of the

COLD WATER INSTALLATION, FIRE-FIGHTING, ETC.

building is the determining factor and varies between 15 m and 60 m throughout the country. Wet risers are permanently connected to the mains supply and must be equipped with duplicate pumps each able to deliver 23 litres/sec against a head of 525 kN/m^2 at the highest outlet.

The pressure in the hoses should not exceed the latter figure and orifice plates should be installed at each valve to restrict the flow when the valve is open. It may be necessary to store 45 m^3 of water based on the need to feed three outlets for 30 minutes at a rate of 7·6 litres per second. Should the height of the building

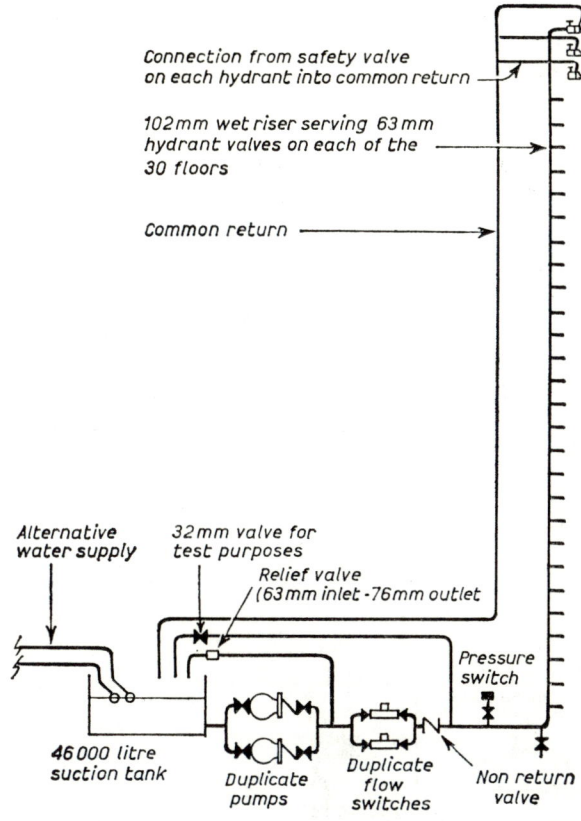

Fig. 10.5 Wet riser.

exceed 60 m it may be necessary to instal a break tank and a second level of pumping (see Fig. 10.5). If there is a suitable standby electrical supply available the prime movers for the pumps may be electric motors, otherwise specially designed diesel engines, which can start automatically on full load from cold, should be used. Pumps should be arranged for both manual and auto setting and it should only be possible to stop the pumps manually. An audible and visible alarm should be given when the pumping plant is brought into operation and direct connection to the fire station is usually required.

10.17.3 Hose reels.

The main design factor is that the fire-fighting system should be

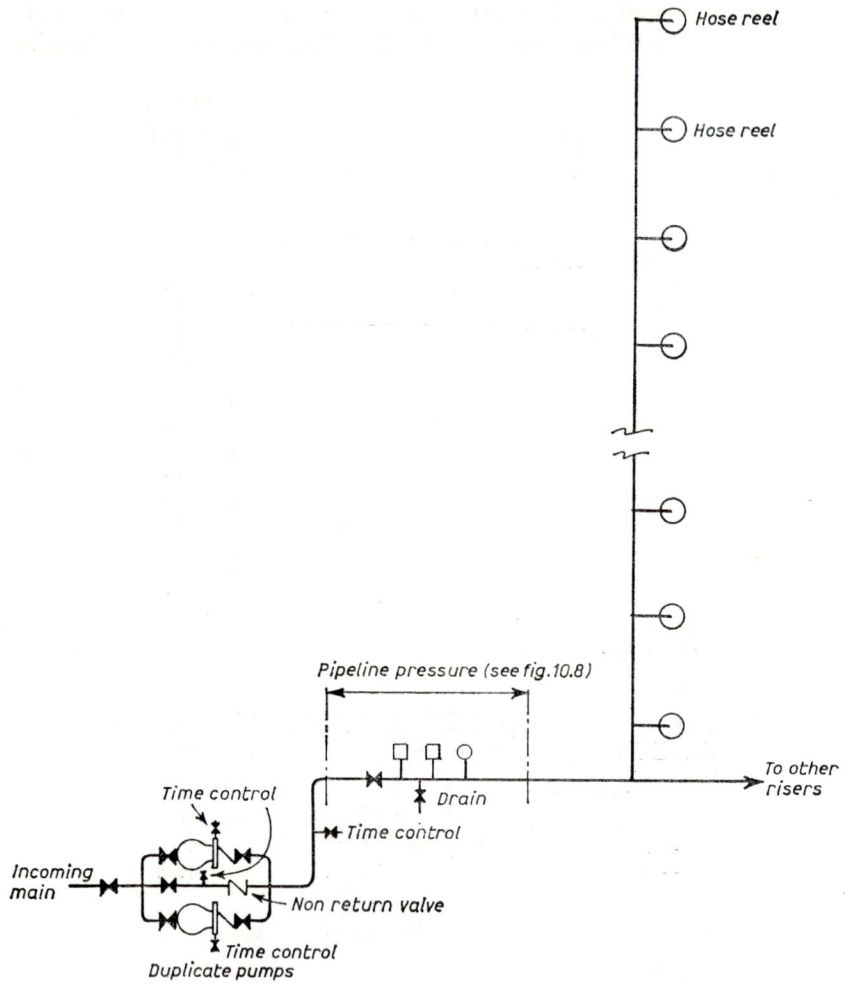

Fig. 10.6 Pumped hose reel installation – with pipeline pressure unit.

capable of operating three reels simultaneously, at a flow rate of 0·38 litres per second at a pressure of 210 kN/m² at the connection to each reel. If the authority's main cannot meet these require-

COLD WATER INSTALLATION, FIRE-FIGHTING, ETC. 99

ments then pumps must be installed. Some authorities insist that a break tank be installed from which the pump supply is provided.

Fig. 10.6 shows a pumped hose reel installation incorporating a pipe line pressure unit, which works as follows: When the system is at rest it is pressurized to the maximum head by the pump and this pressure is retained by the non-return valve. When the non-return valves are opened the pipe line pressure is reduced and then this is equivalent to 137,895 N/m^2 or 1·37895 bars. At the highest hose reel, the pressure switch will start the selected pump. The pump will increase the pressure to 206,840 N/m^2 or 2·0684 bars at the top reel, but if this pump does not raise the pressure in the pipe line after the call from the pressure switch then after a time delay of 10 seconds the stand-by pump will be cut in by the second pressure switch. Once started the pumps will run for a minimum of three minutes to overcome any 'hunting' of the pressure switches.

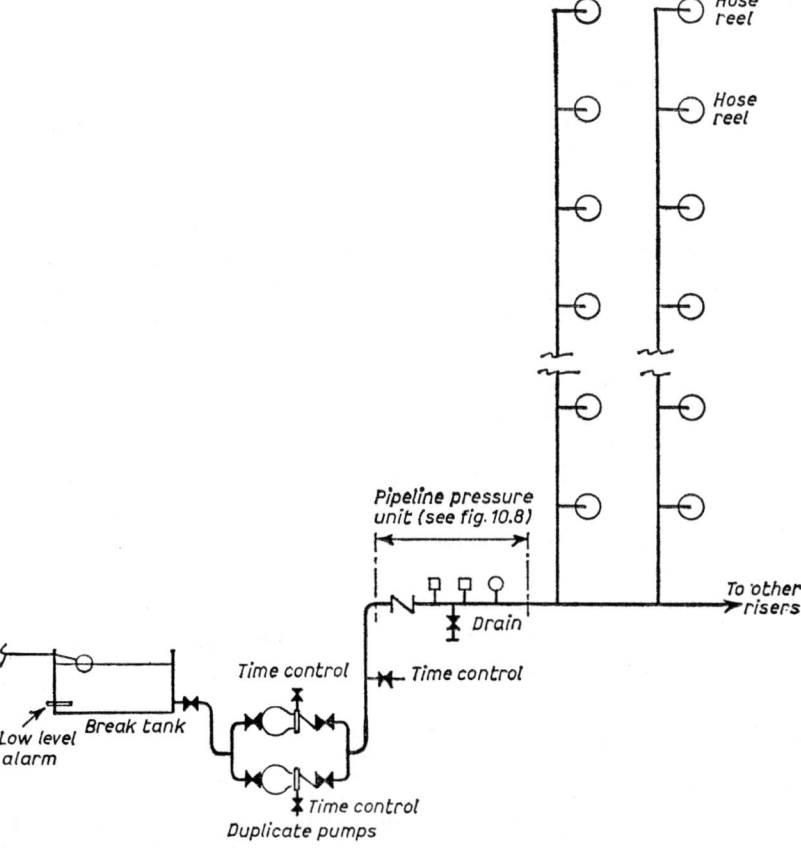

Fig. 10.7 Pumped hose reel installation as Fig. 10.6 but with break tank.

The time switch to provide this minimum running period of the stand-by pump should be incorporated with the other controls in the wall mounted control panel which is usually supplied by the pump manufacturers.

Fig. 10.7 shows the duplicate pump boosted system, but this time incorporating a break tank.

Fig. 10.8 shows a pipeline pressure unit.

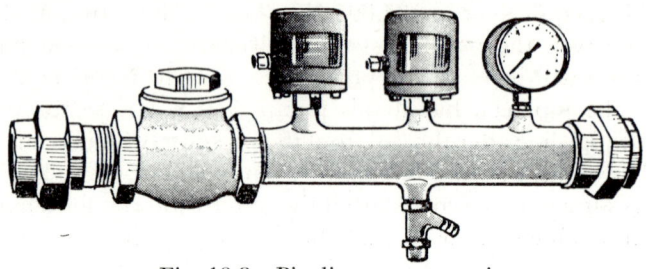

Fig. 10.8   Pipeline pressure unit.

10.18

Measurement – fire-fighting installation. When measuring, note the points included under paragraph 10.11 and in addition:

10.18.1   A test cock should be provided to each pump and to the common discharge from the pumps.

10.18.2   The pipeline pressure unit is available as a composite item from certain manufacturers and it comprises a union inlet, a non-return valve, two pressure switches, a drain cock and a pressure gauge.

10.18.3   The description of the hose reels should state clearly whether they are fixed pattern, swinging pattern, recessed, non-recessed etc., also the method of operating the reel and method of fixing to wall.

10.18.4   That it may be necessary to take down and re-fix the reels for decoration purposes, if so, this should be measured (see SMM, S106).

10.18.5   That hose reel installations are generally in copper tube to BS 659 or BS 3931 or galvanized mild steel tube to BS 1387.

10.18.6   That in dry riser installations $102 \times 102 \times 64$ mm sweep tees are used at each level for the connection of the landing valve. At this point a hexagonal nipple must be provided between the tee piece and the landing valve. As hexagonal nipples are a fitting they must, therefore, be measured.

10.19

Valves and stop cocks – the following are in use on water installations.

10.19.1   Sluice valves.

These are usually cast iron and fullway to BS 1218 and have screwed or flanged ends, or sockets for caulking to cast iron. They are available in sizes from 51 mm to 305 mm and are normally used on large mains. They are fullway in order to reduce resistance of the flow to a minimum (i.e. when open, the bore through the valve is consistent and of equal diameter to the line size).

10.19.2   Copper alloy gate valves.

These are to BS 1952 and have screwed or flanged ends, they are also available with capillary or compression ends. Screwed and flanged gate valves are available in sizes up to 152 mm and the capillary and compression ended valves in sizes up to and including 76 mm.

They are used on heating and hot water installations, cold water supplies from the storage cisterns and low pressure systems. They are obtainable with lock-shield or wheel-head. They offer less resistance to the flow of water than a normal stop cock. Operation is as described for the sluice valves.

10.19.3   Stop valve or stop cock.

These are to BS 1010 and are obtainable in sizes up to 64 mm and are available with screwed, flanged, compression and capillary ends. They have greater resistance to the water flow than fullway valves. They are obtainable in gunmetal or brass.

10.19.4   Copper alloy check valves (non-return valve).

These are to BS 1953 and are available in three types, these being (*a*) piston, (*b*) disc, (*c*) swinging type in sizes from 12 mm to 102 mm with flanged or screwed ends. A check valve allows water to travel one way only and they are used on cold and hot service and heating installations on the discharge side of pumps and on the by-pass. They are commonly installed on thermostatic mixing valves, so that when the hot and cold pressures are unequal the non-return valve will prevent the higher pressure service forcing its way into the lower pressure.

10.19.5   Ball valves.

These are to BS 1212 and are available in sizes from 10 mm to 51 mm. The low pressure type is for systems up to 275,790 N/m^2 or 2·7579 bars 28 m head. Medium pressure from 275,790 N/m^2 or 2·7579 bars to 689,480 N/m^2 or 6·8948 bars 70·5 m head. High pressure 689,480 N/m^2 or 6·8948 bars to 1,378,960 N/m^2 or 13·7896 bars 141 m head. The low pressure type is used on W.C.s connected to storage cisterns giving quieter performance than when directly connected to mains. The fitting of a silencing tube as part of the ball valve will help to reduce noise. Descriptions of all valves should state whether the ball is to be copper or plastic and if a silencing tube is required or not. For sizes over 51 mm flanged ball valves are obtainable. The equilibrium ball valve is suitable for pressures of up to 482,630 N/m^2 or 4·8263 bars depending on size and are available from 39 mm to 152 mm. They can be obtained with screwed inlet, but are usually flanged. The equilibrium ball valve is used where large quantities of water are involved and are quieter than ball valves to BS 1212 of similar size; they are, however, only suitable for medium or low pressure water supplies.

10.20

Typical descriptions might be as follows:

10.20.1 For a cold water tank.

Galvanized pressed steel 54,553 litres nominal capacity externally flanged cold water storage tank as supplied by XYZ size 6·096 × 3·658 × 2·438 m with 3·658 m wide centre division complete with all stays, cleats, nuts and washers and No. 2 internal and No. 1 external access ladders, 3 mm galvanized flat cover with No. 2 457 mm diameter hinged manhole covers and 102 mm diameter cowl ventilator painted internally with one priming coat and two coats of Wailes Dove Bituros solution and two coats of Wailes Dove Bituros hot enamel and tank and lid externally painted one coat of calcium plumbate primer, two coats of Wailes Dove Cream Bitumastic solution except the bottoms, which shall be primed and painted with two coats of Wailes Dove Bitumastic No. 50, including perforations and flange pads for No. 2 152 mm diameter down services, No. 2 102 mm diameter down services, No 2 102 mm diameter overflows, No. 2 64 mm diameter rising mains, No. 2 39 mm diameter wash outs and No. 2 25 mm diameter warning pipes and fixing on supports (by others) in tank room approximately 27·432 m above ground level.

10.20.2 For steel cisterns.

Galvanized mild steel cistern to BS 417 Grade A type SC350 size 1524 × 1143 × 914 mm high 1046 litres capacity with 1·994 mm BG cover with hinged access lined with 25 mm polyurethane as sound attenuation and painted internally with one priming coat and two coats of Wailes Dove Bituros solution and two coats of Wailes Dove Bituros hot enamel and tank and lid externally painted one coat of calcium plumbate primer, two coats of Wailes Dove Cream Bitumastic solution except the bottoms, which shall be primed and painted with two coats of Wailes Dove Bitumastic No. 50, including perforations and flanged pads for 76 mm diameter rising main and down service and 51 mm diameter overflow and fixing on supports (by others) approximately 2·438 m above basement level.

10.20.3 For a hose reel.

Messrs XYZ Fig. No.   automatic recess swinging reel type with 30·480 m of 18 mm hose complete with nozzle, instruction plate, reel mounted on door and cabinet plugged and screwed to wall.

10.20.4 For a landing valve.

64 mm Messrs XYZ Fig. No.   gunmetal gate pattern landing valve flanged to BST 'D' with 64 mm instantaneous female coupling with removable plug screwed and chain including handwheel marked with OPEN and SHUT directions and secured in the shut position with leather strap and padlock.

10.20.5 For a dry riser inlet cabinet.

569 × 539 × 305 mm Dry riser inlet cabinet with door glazed with 6 mm wire glass and indicated by the words LFB DRY MAIN INLET painted on inner face of glass in 76 mm block letters, the door to be fastened with spring lock which can also be operated from inside without key after glass is broken, a permanent notice with 31 mm high letters to be fitted in cabinet with the words 'LOW LEVEL DRAIN VALVE IN BASEMENT STAIR LOBBY'.

10.20.6 For a dry-riser pumping-in breeching.

4-way malleable iron dry-riser pumping-in breeching with four 64 mm instantaneous male couplings each incorporating a back pressure valve and protected by a brass blank cap and secured with a captive chain, the breeching to include a 152 mm outlet at the back flanged to BST 'D' and a 25 mm gunmetal drain valve with brass blank cap, chain and handwheel.

CHAPTER 11

Hot water installation

11.1

A centralized domestic hot water supply system normally comprises the following:

11.1.1 Cold water storage system with its associated cold water supply.
11.1.2 A cold water down-feed pipe from the storage cistern to the hot water storage vessel.
11.1.3 The heating unit which may be operated by solid fuel, oil, gas, electric, a steam to water calorifier, or a water to water calorifier.
11.1.4 The hot water storage vessel.
11.1.5 The pipework installation complete with valves, cocks, draw-off taps, thermostats and controls.
11.1.6 Supplementary fittings such as towel rails, drying coils, etc.
11.1.7 Pump sets where required.
11.1.8 Thermal insulation.

11.2

Domestic hot water may either be heated directly by exposing the water supply to the heat source, or indirectly in which case the supply is heated by a coil through which passes a heating medium (water or steam) in the hot water storage vessel.

When the indirect system is used the heating medium (known as the primary supply) is recirculated through the coil and does not mix with the water in the vessel (known as the secondary supply) which is drawn off for domestic use.

11.3

As the central heating installation is not normally required in summer it is often necessary to provide a heat source for the domestic hot water system, this can be a small boiler or an electric immersion heater which should be installed in the storage vessel for summer use.

11.4

It should be noted that the cold water storage system and its associated supply are normally measured as part of the cold water installation.

11.5

Cold water feed to the system. The main consists of a feed pipe from the cold water storage vessel to the hot water storage vessel complete with a lockshield isolating valve in order that the supply can be turned off should the hot water system require to be drained. In some circumstances a cold water meter is installed on this feed – the meter, if installed, should be provided with a by-pass of the same diameter as the main feed – the by-pass should be valved. A drain-off cock should be installed in such a position that will permit the cold feed to be drained down.

11.6

Calorifiers – see section 12.6 and Figs. 11.1, 11.2 and 11.3.

11.6.1 Calorifiers are generally provided in duplicate to permit the closing down of one calorifier so that maintenance may be carried out without affecting the hot water system.

11.6.2 The following should be noted when describing calorifiers:
   (a) galvanized or copper or copper lined mild steel.
   (b) BS 853 covers calorifiers for use in domestic hot water supply and is applicable to all sizes of steam to water, and water to water calorifiers and indirect cylinders where the holding capacity exceeds 227·30 litres.
   (c) For calorifiers below 227·30 litres (pending the issue of a British Standard for the smaller sizes) calorifiers must have a shell thickness of not less than that stated in BS 417 or BS 699.

11.6.3 Each calorifier should have the following mountings:
   (a) Where the capacity exceeds 454·61 litres a thermometer to indicate the temperature of the storage water.
   (b) A pressure relief valve must be fitted to all water to water calorifiers over 227·30 litres capacity and to all steam to water calorifiers.
   (c) A safety valve on the primary supply when an immersion heater is fitted or when a separate boiler is coupled directly to the storage vessel.
   (d) A pressure gauge complete with syphon and cock should be provided to the steam side of each steam to water calorifier.
   (e) An altitude gauge with cock fitted to the water side of each steam to water calorifier and the secondary side of each water to water calorifier should be provided where the holding capacity exceeds 682 litres.
   (f) An automatic temperature regulator should be provided on all steam to water calorifiers and water to water calorifiers where the working temperature of the primary supply is likely to cause an excessive rise to the secondary supply, above its

designed working temperature. A control thermostat should be positioned so that it is not unduly influenced by local heat and clear of the heating coil.

(g) A drain cock should be provided to the secondary side of the calorifiers.

(h) An air relief valve or pipe should be provided to the primary section of the calorifier where air could be trapped during filling and starting operations.

(i) A bolted neck should be provided to permit the removal of the heating coil.

(j) A hand hole and bolted cover should be provided for maintenance purposes.

11.6.4 Calorifiers should be properly insulated and supported, either by means of cradles or brick or concrete piers. Cradles may need lining.

11.6.5 The primary pipework and secondary pipework should be provided with flanges, unions and/or gate valves as required so that the calorifier can be disconnected.

11.6.6 A typical description of a calorifier might be as follows:

Copper calorifier of brazed construction 1422 mm diameter by 2616 mm overall height, 2273 litres capacity to BS 853:1960 Part 2 suitable for a working pressure of 275,790 N/m^2 or 2·7579 bars on the shell and 1,034,210 N/m^2 or 10·3421 bars on the battery and tested at the manufacturer's works to 413,690 N/m^2 or 4·1369 bars on the shell and 1,551,329 N/m^2 or 15·51329 bars on the battery and to be suitable to raise the contents from 10°C to 65·6°C in two hours when fed with primary high pressure hot water at 146·1°C flow and 96°C return. The battery is to be formed from solid drawn copper 'U' tubes and should be removable for cleaning and inspection. The calorifier to be complete with mild steel cradles and the following connections:

25 mm primary flow return flanged table H.
64 mm secondary flow flanged table D.
25 mm secondary return flanged table D.
51 mm cold water feed flanged table D.
39 mm BSP screwed drain connection.
31 mm screwed BSP boss for open vent.
51 mm BSP screwed boss for safety valve.
19 mm BSP screwed boss for 2 No. stats.

and 1 No. bolted inspection cover, including all necessary assembling, placing in position and jointing and 4 times bolting cradle to concrete floor. (All mountings, i.e. safety valve, altitude gauge, thermometer, stats, drain cock and insulation have been measured separately.)

11.6.7 It should be noted that the working pressures and testing pressures are stated within the description of the calorifier as this affects the thickness of the materials to be used, and likewise the cost.

11.7

Copper cylinders for domestic purposes are to BS 699 and galvanized mild steel cisterns, tanks and cylinders to BS 417.

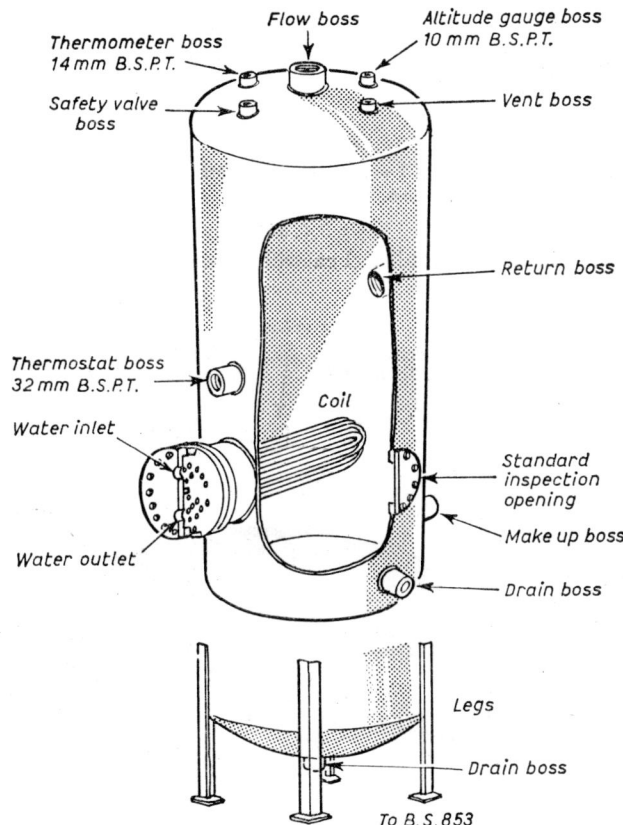

Fig. 11.1 Galvanized mild steel calorifier – water to water vertical.

11.8

Galvanized mild steel cylinders are available to BS 1565 and range in size and capacity from 457 mm internal diameter × 762 mm height over dome, 110 litres capacity to 610 mm internal diameter × 1753 mm height over dome, 455 litres capacity.

11.9

Copper indirect cylinders to BS 1566 are available in sizes ranging from 760 mm external height over dome × 457 mm external diameter, 100 litres

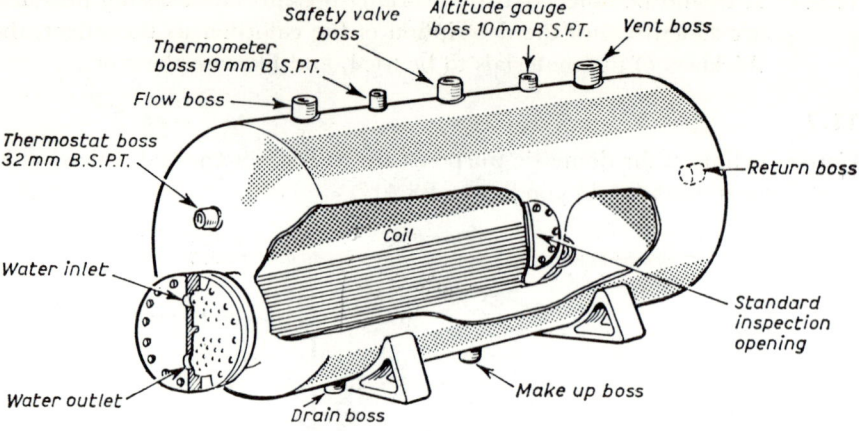

Fig. 11.2 Galvanized mild steel calorifier – water to water horizontal.

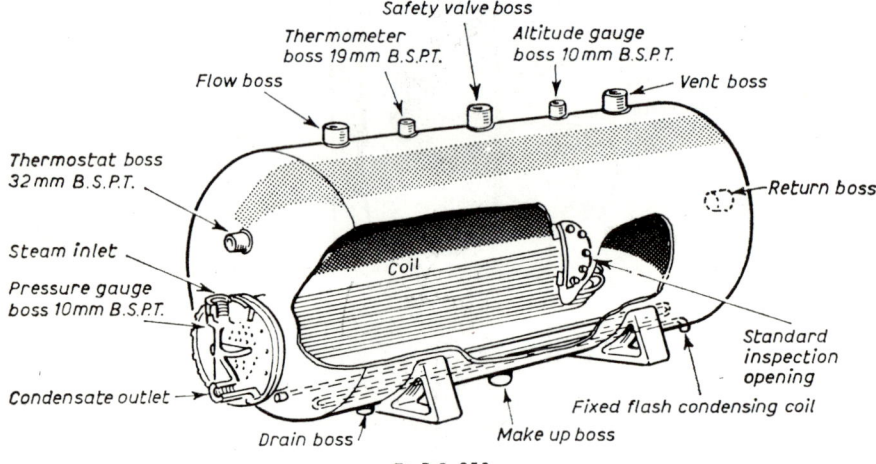

Fig. 11.3 Galvanized mild steel calorifier – steam to water horizontal.

storage capacity to 1758 mm external height over dome × 610 mm external diameter, 418 litres storage capacity.

11.10

Secondary pipework installation comprises the following:

11.10.1 An open vent from the top of the calorifier running over and discharging into the cold water supply tank.

11.10.2 A secondary flow connection from the calorifier to the various hot water outlet points together with the secondary return pipework.

Flow and return pipework should be run to all fittings in order that there is a continuous circulation of water within the system and dead legs are thus avoided. To each fitting or range of fittings there should be an isolating valve on the flow with a drain-off cock installed on the dead side of the isolating valve and a regulating valve on the return.

Appliances such as towel rails, drying coils, should be connected into the hot water pipework and each should be provided with a vent to release air from the system and be suitably isolated.

11.11

Provision should be made within the hot water piping system for the elimination of air, either by means of air bottles at the high points or automatic air eliminators. An air bottle should comprise a length of tubing capped off each end, with a branch on one side connected into the hot water service pipework. From the top of the air bottle a further branch should be connected and this is run to low level and terminated with an isolating valve or air cock.

11.12

Pumps may be required to aid circulation in the secondary flow. A typical system should consist of a pair of in-line pumps connected to the secondary flow with a by-pass to the pumps incorporating an isolating valve and non-return valve in order that the hot water service may be kept working by gravity in the event of pump failure. The pumps should be arranged so that each is isolated on both the suction and the discharge side, and each should have a non-return valve on the discharge. The size of the pump connections are usually smaller than the line size. It should therefore be confirmed with the engineer whether or not the isolating valves adjoining the pumps are to be of line size or pump bore size – the latter being the cheaper – in either situation the necessary reducers to the pumps must be measured.

A typical description of a pump might be as follows:

'Messrs. XYZ model No.   or other approved vertical spindle in-line accelerator to handle 82·273 litres/sec (0.206 bars) at 2·44 m head, having casing and motor support bracket constructed from gunmetal of ample thickness and pressure tested. A fully shrouded gunmetal impeller shall be pinned to the motor shaft with extended hub to carry the crane mechanical seal, and also seal against leakage to the motor shaft. The 0·2496 kW motor shall be of ball bearing design specially selected for quiet running and shall be suitable for 240/1/50 supply. Motor rev./min. 1450. Pump to be complete with air valve, drain plug and water rubber thrower. Pump shall have flanged BST 'D' connection. Pump to have a stable characteristic performance curve and the motor shall be fully non-overloading at all duties. Pump to be fixed at high level on and including hangers incorporating a spring hanger assembly. (*Note:* Starters and flexible connections are measured separately.)'

11.13

Hot water service pipework is usually in copper tube to BS 659 or 3931 with compression or capillary fittings or galvanized mild steel tube to BS 1387 with galvanized malleable iron fittings – the latter is more expensive to install than the former, the introduction of thin wall copper tubes (BS 3931) has assisted in reducing the cost difference between copper and galvanized tube.

11.14

Measurement – domestic hot water installations – where necessary note the points included under section 10.11 and the following additional points:

11.14.1 It may be necessary (or required by the engineers) to provide insulated valve boxes for valves over 44 mm diameter.

11.14.2 That the in-line pumps usually require a set of supports or hanger supports.

11.14.3 That a drain-off cock should be provided generally at all low points within the system to enable a section or all of the system to be drained.

11.14.4 That valves on hot water services should be gunmetal or bronze.

11.14.5 That the pumps on the hot water service systems should have gunmetal impellers and usually gunmetal or bronze bodies.

CHAPTER 12

Low pressure hot water heating installation

12.1

A low pressure hot water heating installation normally comprises the following:

12.1.1 Heat source – boiler, solid fuel, gas, oil fuel or electrode.
12.1.2 Steam to water, or water to water calorifier.
12.1.3 Feed and expansion tank and cold feed.
12.1.4 Distribution system consisting of pipework, fittings and valves.
12.1.5 Heating appliances, radiators, convectors, unit heaters and radiant panels.
12.1.6 Thermal insulation.
12.1.7 Supplementary appliances such as automatic controls, circulating pumps.

12.2

Heat source. When describing boilers it is essential to obtain the manufacturer's literature to ascertain (particularly in package type boilers) what is included with the boiler unit and what mountings are required. In most circumstances the following mountings are required: safety valve, thermometer, altitude gauge, drain-off cock, open vent pipe, automatic damper regulator and boiler temperature limit thermostat. Gas boilers should have a flame failure protection device, gas governor, main control cock and pilot lights. Solid fuel boilers should have a set of stoking and cleaning tools. With oil-fired boilers there should be an oil burner, safety flue stat or photo-electric flame failure device, a control thermostat, a self-closing oil valve in the supply line between the tank and burner with a fusible link release mechanism to operate in the event of fire. (See chapter 13.)

12.3

A typical description of a large boiler for a hotel, hospital or similar building might be as follows:

'Messrs. XYZ or other approved oil-fired radiant heat boiler rated at

10,000,000 Btu/h (2931 kW) reference No. ... of the oil-fired radiant heat type completely insulated and enclosed in an enamelled sheet metal casing suitable for LPHW and constructed to BS 855/2790 and to suit a design working pressure of 999,740 N/m^2 or 9·9974 bars and test pressure 1,310,000 N/m^2 or 13·1 bars and flow and return temperatures of 87·8°C and 71·1°C respectively, and suitable for use with 960 sec. Redwood No. 1 at 37·8°C. Boiler efficiency to be not less than 80% based on the gross calorific value. Each boiler to be of welded mild steel construction and of the three pass pattern and complete with a purpose made fully automatic oil burner. Each boiler to be tested to 1,310,000 N/m^2 or 13·1 bars after installation, and to be complete with drain valve, safety valve, explosion door and regulating damper altitude pressure gauge, flow thermometer, return thermometer, burner thermostats and a complete set of flue clearing tools. A boiler number plate shall be provided on each boiler. The firing method of the boiler shall comply with the *Clean Air Act*. The oil burner shall be a fully automatic pressure jet type suitable for low and high firing. The minimum rating for each burner shall be equal to maximum load at high efficiency. Each burner to be fitted with fully automatic equipment for ignition, and on/off and high/low firing including photo-electric flame-failure device. A spare atomizer shall be provided for each burner. Burner shall be fitted with a gas tight flange at the joint to the boiler front plate. The burner pump to have an air release cock. Motors driving the burners to be generously rated for continuous running on an electric supply of 440 volts 3 phase 50 cycle and conform to relevant BSS and protected against single phasing. The burners and their installation to conform to relevant BSS. Each boiler shall be complete with a pre-wired control panel fitted to the side of the boiler and shall include: (*a*) Fully automatic firing equipment to give high/low/off thermostat control with electric ignition comprising burner assembly with air director, electric ignition equipment, oil preheater with thermostatic control. (*b*) Safety controls including photo-cell flame failure equipment, similar signal lamp. Audible warning lockout shall be given by an electric gong with muting switch, which shall incorporate a time delay to reset the circuit after 30 secs. Boilers to be fixed in position on bases (by others) and including for all necessary commissioning and testing by the boiler manufacturer.'

12.4

Boiler flues are generally of mild steel or cast iron, the size and type of the connection to the boiler should be checked so that the necessary mating flange or transformation piece is described. It is good practice to provide a draught stabilizer at the base of the flue, also an access door with a gas tight seal. An explosion door is provided either on the flue box of the boiler, or should be provided on the flue if insulated normally. Alternatively a combined draught stabilizer, access door and explosion door can be fitted at the base of the flue.

12.5

The burning of town gas results in the formation of water vapour which must be dispersed to the atmosphere before it has cooled sufficiently to condense in the flue. Flues from gas boilers are generally made of asbestos and frequently have a condensate pocket formed at the base from which a condensate pipe is led away. The provision of smoke density equipment, CO_2 sensors and draught gauges may be considered necessary.

12.6

Calorifiers (see 4.6). Calorifiers are required when the boiler is required to provide the heat source for the domestic hot water services as well as the low pressure hot water heating.

The primary flow and return from the boiler to the calorifier provides the heat source. A calorifier is, as described in section 11, an appliance in which water is heated by another fluid or gas, generally water or steam, through the medium of an internal heating surface. Indirect cylinder is a term commonly applied to small storage calorifiers. Calorifiers are made of mild steel, cast iron or copper to BS 853.

12.7

Calorifier mountings are discussed in section 11.6.3 and a typical description is given in section 11.6.6.

12.8

The primary heating circuit should be fitted to permit free venting by means of a vent pipe, manual air release, or automatic air vent.

12.9

The heating capacity of a calorifier should be specified in accordance with the required hot water storage recovery rate, e.g. horizontal indirect calorifier with removable solid copper U-tube battery expanded into a copper lined steel chest to raise the contents from 10°C to 65·6°C in one hour when fed with primary water at 82·2°C flow and 71·1°C return.

12.10

Access should also be provided to each calorifier for maintenance and inspection of all parts of the vessel, especially the tube heater batteries.

12.11

Feed and expansion tank cold feed and open vent. Water, when heated, expands and provision should, therefore, be made to accommodate the increased volume. The feed and expansion tank has a dual purpose; to accommodate the water created as a result of expansion and to top up the water in the installation that is lost due to evaporation and leakage. The tank should be positioned above the level of the highest point of the system and the open vent pipes are turned over the tank. The cold feed connection to the boiler should be taken from the side of the tank, which should be fitted with a ball valve and stop cock and also an overflow which discharges in a visible external position. Feed and expansion cisterns may be constructed of painted mild steel, galvanized mild steel, asbestos or plastic and should be provided with a lid and suitably insulated.

A typical arrangement is shown in Fig. 12.1.

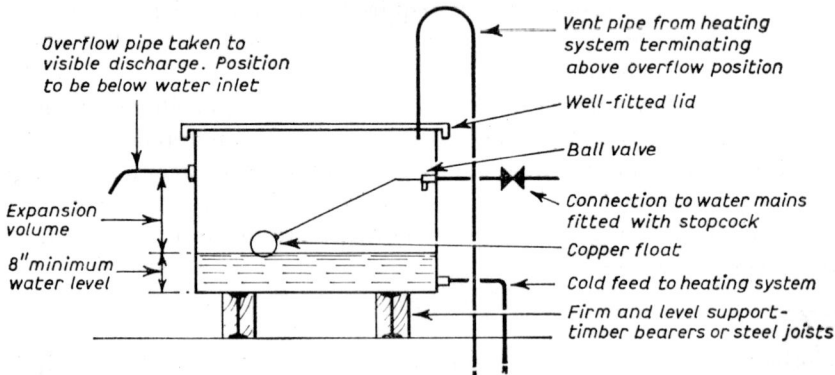

Fig. 12.1 Feed and expansion tank.

12.12

Distribution system. The following pipes and fittings are commonly used for low pressure hot water heating installations:

BS 864   Capillary fittings and compression fittings of copper and copper alloy for use with copper tube complying with BS 659, BS 1386 and BS 3931.

BS 66   Copper alloy three-piece unions (for low- and medium-pressure screwed copper tubes).

BS 99   Copper alloy pipe fittings screwed for low- and medium-pressure BS copper tubes.

BS 1710   Colour identification of pipe lines.

BS 659   Light gauge copper tubes.

BS 143   Malleable cast iron and cast copper alloy pipe fittings (screwed BSP taper thread).

BS 1256   Malleable cast iron and cast copper alloy pipe fittings for steam, air, water and gas, screwed BSP taper male thread and parallel female thread.

BS 21   Pipe threads, Part 1: Basic sizes and tolerances.
BS 61   Screw threads for copper tubes.
BS 1387   Steel tubes and tubulars suitable for screwing to BS 21 pipe threads.
BS 10   Tables of pipe flanges (for land use).
BS 1740   Wrought pipe fittings, iron and steel, screwed BSP thread.
BS 1965   Butt welding pipe fittings for pressure purposes.
BS 1724   Bronze welding.
BS 1737   Jointing materials and compounds.
BS 3931   Hard-drawn thin-wall copper tubes.

12.13

Steel pipes to BS 1387 covers sizes from 13 mm to 152 mm which can be light, medium or heavy weight. Sizes above 152 mm are covered by BS 3601.

12.14

It is usual to use medium weight tube for low-pressure hot-water heating with either screwed fittings to BS 143 or welded fittings to BS 1965.

12.15

Pipelines should be provided with a sufficient number of joints to permit easy dismantling; for pipe sizes up to 64 mm pipe unions are commonly used. For larger pipework flanged joints are normal and BS 10 specifies flanges and boltings for pipes, valves and fittings. Those most commonly used are those conforming to Table D (working steam pressures up to 344,740 N/m² or 3·4474 bars) Table E (up to 689,480 N/m² or 6·8948 bars) Table F (up to 1,034,220 N/m² or 10·3422 bars) and Table H (up to 1723,700 N/m² or 17·237 bars). Flanges should be jointed by inserting a corrugated brass ring, asbestos or special compound joint ring coated with jointing compound and the bolts tightened.

12.16

Light-gauge copper pipe to BS 659 can also be used for low pressure hot water heating, this tube is more expensive than mild steel tube.

12.17

Hard-drawn thin-wall copper tube to BS 3931 is often used for smaller installations, but manufactured bends and fittings should be used.

12.18

Copper pipe should be jointed by means of compression or capillary fittings to BS 864 which specifies fittings up to 64 mm. Compression fittings are manufactured also for pipes larger than 64 mm but it is more common and cheaper to braze or silver-solder joints in large copper pipes.

12.19

Drain cocks fitted with hose unions should be provided to permit items of plant, main circuits and sub-circuits or the complete or part of the installation to be drained. In large installations drain cocks in all these locations should be provided.

12.20

An open vent of not less than 19 mm should be installed at the highest point of each circuit where air is likely to accumulate.

12.21

Where air pockets are likely to occur on large circuits and it is not practical to connect open vents to the atmosphere, air bottles should be installed with an air emptying pipe connected to the top of the bottle, the air emptying pipe is terminated with a valve within hand reach. Alternatively automatic air vents should be provided, but each should be fitted with an isolating valve to enable them to be removed for repair.

12.22

Valves on pipelines are required for either isolation of sections or for regulation, i.e. for balancing the flow between various sections of the system.

12.23

Valves for isolation are generally wheelhead full-way gate pattern or seated pattern valves and should be provided on each main and branch circuit. These normally have screwed ends up to 51 mm, above 51 mm flanged valves are usual.

12.24

Regulation valves should be installed on branch returns and appliances connected to these. Valves provided for regulation purposes should be lockshield where the setting of the valve should not be altered, after initial commissioning, lockshield valves require a special valve key.

12.25

Provision for expansion must be provided where there are long runs of pipes. This can often be achieved by changing the direction of the pipe run. Where this is impractical, when for instance there is a straight run of pipe the length of a building, various methods are adopted. One is to use expansion loops, as shown in Fig. 12.2.

Loops should have flanged ends for connecting to the main pipes and be in

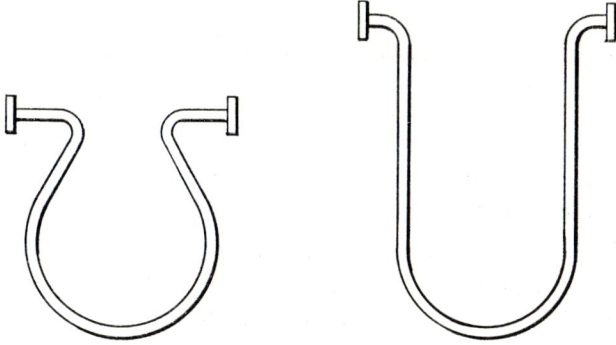

Fig. 12.2 Typical flanged expansion loops.

wrought iron or mild steel or alternatively copper, which expands and contracts more readily. Alternative standard expansion joints (several types are available) may be used.

12.26

Standard sliding expansion joints consist of two sliding parts, one inside the other and fitted with a gland with suitable packing to make them watertight. These are made either in gunmetal or cast iron as shown in Fig. 12.3.

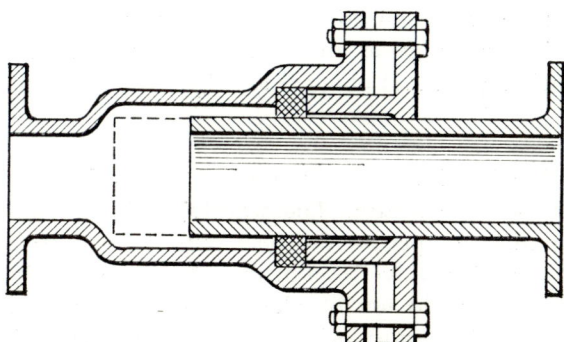

Fig. 12.3 Typical sliding expansion joint.

12.27

Expansion bellows can in the main cope with expansion movements up to 51 mm. Manufacturer's information will give the following:

    Size of connection
    Overall free length
    Total axial traverse from cold-pull-up (CPU)
    Extended length with 50% CPU
    Spring rate
    Effective area
    Working pressure

12.28

Pipe anchor points for expansion devices and pipe supports generally are described in section 17.

12.29

Heating appliances. Radiators are one of the cheapest forms of heat emitters. When describing radiators the following should be stated:

12.29.1 Manufacturer's name, material and type, cast iron column, hospital or panel, pressed steel single or double panel.

12.29.2 Size, number of sections, heating surface or physical dimension, number of panels.

12.29.3 Connections, size and position of tappings for valves, air vent and blank plug.

12.29.4 Finish, unpainted, primed, stove enamelled.

12.29.5 Fixings, floor mounted with legs and wall fixing brackets, concealed brackets.

12.29.6 Working pressure.

A typical description of a panel radiator might be:

'Messrs. XYZ pressed steel single panel 60 section radiator 2235 mm long × 584 mm high for use with LPHW at 82·2/71·1°C with 13 mm bottom opposite end connections, brass air vent and blank plug with primed finish and fixing on and including standard pattern concealed brackets coachscrewed and plugged to brick wall.'

12.30

Radiators are fitted with two valves, a wheel head valve on the flow and a lockshield valve on the return. The wheelhead is an on/off valve with intermediate settings to permit the heat output from the radiator to be adjusted. The lockshield valve is set at the time the system is commissioned and balanced, and should not be altered unless the system becomes unbalanced. The wheelhead and lockshield valves may be straight pattern or angled, brass finish or chromium plated and with male screwed union end for connection to the radiator and the other end for connection to copper or mild steel tube.

12.31

Convection heaters are divided into two types, natural convectors or fan assisted. Both types comprise a box containing the gilled tubular heating elements with flow and return headers with suitable connections to suit the circulating pipework. A 3 mm diameter tapping is provided at a suitable high point for fitting an air cock to allow the release of air. The front panel is removable to allow access to the elements and other equipment within the casing. When the convector is of the recessed type, grilles are provided at the top and bottom of the front panel to allow cool air to enter by natural draught, via the bottom grilles, after passing over the heated elements the warm air is emitted via the top grilles. If the unit is a wall fixed model the grilles may be in the top and bottom of the casing. Alternatively if the convector is a model that stands upon the floor, the bottom grille is situated at the bottom of the front panel and the discharge grilles can be at the top of the front panel or in the top of the casing.

12.32

A fan assisted convector incorporates an electric fan which boosts the output of heated air. The fan motor is generally provided with a three-speed control, i.e. low, normal and boost.

12.33

The heat source can be low-pressure hot water or steam. Special elements suitable for medium- and high-pressure hot water can be obtained.

12.34

A typical description for a convector heater should include the following:

12.34.1 Manufacturer (if specified).
12.34.2 Heating medium.
  Two pipe accelerated low pressure hot water.
  Two pipe gravity low pressure hot water.
  Steam.
  High pressure hot water.
12.34.3 Type and finish.
  Recessed.
  Wall mounting.
  Floor mounting.
12.34.4 Size.
  Length.
  Height.
  Depth – this is dependent upon the number of finned elements within the casing.
12.34.5 Connections.
  Diameter and handing.
  Horizontal or vertical.
  Plain tails for welding.
  Screwed BSPT male or female.
  Flanged to BS 10 Table to be stated.
  Compression joint for copper BS 864.
  Plain tails for copper joint to BS 864 (compression or capillary).
12.34.6 Damper. State if manual control damper is to be fitted.
12.34.7 Automatic. State if individual thermostats are to be fitted.

12.34.8 Venting. If individual air cocks required to each unit.

12.34.9 Other accessories. Check manufacturer's catalogue and consult engineer.

12.35

A typical description for a fan assisted convector heater as shown in Fig. 12.4 should include 12.34.1 to 12.34.9 plus the following:

12.35.1 Electrical supply. Voltage, phase and frequency.

12.35.2 Wiring. Dependent on optional extras required with unit, i.e. thermostat, clock control, automatic speed control.

12.35.3 Starters. Check if electrical contractor is supplying and/or fixing.

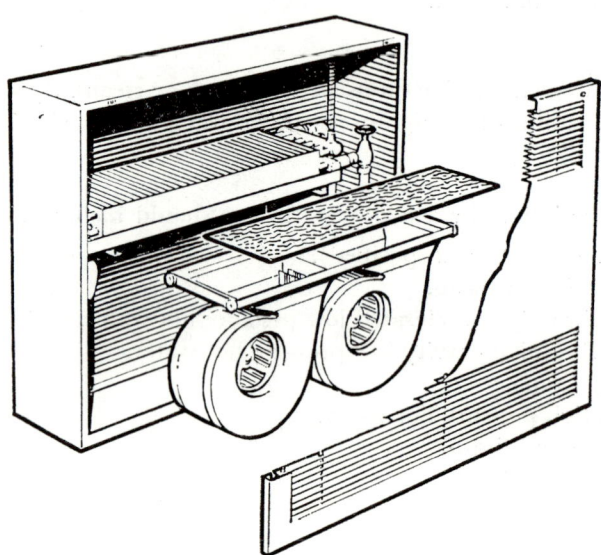

Fig. 12.4 Fan assisted convector heater.

12.36

Unit heaters are similar to a fan assisted convector heater in that they consist of a heater battery and a fan. This type of heater is installed in large open areas where floor space is at a premium, or heaters at floor level are not convenient.

The fan is a more powerful unit than those fitted to convectors, some types are designed to discharge horizontally, and others downwards, from the bottom of the unit. The louvres are adjustable in order that the direction of the air can be varied to suit the requirements. Heat source can be low pressure, medium pressure or high pressure hot water or high or low pressure steam. Fan motors can be extra low speed, low speed or normal speed.

Horizontal discharge units are ideal for creating a flow of warm air along exposed walls or discharging into narrow aisles, blanketing large doorways or projecting heat towards points of high heat loss. The vertical discharge type are useful for projecting heat downwards, regardless of obstacles which would impede the flow of air from a horizontal blow heater.

When the heat source is low pressure hot water it is important that the temperature of the blown air be higher than blood heat – blown air below this temperature tends to cause discomfort due to its apparent coolness.

A typical description for a unit heater as shown in Figs. 12.5 and 12.6 should include the following:

12.36.1 Manufacturer. Model reference and type.
12.36.2 Heating medium.
  LPHW (flow and return temperature)
  MPHW (flow and return temperature)
  HPHW (flow and return temperature)
  Steam pressure (also temperature when superheated)
12.36.3 Fan speed.
  Extra low speed (approx. 700 rev./min.)
  Low speed (approx. 900 rev./min.)
  Normal speed (approx. 1400 rev./min.)
12.36.4 Electricity supply. Voltage, phase and frequency.
12.36.5 Connections. As for convector heaters.
12.36.6 Intake.
  Recirculating air type.
  Flanged for ductwork.
12.36.7 Outlets.
  Standard.
  Flanged for ductwork.
  Two way discharge (horizontal and vertical).
12.36.8 Starters ⎫
12.36.9 Thermostats ⎬ If required state type.

12.37

Unit heaters often require purpose-made and special supports.

12.38

Radiant panels are normally utilized for heating warehouses or large workshops in lieu of unit heaters and are available in two standard sizes having nominal dimensions: 914×1829 mm or 1219×2438 mm. The sinuous coil can run parallel with either the shorter or longer side according to the design of the pipework layout for the proposed installation. Panels are manufactured to offer radiant emission from both sides or one side only and can be fixed to provide heat from the following positions:

12.38.1 Vertical single-sided panels – mounted along the outer walls of a building radiating inwards.

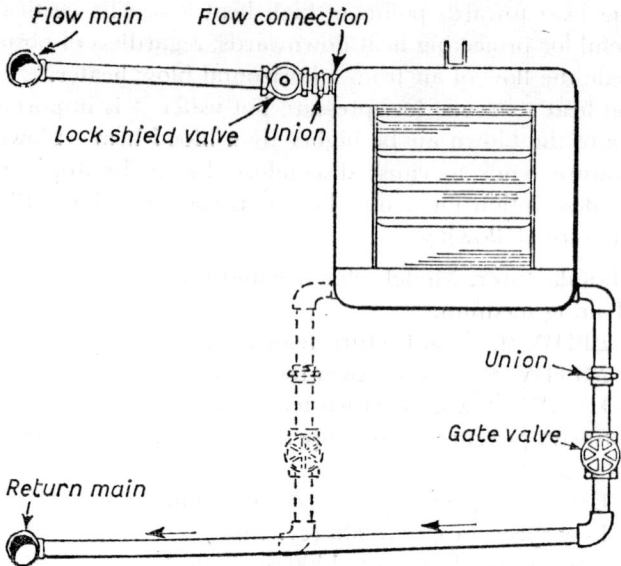

Fig. 12.5 Horizontal discharge pattern unit heater.

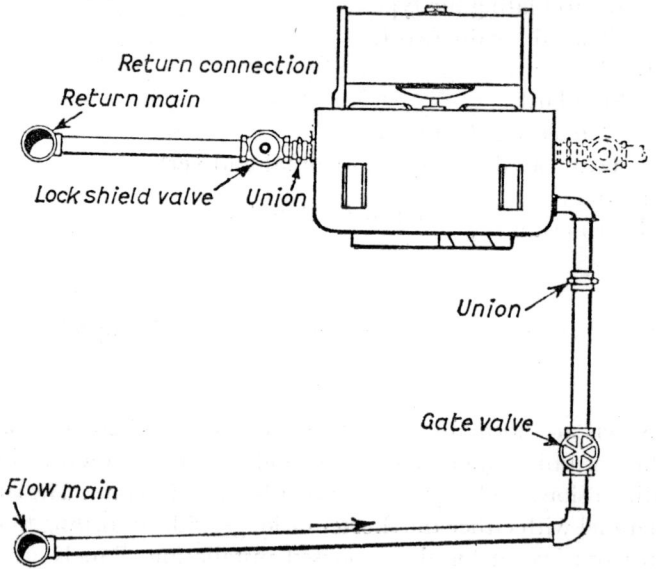

Fig. 12.6 Vertical discharge pattern unit heater.

12.38.2 Vertical double-sided panels – mounted between bays radiating outwards in both directions. Approximately half the heat emission in cases 1 and 2 is radiated upwards.

12.38.3 Horizontal single-sided panels – distributed over the area to be heated radiating downwards is the most economical installation in terms of fuel consumption, but involves a higher capital expenditure. Structural considerations sometimes outweigh running costs.

12.38.4 Enclosed single-sided panels – mounted at the sides of the building or between bays radiating outwards and downwards.

12.39

Fig. 12.7 shows a section through an industrial building and indicates the spread of radiant heat from three types of radiant panels.

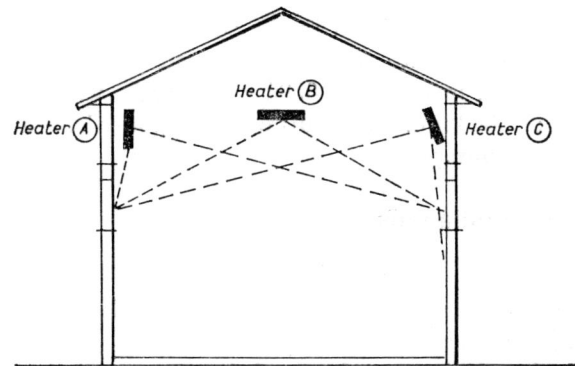

Fig. 12.7 Spread of radiant heat from wall or ceiling mounted panels.
A. Single-sided vertically mounted – 39% of radiant heat used direct.
B. Single-sided horizontally mounted – 95% of radiant heat used direct.
C. Single-sided inclined at 45° – 70% of radiant heat used direct.

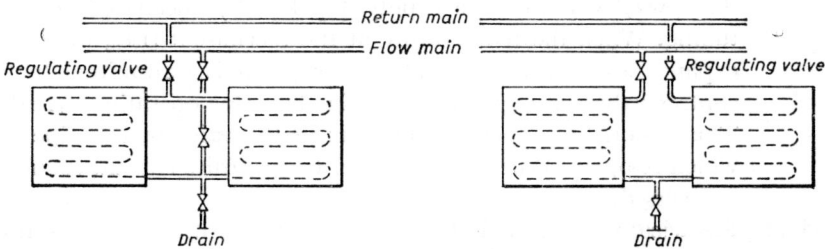

Two panels connected in parallel with two valves. Flow taken to lower connections to assist in purging air from the sinuous coil.

Alternative connections for panels connected in series with one isolating and one regulating valve.

Fig. 12.8 Typical piping arrangements for low pressure hot water vertical or inclined panels.

12.40

A typical description for a radiant panel heater as shown in Fig. 12.8 should include the following:

12.40.1 Manufacturer.
12.40.2 Size and type. Watt output, flow and return temperature.
12.40.3 Connections.
        (a) Plain ends for welding.
        (b) Screwed BSPT.
        (c) Flanged to BS 10 table F or H.

12.41

As an alternative to radiant panels it is possible to use 'Raystrip' which comprises one, two, three or four tubes 32 mm diameter bonded to high conductivity corrugated aluminium sheets. Heat emissions vary according to the number of tubes contained in the strip and range from 240–3,310 watt/h/m. This type of unit can also incorporate fluorescent light fittings. Each strip is supplied in standard 6096 mm lengths with make-up pieces either 1524 mm or 3048 mm long, thus permitting any length to be created in multiples of 1524 mm.

Supplementary appliances

12.42

Automatic controls in common use are self-acting and electrically operated. Other forms include pneumatic and hydraulic.

12.42.1   Self-acting. This type of control does not require auxiliary power (such as electricity). An example of this form of control is a self-acting water temperature controller comprising an immersion water thermostat containing a volatile liquid and a metal bellows. The thermostat unit is fixed into the calorifier and connected to a three way valve in the supply pipeline by means of capillary tubing. When the temperature at the thermostat rises, the liquid expands and the corresponding movement is transmitted to the control valve through the piston in the valve operating cylinder. This action then operates the part in the valve in the pipe run which re-opens. When the calorifier temperature falls the sequence is reversed.

12.42.2   Electrically controlled. Room thermostats are fixed in positions where minimum/maximum temperature control is required, such as offices or living rooms in houses. When the temperature in the controlled area drops to the minimum setting the thermostat opens a mechanically operated valve to allow heated water to circulate to the heating appliance (radiator, convector heater, etc.) which in turn raises the ambient temperature until such time as the

HOT WATER HEATING INSTALLATION

maximum temperature setting is reached and the sequence is reversed diverting the heat supply to other sections of the system.

12.43

An electric wiring system which links the various components may incorporate fuse protection, relays, air flow switches, time delay units, contactors and the various other accessories to provide a complete and safe wiring installation.

12.44

A centralized control station, at which the various controls are usually grouped together, is often installed. This may take the form of an assembly of the various items of equipment fixed directly on to the wall of a plant room or a comprehensive factory constructed pre-wired control panel.

When the latter installation is required the following should be measured:

12.44.1   Provisional sum for the supply of the control panel and individual control valves by a nominated supplier.
12.44.2   Measured items for fixing the control panel and valves only by the mechanical services sub-contractor.
12.44.3   Electrical power to the valves and panel by the electrical services sub-contractor.
12.44.4   A provisional sum for the wiring of the individual controls to the panel and commissioning and testing.

12.45

Circulating pumps fall in three categories according to the size of the installation.

12.45.1   Glandless pipeline circulating pump for domestic central heating installations (incorporating a variable head adjustment) which can be installed vertically or horizontally.
12.45.2   In-line pumps which are fitted into the pipe line with the electric motor mounted above the water way. Up to 51 mm diameter are fitted with unions for connections to the pipework and over 51 mm diameter have flanged ends.
12.45.3   Centrifugal pumps are floor mounted with the electric motor at the side of the impeller. This type of pump is normally installed in plant rooms and is available over a wide range of duties.

12.46

Pumps should be installed with isolating valves on the suction and discharge and a non-return valve on the suction side. In order that the installation may function to a limited extent by gravity should the pumps fail, a bypass should be fitted with an isolating valve which is shut down when the pump is in operation. In order to prevent noise transmission through the pipework when in-line or centrifugal pumps are installed, the connections to the suction and discharge ports should be by means of flexible bellows with flanged or screwed ends. In-line pumps should be adequately supported. Floor mounted pumps should be mounted on a concrete block with a spring loaded frame to absorb vibration to prevent noise transmission via the building fabric. As an alternative to this method the pump can be mounted on a concrete block and a 51 mm thick layer of cork both normally supplied and fixed by the main contractor.

12.47

Typical descriptions for pumps might be as follows:

'Messrs XYZ or other approved horizontal floor mounted heating pumps constructed of a close grained cast iron body, gunmetal impeller, stainless steel shaft and lubricated sleeve bearing and motor. Pump shall be of direct drive type and to have pump head and drive motor mounted on a common baseplate suitably cast with drip drain connection and holes for and including holding down bolts. Motors to be – hp (kW) of squirrel cage type suitable for 400–440/3/50 cps supply. Pump connections to be flanged BS 10 table D. Pump to handle – litre/s at – m head (bar) when running at – rev./min. starter to be direct on line suitable for 400–440/3/50 supply.'

or

'Messrs XYZ model 203 mm or other approved to handle 143·25 litre/s at 12·19 m head (1·17 bar) horizontal end suction ball bearing centrifugal pump having volute formed casing constructed from close grained cast iron of ample thickness and pressure tested. Impeller to be of cast iron keyed to high tensile steel shaft of extra large diameter, giving maximum stiffness and free from vibration; provided with passage through hub to relieve stuffing box pressure and to give hydraulic balance. Shaft sleeve to be provided to prevent packing wear on shaft. Renewable impeller rings to be fitted. The stuffing box to be of extra depth fitted with appropriate grade packing. The driving head to be of cast iron, of substantial design, providing rigid support to bearings and pump. The pump to be provided with flexible coupling for connection to the driving motor and the whole to be mounted on a combination base plate. Pump to be complete with air valve, drain plug, grease caps, shaft and impeller nut spanners. 30 kW motor shall be suitable for 415/3/50 supply running at 1450 rev./min. and having drip proof enclosure and class "E" insulation. Pump connections to be flanged BS table "E". Pump to have stable characteristic performance curve and provided with a motor which is fully non-overloading at all duties.'

(*Note:* Starters and flexible connections measured separately.)

12.48

Each pump should have a pair of altitude gauges mounted adjacent to the pump and connected to the bosses on the suction and discharge. Provision should also be made for thermometer wells in the pipe runs on each side of the pump and an air bottle on the discharge.

12.49

A typical description for a gauge might be as follows:

'Messrs XYZ or other approved, stove enamelled steel gauge board fixed with angle iron over pump set and including 2 No. 102 mm diameter altitude gauges, each complete with 10 mm pipework and connections and cocks with bronze plugs.'

12.50

A typical description for an air bottle might be as follows:

'Purpose made mild steel air bottle comprising 305 mm length of 64 mm diameter tube blanked off each end with 152 mm length of 64 mm diameter tube one end branch welded into main and the other end branch welded to air bottle with approximately 6096 mm of 10 mm diameter pipe as air line to low level, one end branch welded into 64 mm tube and the other end fitted with 10 mm air cock including bending as necessary.'

12.51

The outlet from the drip tray or gland of the pump should be fitted with a short spout with a visible discharge. This may be turned either directly over an adjacent gully to the pump or over a tundish with a pipe connection (not less than 25 mm diameter) carried to the nearest gully, drain or sump. All changes in direction to such drain pipes should be in the form of plugged crosses.

It should be noted that the size of the suction and discharge pipework connections on the pumps is often less than that of the service in which they are mounted, therefore reducers must be measured. The point at which the service should be reduced should be ascertained from the engineer, as it is cheaper to reduce the diameter of the pipe prior to the isolating valves, flexible connections etc., which are normally provided on the suction and discharge pipework. Drain cocks should be provided on the suction line to each pump and strainers may be required on the suction side of the pumps.

CHAPTER 13
Fuel oil installation

13.1

Fuel oil used for boilers is normally delivered in road tankers of around 27,276 litres capacity. On particularly large installations it may be delivered by rail tanker or by a pipe line direct from the refinery. Private dwellings normally have a minimum storage capacity equivalent to 3 weeks' consumption or an economic delivery.

13.2

Oil storage tanks are generally constructed of black mild steel and are either pre-fabricated or welded on site and installed above or below ground. Mild steel tanks up to 54,552 litres capacity are covered by BS 799 and may be rectangular or cylindrical and suitable for vertical or horizontal mountings. The BS classifies the tanks in relation to the pressure, their shape and latitude. Generally speaking the lower the pressure the cheaper the tank. The pressure on the tank will be determined by the highest level to which the oil may rise and this will be usually the termination point of the vent pipe from the tank. Tanks should have the following connections and mountings (*a*) connection for fill pipe, (*b*) connection for vent pipe, (*c*) sludge outlet at base – for cleaning out, (*d*) an access manhole in an accessible position, (*e*) a contents gauge in a visible position and (*f*) sometimes a pre-heater unit (depending on the grade of the oil). Oil storage tanks can, alternatively, be in reinforced concrete. Typical descriptions of a mild steel oil tank and accessories might be:

'Horizontal mild steel fuel oil storage tank to BS 799 part 1 type "K" of site welded construction size 6·70 m long × 3·05 m wide and 3·05 m high each to be complete with 457 mm diameter manhole, 51 mm flanged outlet BST "D", 51 mm flanged sludge outlet BST "D", 76 mm flanged vent BST "D", 76 mm flanged fill BST "D", tappings for high and low level float switch; and hydrostatic contents gauge, and with flanged stool to suit $7\frac{1}{2}$ kW outflow heater. Tank to be fixed in position on supports (by builder).

'Calibrated dip-stick or tape with varnished calibrated chart'.

FUEL OIL INSTALLATION

'Messrs XYZ magnetic level switches for high and low level alarm in oil tanks.'

13.3

Contents gauges – the following are in common use:

13.3.1 Direct reading, including:
    (a) Sight tube of transparent material.
    (b) Cat and mouse gauge – consisting of a float, an indicator, gauge board plus pulleys and wires.
    (c) Float gauge – consisting of a float and dial indicator gauge.

13.3.2 Remote reading gauges which are either hydraulically or electrically operated by a sensing element installed in the oil tank from which a capillary tube is run to the gauge. A typical description might be: 'Hydrostatic contents gauge of continuous indicating type complete with approximately 25 m of capillary 2 No. gauges, one mounted at oil fill point, the other handed to control panel manufacturer for fixing in panel. Gauge to be marked 'FULL' and 'EMPTY' to indicate limits of useable oil in tank (i.e. to correspond with high level alarm and fuel outlet level respectively) and marked 'REFUELLING' at a level that will allow a full delivery of oil. Unit to be complete with transducer transmitter and alarm unit for mounting at fill point.'

13.4

Fill pipe connection is generally blanked off with a gunmetal cap and chain and padlocked. The fill pipe is housed in an oil storage inlet box. Typical descriptions might be:

'Messrs XYZ oil-intake box size 610 × 305 × 203 mm as catalogue No. X, suitably lettered "oil-fill point" and hand to builder for building-in. Box to also have perforations for 2 No. hydrostatic contents gauges (measured separately).

'Drip tray to suit oil fill box and place in position.

'229 × 102 mm non-corrodible plate bearing indelible markings showing grade of fuel oil to be used.'

13.5

Fill pipe bore – this will depend on the extent of the storage capacity, the length of the fill pipe and the grade of oil being used. If the point of fill is at a lower level than the top of the oil storage tank then an isolating valve is required to prevent back flow when the tanker's filling hose is removed. The fill pipe is jointed to the oil tank, usually with a flanged or screwed connection.

13.6

Alarms should be installed on all storage tanks to give warning and thereby prevent overfilling. One type of alarm is set off electrically by means of a float switch set at the desired height in the oil tank, operating an audible alarm.

13.7
Ventilation pipes are required to release the air from the tank when filling. If there is a series of tanks then these will be coupled to form one outlet point at high level and located to avoid nuisance from oil fumes. The end of the ventilation pipe should be an open outlet looking down, constructed with a return bend with the end covered with a balloon grating.

13.8
Drain valves – BS 799 recommends the following sizes:

Tanks up to 1364 litres – 19 mm
1364 litres to 3410 litres – 25 mm
3410 litres to 6818 litres – 38 mm
6818 litres to 22,730 litres – 51 mm
Over 22,730 litres – 64 mm.

13.9
Access – internal or external access ladders may be required for maintenance purposes.

13.10
Pre-heaters – commonly used gas oil of maximum viscosity of 45 s requires no pre-heating. Light fuel oil of maximum viscosity of 250 s needs to be at a temperature of 7·2°C at outflow – heavy fuel oil of maximum viscosity of 1000 seconds needs to be at a temperature of 26·7°C at outflow.

Pre-heating is achieved by either an electric immersion heater, high pressure hot water coil or a steam coil. A typical description of an electric immersion heater might be:

> 'Outflow immersion heater $7\frac{1}{2}$ kW of the permanent submerged shrouded element type, designed to allow for element withdrawal without draining tank. Loading of element to be not less than 90 watts for 960 s oil (Redwood No. 1 at 37·8°C) per 4·55 litres per hour of oil flow. Heater to incorporate internal rod type immersion stat controlling the elements, outflow oil temperature indicator and water-tight terminal box.'

13.11
Oil feed – is run from the tanks to the boilers, and may require pumping – in which case duplicate pumps are installed with isolating valves on the suction and discharge sides, a non-return valve. In an accessible position it is advisable to install a duplex oil filter to prevent sludge from the oil tanks damaging **the oil burners.**

13.12

Fire precautions – it is necessary to turn off the oil supply quickly in case of fire. This can be achieved by installing fire precaution valves in the oil feed pipe. The basic fire valve consists of a weight operated free fall valve – the weight being held in position by a system of stainless steel wires and pulleys in which is fitted a fusible link, with a break temperature of 65·6°C, situated over the oil burner. More sophisticated forms of fire precautionaries can be achieved by using a mercury switch mounted on the fire valve lever. When the valve lowers, the mercury switch sets an alarm, and shuts down the oil burner's motor. It is a wise precaution to design the installation so that the fire valve can be operated by the boiler house staff from a point adjacent to the boiler house exit. This can be achieved by installing a manually operated quick release mechanism, consisting of a push button unit to which the fire cable is attached – when the button is pushed (or hit) the pin holding the cable is released thus operating the weight which rapidly closes the fire valve. Typical descriptions of fire precaution equipment might be:

'Push button mushroom head surface mounting emergency release suitably labelled "FIRE CONTROL VALVE" in red letters 483 mm high on 3 mm thick durable plastic.

'76 mm fire valve of the free fall weight type complete with mercury switch; weight of fire valve to be minimum 10 lb (4·53 kg).

'Electric thermal link fused to break circuit at 68·3°C.

'Float switch sump similar to Messrs XYZ Fig. No. X 419 mm diameter at top, 356 mm high complete with magnetic level switch.

'Allow for approximately 30 m of stainless steel tensioning wire, 10 pulleys and connect up fusible links, fire valves and manual quick releases, etc.'

13.13

Oil burners are normally protected by a foam inlet installation which comprises a foam inlet box from which pipe work (usually 64 mm and 76 mm diameter) is run to discharge over the oil burners; the pipe work should be terminated over the oil burners; with a foam spreader fitting. Typical descriptions might be as follows:

'76 mm Gunmetal funnel type inlet adaptor as manufactured by Messrs XYZ No. X and complete with identification label.

'64 mm Messrs XYZ foam spreader No. X.

'Messrs XYZ foam inlet box No. X size 610 × 305 × 203 mm and suitably lettered "F.B. FOAM INLET" and hand to builder for building in.'

CHAPTER 14
Gas installation

14.1

A typical gas installation is shown in Fig. 14.1 suitable for natural or coal gas.

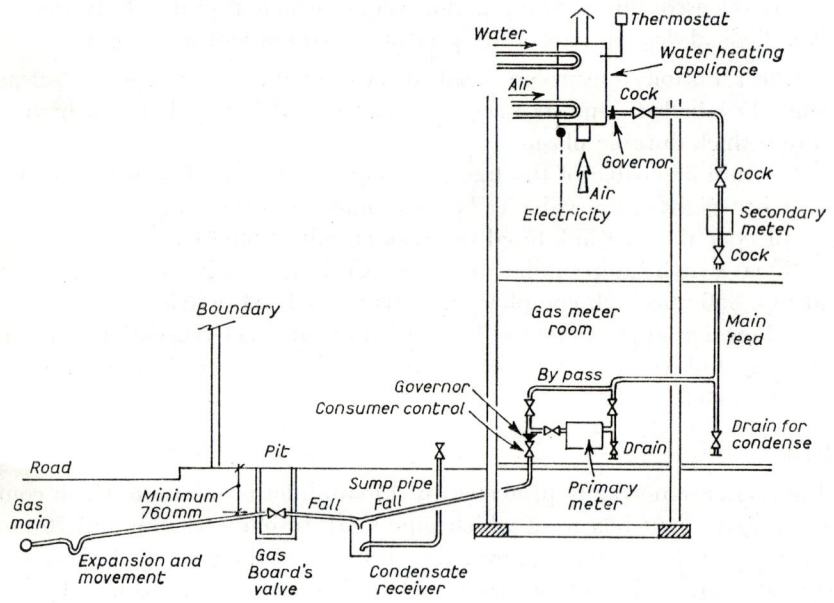

Fig. 14.1 Typical gas installation

14.2

In small domestic installations where the service pipe is less than 51 mm diameter, the Gas Board make the connection from the gas main to and including the meter.

14.3

In other installations the Gas Board make the connection from the gas main to and including the main valve, just inside the site boundary.

GAS INSTALLATION   133

14.4

Gas mains are subject to frost action and should be laid at a minimum depth of 762 mm and to a slight fall if a condensate receiver is installed.

14.5

Gas service pipes are generally of galvanized mild steel or cast iron; sometimes copper or plastic pipes are used. The following apply:

BS 78   Cast iron pipes for gas.
BS 143   Malleable cast iron and cast alloy pipe fittings for gas.
BS 534   Steel spigot and socket pipes for gas.
BS 1211   Centrifugally cast iron pipes for gas.

14.6

The Gas Board's valve is housed in a brick or concrete valve pit (similar to a water pit) with hinged cast-iron cover.

14.7

A condensate receiver or syphon box is sometimes required to collect condensate between the Gas Board's valve and the primary meter. A condensate

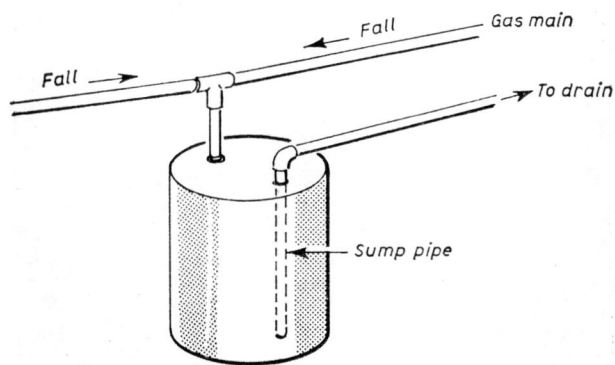

Fig. 14.2   Condensate receiver.

receiver is a cylindrical container of varying capacity to collect condensate and with an outlet sump pipe to facilitate emptying by pump or other means – as Fig. 14.2.

14.8

Consumer control is brass or gunmetal gas cock with a square head operated by a black iron 90° lever – it permits the supply to be turned off for repairs and/or maintenance.

14.9

Service governor fitted between the consumer control and meter – governs the gas flow which is usually below 5000 MN/m² (20·0 in wg.). In some circumstances the governor needs venting via a relief valve.

14.10

Gas meters record the volume of gas passing through a pipe. Primary gas meters record all the gas entering a building. Secondary meters record gas consumption by sub-tenants or particular processes in factories. Where continuity of gas supply is essential a by-pass pipe should be installed to permit the removal of the meter in case of breakdown. The by-pass is fitted with a sealed valve (or valves) – union nuts (to BS 746) are used either side of the meter to allow its removal and replacement. On meters over 1200 m²/h capacity flanged connections conforming to BS 10 Table A should be used. Alternatively connector sockets should be used.

Fig. 14.3 A built-in type meter compartment.

14.11

Meter compartment for small installations should be 533 × 533 × 305 mm which will accommodate an average domestic (100 cu ft/m) meter with reasonable space to make the necessary connections, and where possible meter dials should be about 1372 mm above floor level for ease of reading.

14.12

Gas installation pipework and fittings may be any of the following:

Steel pipes and fittings.

- BS 143   Malleable cast iron and cast copper alloy pipe fittings. Screwed BSP taper thread or API line pipe thread.
- BS 1256 Malleable cast iron (whiteheart process) and cast copper alloy pipe fittings. Screwed BSP taper male thread and parallel female thread.
- BS 1387 Steel tubes and tubulars suitable for screwing to BS 21 pipe threads.
- BS 3601 Steel pipes and tubes for pressure purposes. Carbon steel; ordinary duties.

Solid drawn copper pipe with copper alloy fittings.

- BS 61   Copper tubes (heavy gauge) for general purposes.
- BS 659   Light gauge copper tubes.
- BS 864   Capillary and compression fittings of copper and copper alloy for use with copper tube complying with BS 659 and BS 1386.

Lead pipe (for limited use).

- BS 602   Lead pipes for other than chemical purposes.

Cast iron and spun iron pipes and fittings; steel spigot socket pipes and fittings.

- BS 78 Part 1   Cast iron spigot and socket pipes (vertically cast) and spigot and socket fittings.
- BS 534   Steel pipes, fittings and specials.
- BS 1211 Centrifugally cast (spun) iron pressure pipes.

Jointing materials.

- BS 1737 Jointing materials and compounds.
- BS 2494 Rubber joint rings.

14.13

A pressure test point should be provided in a convenient position on or near the outlet from the meter.

14.14

Installation pipes which pass through floors constructed of a corrosive material, or which would be exposed to, or in contact with, chemical effluents should be encased in a non-corrodible sleeve. Steel pipes should be painted. Steel pipes buried in concrete floors should be wrapped with a suitable wrapping tape. Copper pipes should be protected by a factory-bonded PVC sheath.

14.15

Branch installation pipes to sections or to different floors should be isolated by a cock or valve.

14.16

A condensate receiver or a suitable drain point (to enable condensate to be removed) should be installed at the bottom of all risers.

14.17

Where pipes pass through walls, floors or ceilings, a metal sleeve should be allowed with suitable cover plates at the point where the pipe enters the sleeve if exposed to view. The annular space may be packed with bituminous filling to prevent the ingress of water, or with asbestos where fire resisting floors or walls are penetrated.

14.18

Gas appliances are many and various; reference should be made to the manufacturers' catalogues to ascertain the size and type of connection required, e.g. BSP male/female, flanged, flexible hose, and whether the governor, isolating valve and union is included with the appliance or should be provided on the branch. Safety devices such as bimetallic spring valves, flame failure devices, low-pressure cut-off valves, etc., are normally included with the appliance.

14.19

Testing. It is essential that gas installations or alterations are properly tested for soundness by, or under, the direction of the Gas Board, prior to covering over, if the work is below ground or in ducts or trenches or before treating with protective coating or connecting to the meter. The Gas Board will direct the method of testing.

CHAPTER 15

Compressed air installation

15.1
Compressed air is used for innumerable industrial processes such as paint spraying, power for machinery and as a control medium for delicate instruments.

15.2
Compressed air is one of the most expensive of all mechanical services, for instance to compress 2·8 cubic metres of free air in a minute to a pressure of 6·8948 bars requires an input of about 15 kW.

15.3
A compressed air installation normally comprises:
15.3.1   A compressor – single- or two-stage – plus starter, motor, etc.
15.3.2   An after-cooler.
15.3.3   An air receiver.
15.3.4   An air dryer (optional).
15.3.5   Distribution pipework and outlet point.

15.4
There is a wide range of compressors available. A typical description might be as follows:

'Automatic, reciprocating, oil-fused-type air compressor having a free air delivery duty of 0·092 m² per second at a pressure of 4·1369 bars gauge pressure, all as Messrs XYZ Model X – having a two-stage air-cooled unit equipped with air intake filter, dual control and air cooler intercooler with fan. The compressor to be mounted on, and including a combined base plate securely fixed to concrete base (base by others) with a three phase 37·5 kW screen protected slip ring electric motor running at 1450 rev./min. and coupled to the compressor by a V-rope drive with belt guard. The compressor is to be complete with intermittent control through an "Erskine Heap" floor mounted automatic stator/rotor starter with three overload releases and a fine pressure control giving a continuous running to within plus or minus 2% of the set pressure.'

15.5

Packaged type compressed air units are also available and these may incorporate the after-cooler and the air-receiver, and the above description should be extended accordingly.

15.6

A typical description for an air cooler might be as follows:

'Air-cooled after cooler as Messrs XYZ model No. X fixed to concrete base (base by others), having a cold temperature difference of some −6·7°C with a 1·125 kW three phase electric fan, and complete with safety valve, moisture separator, drain trap.'

15.7

A typical description of an air-receiver might be as follows:

'914 mm diameter × 1829 mm high vertical air-receiver as manufactured by Messrs XYZ complete with 2 No. hand holes and covers with flanged pads for 64 mm inlet and outlet and with tappings for and including the following mountings – safety valve, pressure gauge and drain valve. The receiver to be complete with supporting feet and to be constructed to BS 487 for a working pressure of 4·1369 bar and be complete with a trap set on the drain.'

15.8

Adequate anti-vibration mountings should be provided for the compressor. Flexible connections from the compressor to the pipework may sometimes be necessary. The drain trap on the after-cooler and the air-receiver requires a length of pipework so that it discharges over a drain or gully. The object of these drain traps is to remove water which condenses when the air is compressed – the amount of water depends on the relative humidity of the air entering the air filter en route for the compressor. Water in compressed air lines causes corrosion, which increases the resistance within the pipe and builds up a pressure drop which wastes power. Corrosion causes valves, joints and traps to leak with the resultant drop in air pressure at the receiving end. Water and sludge can also damage the plant, particularly pneumatic instruments which control the plant, by the closing up of orifices.

15.9

An air dryer is installed when it is essential to have 'dry compressed air'. The following are common types of air dryers:

15.9.1 Thermal mass refrigeration. This air dryer removes moisture by cooling the air by refrigeration to a pressure dew point at a temperature of between 1·7 and 10°C. The only power input required to this type is the electricity to operate the refrigeration system. This type of air dryer is efficient and more economical to operate than the two given below.

15.9.2 Desiccant. Moisture is removed by absorption.

15.9.3 Chemical. Salt is used which reacts with the moisture to form a solution which is drained off, and the equipment then has to be replenished.

15.10

Cooling compressors. Depending on the type of compressor used, it may be necessary to have cooling water to carry the excess heat created by the compressor to waste. With a piston-type compressor, for example, it is essential to treat the air temperature down to a reasonable level so that satisfactory lubrication of the working parts is obtained. Water is the most common cooling medium used and this is circulated in a jacket around the cylinder of the compressor. Where the cooling water is an open cooling circuit (i.e. the water from the compressor is run to waste) it is usually advantageous to restrict the amount of water used to the minimum for the satisfactory cooling of the compressor (mains water can be costly). This is usually done by installing a reverse acting valve which is actuated by a thermostat to open and close down the water supply as called for by the thermostat (see Fig. 15.1). The same principle is applied if the compressor is

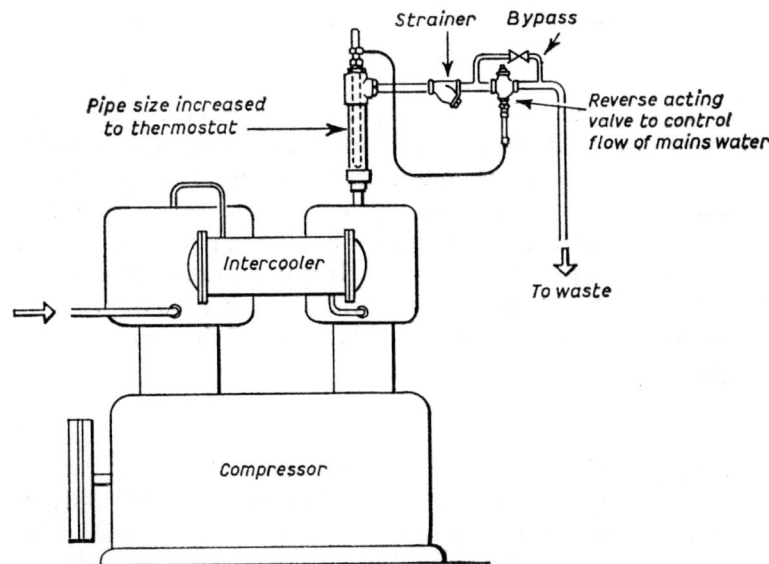

Fig. 15.1 Multi-stage compressor – mains water cooling.

of a multi-stage type. Alternatively the compressor may be cooled by a closed circuit system such as that indicated in Fig. 15.2.

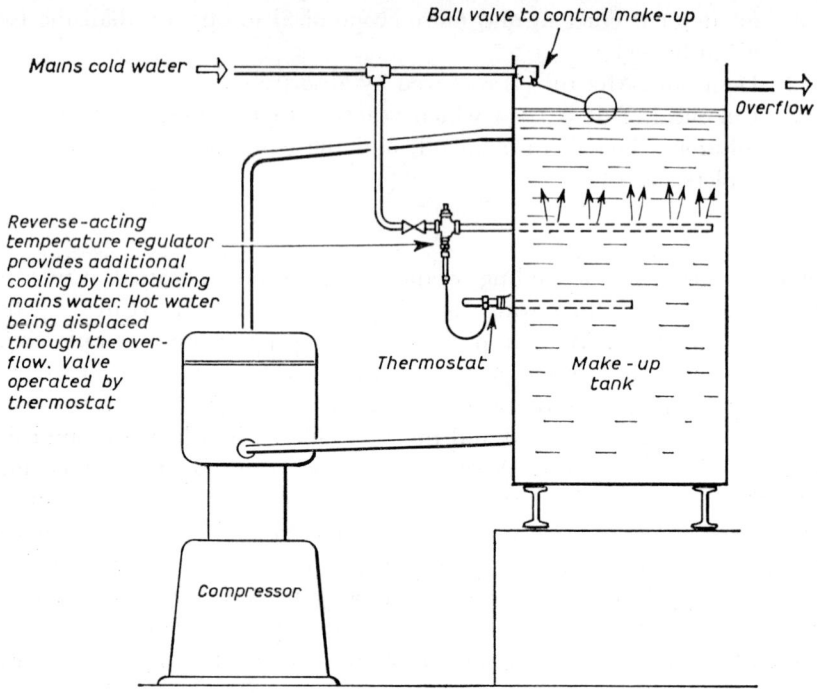

Fig. 15.2 Closed circuit cooling with cooling tank.

15.11

Air drain traps are installed in compressed air installations to remove moisture from low points in the distribution pipework – they consist of a float-operated valve that opens and shuts according to the position of the float within its chamber. They usually have a screwed female inlet and outlet and a 13 mm female connection for a balance pipe that is connected back into the compressed air installation. It is usual to install a strainer on the inlet side of the trap to prevent impurities entering the trap.

Fig. 15.3 details an air trap and Figs. 15.4 to 15.7 show some of the uses of air traps.

15.12

Distribution pipework. Compressed air installations are usually carried out in copper tube to BS 659 or in galvanized mild steel tube to BS 1387. Where high-pressure compressed air is installed the pipes usually should be jointed with flanges to the respective table of BS 10. Ideally all cooling and condensing should take place before the air leaves the air receiver; in practice this is

COMPRESSED AIR INSTALLATION

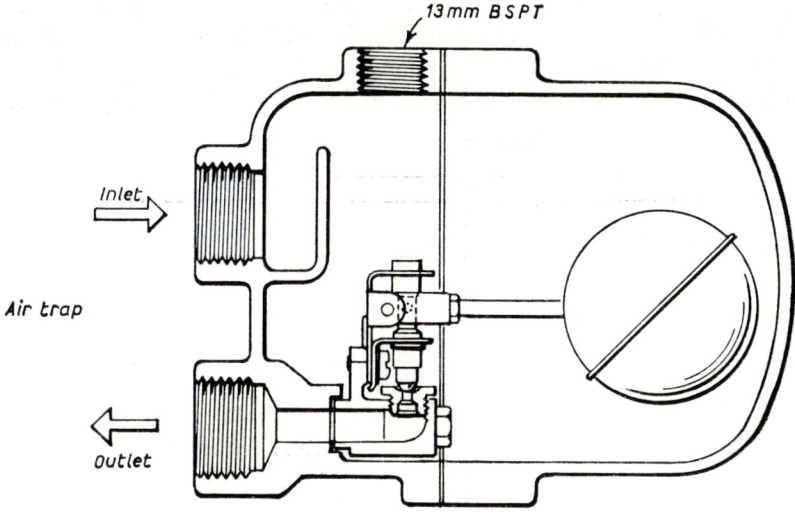

Fig. 15.3 Details of an air trap.

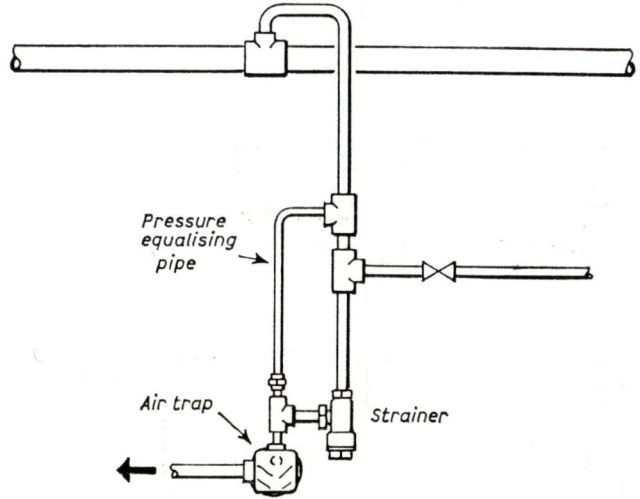

Fig. 15.4 Air trap draining air service line.

not often achieved, unless after-coolers are installed. When an after-cooler is not installed the pipework in the compressed air installation acts as a cooling surface and condensation results; because of this care must be taken in the layout of the compressed air mains so that pipes fall to a drain point: a fall of not less than 25 mm in 3048 mm in the direction of the air flow is recommended and the maximum distance between drain points should not exceed 30·48 m. Fig. 15.8 illustrates a typical ring main installation. Branches from compressed air mains should be taken off the top of the main and then drop to the required level with an air trap set on the lowest point, as shown in Fig. 15.5. Compressed air operated tools and hoists can be troublesome if supplied with wet air, as there will inevitably be some water particles in air which cannot be eliminated by the normal drain points on the pipework: in

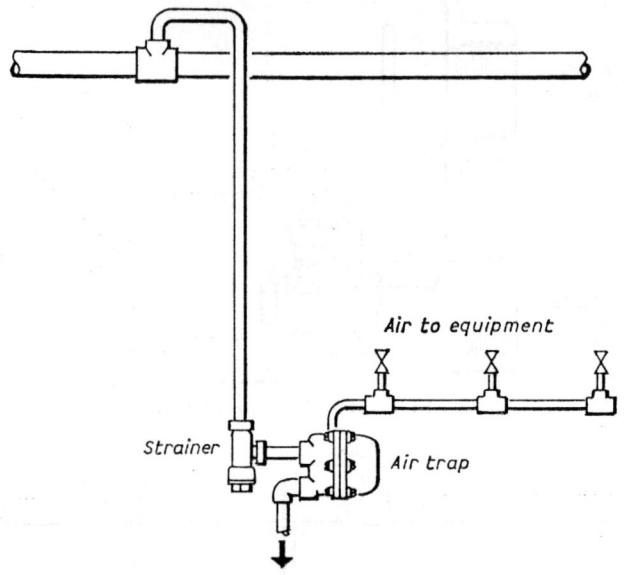

Fig. 15.5 Air trap draining air service line to several points.

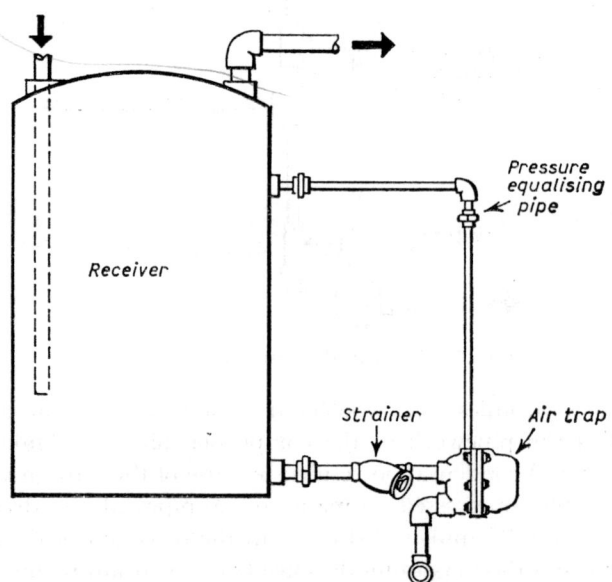

Fig. 15.6 Air trap draining receiver. (Trap installed with pressure equalizing pipe to prevent air locks.)

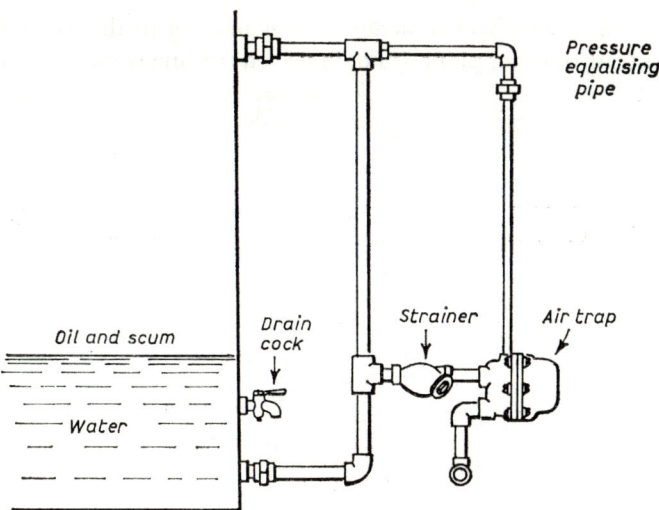

Fig. 15.7 Air trap draining receiver when oil and scum are present (oil can be run off without passing through trap).

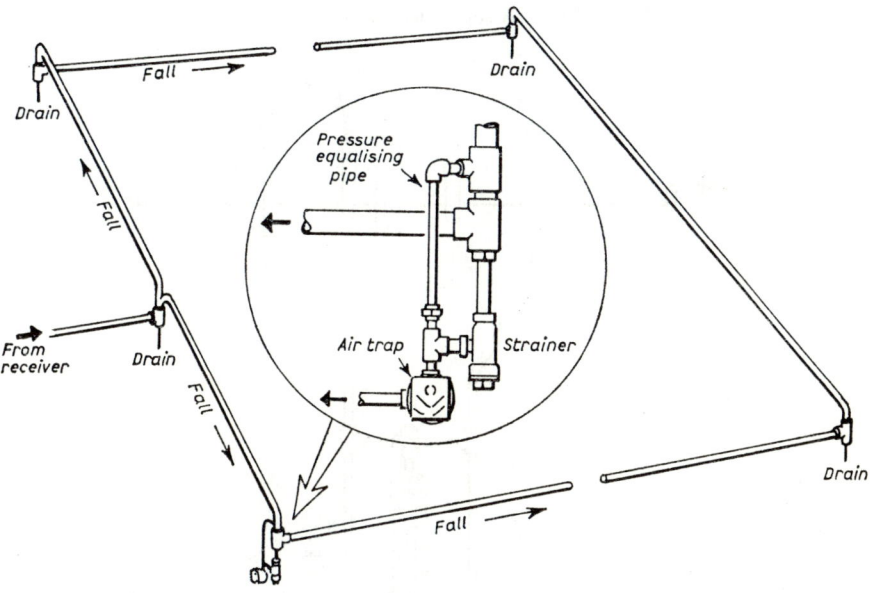

Fig. 15.8 Typical ring main.

such a case a separator, as shown in Fig. 15.9, is fitted in the line serving the equipment, immediately after the receiver.

15.13

Flow meters can be installed in compressed air installations so that leaks can be readily detected. A manometer and flow meter are installed as shown in

Fig. 15.10 – this meter will indicate if air is moving in the main at periods when industrial, or other plant, is not in use – a reading would indicate a leak.

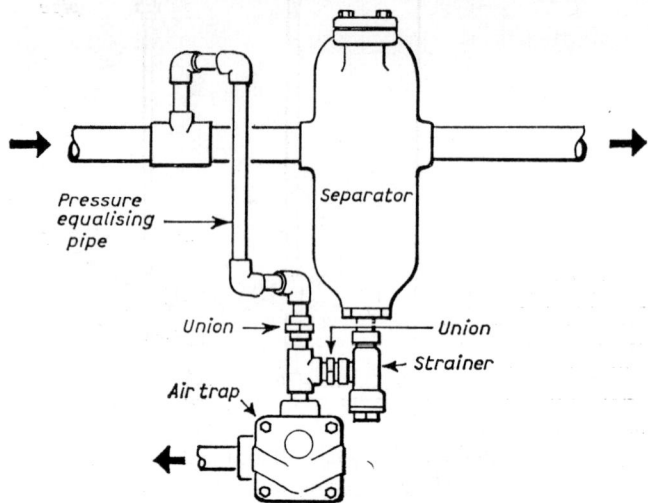

Fig. 15.9 A separator on an air main.

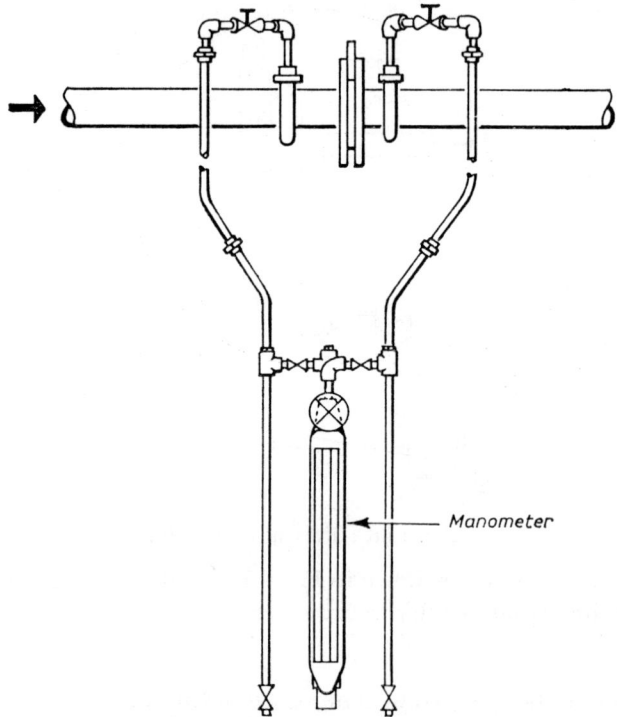

Fig. 15.10 Installation of a manometer and flow meter.

CHAPTER 16
Mechanical ventilation

16.1
The object of a mechanical ventilation installation is to circulate air to those parts of a building that require ventilation and make provision for this air to be expelled either by mechanical or natural means. Circulation of air is achieved in its simplest form by a system of fans and ductwork, into which a filter and heater battery is normally added to clean and heat the incoming air.

16.2
The number of air changes required in a particular area will be conditioned by the level of comfort required, the activity planned for the particular area, the degree of air pollution anticipated (e.g. isolation wards, industrial processes, etc.), the geographical location (e.g. its aspect, its latitude) and the building regulations (e.g. internal bathrooms, kitchens, etc.). A broad indication of usual hourly air changes is given below:

	Air changes
Internal bathrooms and kitchens	8 to 10
Offices	10 to 12
Libraries	10 to 12
Gymnasiums and swimming pools	8 to 12
Cinemas and theatres	8 to 12

16.3
A fully ducted system of mechanical ventilation is often designed to permit the warm air that is removed through the extract ductwork to be recirculated through the supply ductwork. This reduces the volume of cold fresh air to be heated from outside conditions to a minimum and is therefore more economical. The volume of air to be recirculated will vary, depending upon the number of air changes required. Air must not be recirculated from areas where undesirable dust, fumes or contamination may exist.
   Fig. 16.1 shows the diagrammatic arrangement of recirculation ductwork.

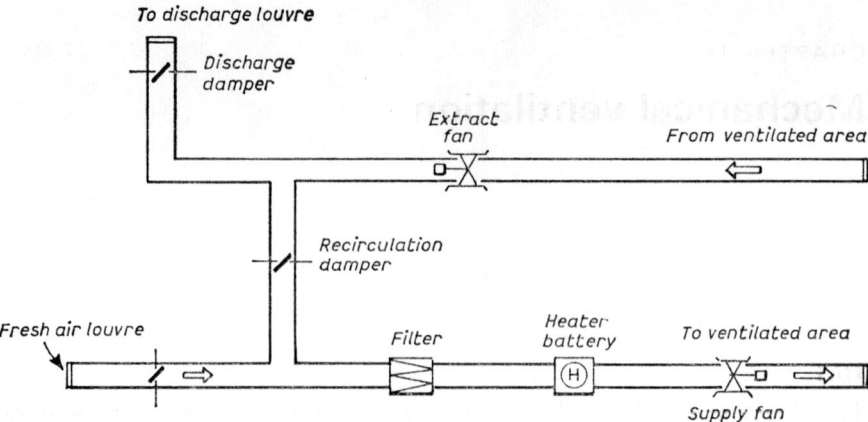

Fig. 16.1 Recirculation duct work.

16.4

Fans are normally axial flow or centrifugal and their 'duty' is expressed by the number of cubic feet (metres) of air that it is capable of handling against a particular resistance. Fans are connected to the ductwork system with flexible connections and are supported on anti-vibration pads of cork or felt. When fans are supported at high level it is necessary to provide anti-vibration mountings within the supports. Fans must be supported independently because of their weight – they must not rely on the ductwork for support.

It is a public health requirement for standby fans or motors to be provided to areas where ventilation is essential at all times, e.g. internal bathrooms and lavatories, etc.

16.5

Axial flow fans as shown in Figs. 16.2 and 16.3 take the form of a hub with a number of impellers, driven by an electric motor. They are capable of moving large quantities of air by drawing air in on the intake side and discharging

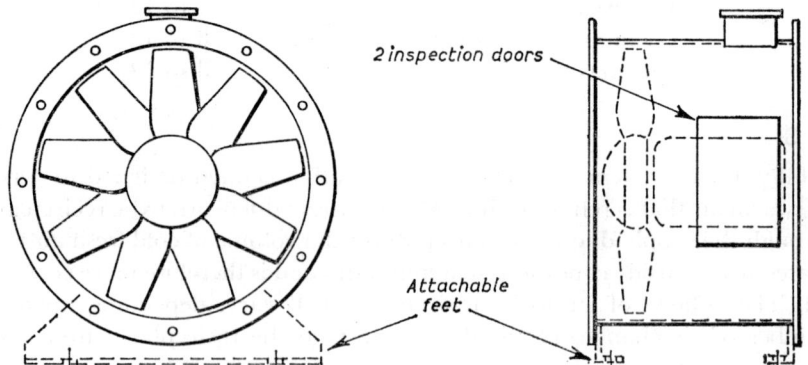

Fig. 16.2 Section through single stage axial flow fan.

MECHANICAL VENTILATION 147

in a direction parallel to its shaft on the discharge side. Axial flow fans are available with sheet metal casings for mounting within ductwork and in one, two, three or more stages. When fans have integral casings or are mounted inside ducts, flanged joints should be provided to permit easy removal of the unit. Access doors should be provided opposite the fans, electric motor or the driving pulley. The ductwork into which an axial flow fan is fitted should be

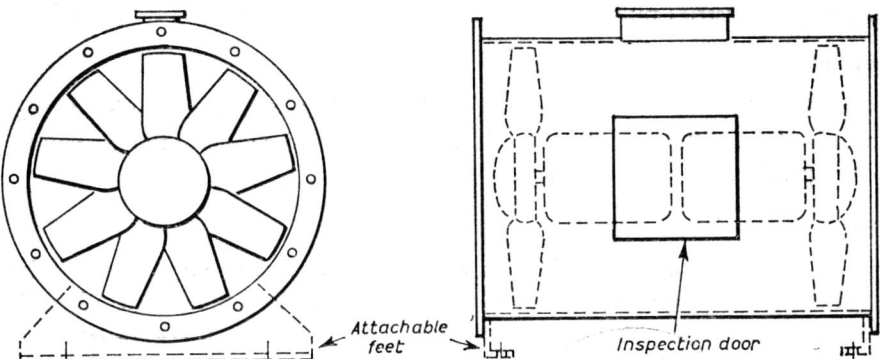

Fig. 16.3   Section through two stage axial flow fan.

the same diameter as the fan. If the fan is being connected into larger or rectangular ducts, tapers or change-section pieces should be provided.

16.6

Centrifugal fans vary considerably, but basically they consist of a multi-bladed impeller mounted on a spindle and housed in a scroll or casing. They operate by drawing air in at the centre of the fan wheel and discharging it tangentially from the circumference. The blades of the fans are shown in Fig. 16.4 and may be forward curved, backward curved or radial, according

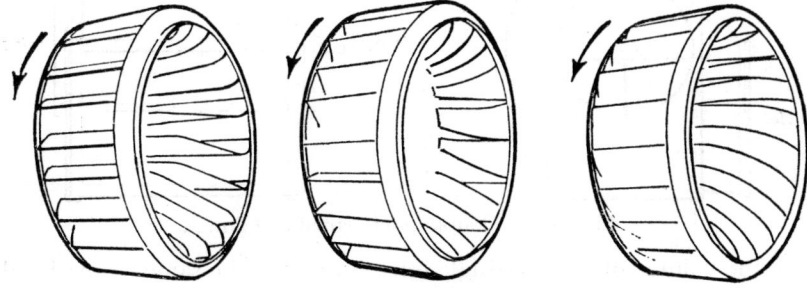

Fig. 16.4   Centrifugal fans.
Left – forward bladed.
Centre – radial bladed.
Right – backward bladed.

to the requirements of the installation. Forward curved fans are most commonly used and are effective in handling a large volume of air at a comparatively low speed. Backward curved fans require a larger fan wheel and run at a higher speed than forward curved fans for a given duty. They generally have a higher efficiency than other centrifugal fans and are especially suitable where two fans are working in parallel. Radial fans may be used as an alternative to the forward curved fans. This type of fan is often used for industrial purposes such as fume and dust removal.

16.7

Centrifugal fans can be driven direct by an electric motor coupled to the shaft or by a belt drive; the latter is more usual, as the duty of the fan can be changed by altering the pulley system.

16.8

Centrifugal fans are available with a variety of discharge angles, single inlet and double inlet are available as Figs. 16.5 and 16.6 – the latter can handle

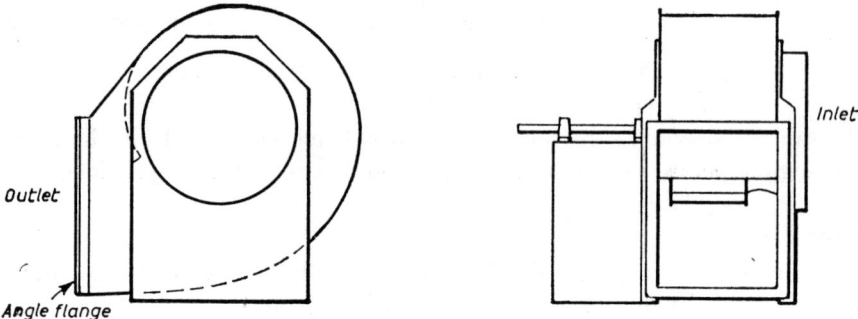

Fig. 16.5   Single inlet centrifugal fan.

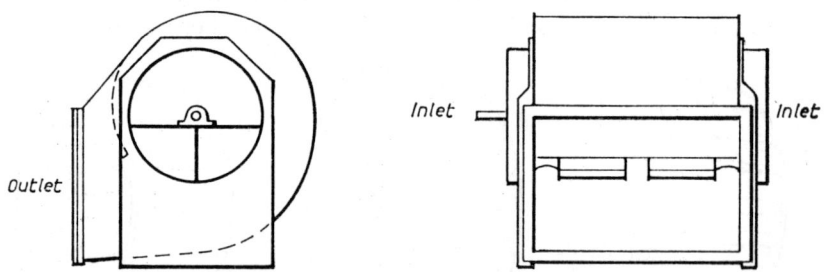

Fig. 16.6   Double inlet centrifugal fan.

double the volume of air of a single inlet fan within the same casing height. Fan casings should be constructed to prevent drumming or vibration and protection guards should be fitted to the open end when operating under open inlet, and open outlet conditions. Since centrifugal fans are quieter than axial flow fans they are more often incorporated in air handling installations.

16.9

Air heaters are used to warm the air in an air handling installation. There are several types of air heaters available, they use either steam, water, gas or electricity as the heating medium. The most usual form of air heater is shown in Fig. 16.7 – the hot-water heater battery.

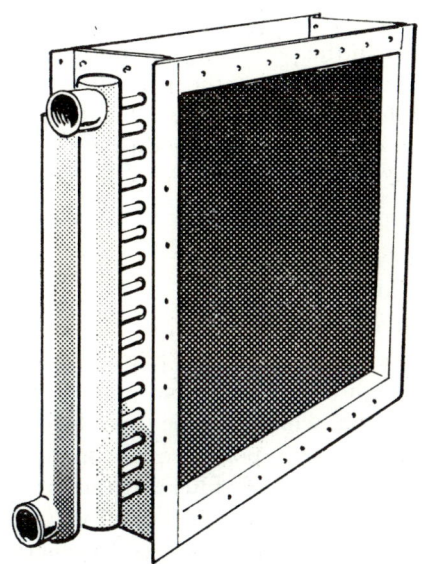

Fig. 16.7 Typical hot-water heater battery.

The fan should be arranged so that air is drawn through the heater battery, otherwise the air velocity produced by the fan is lost on passing through the heater, in addition the heater battery should be situated after the filter to avoid the problems created by dirt and dust blocking the tubes. Air heaters must be supported independently because of their weight – they must not rely on the ductwork for support. Hot water heater batteries as shown in Fig. 16.7 consist of banks of finned tubes through which hot water is pumped. In the past tubes were common, but finned tubes are now more generally used in order to economize space and provide a larger heating surface. The tubes can be arranged into one, two, three or more banks, depending on the capacity required. As the tubes are more liable to become blocked with dirt and dust than plain tubes, access for cleaning must be provided in the ductwork. Where heater batteries comprise more than two rows of finned tubes or three rows of plain tubes, access should be provided to both front and back of the heater battery for cleaning. Where it is not possible to provide adequate access, provision should be made for the easy removal of the heater battery to permit cleaning. The heater batteries are served by hot water flow and return mains of sufficient size to give uniform distribution of heat throughout the battery; the flow connection should be at the highest point of the heater and the return at the lowest point, to permit proper venting and draining.

16.10

Air filters are required to clean the air before it is circulated around the building. The removal of dirt and dust prolongs the life of the operating equipment (e.g. fans, heaters, etc.), the decoration and the furnishings. The choice of filter depends on the prevailing conditions and the efficiency of the filter required – in other words by the percentage of weight of the dust retained by the filter under a standard test. The larger particles which constitute the greater part of the weight of the dust are the most easily collected, therefore even a poor filter can have an efficiency of perhaps 95% or more.

16.11

Filters fall into the following categories:

16.11.1 Dry type filters consist of a casing containing frames covered, or filled, with cotton wool, cloth, paper, fibreglass or some similar material through which the air passes, the dirt being retained on or in the filter media, which may be suitable for re-use after cleaning, or of the throw-away type. Adequate spares must be provided to ensure continual use of the filters. If the throw-away type of filter is used the design must permit the simple replacement of the cells and the provision of adequate spares. In general filter cells as shown in Fig. 16.8 are installed in banks in a flanged sheet metal housing which is bolted to the adjoining ductwork.

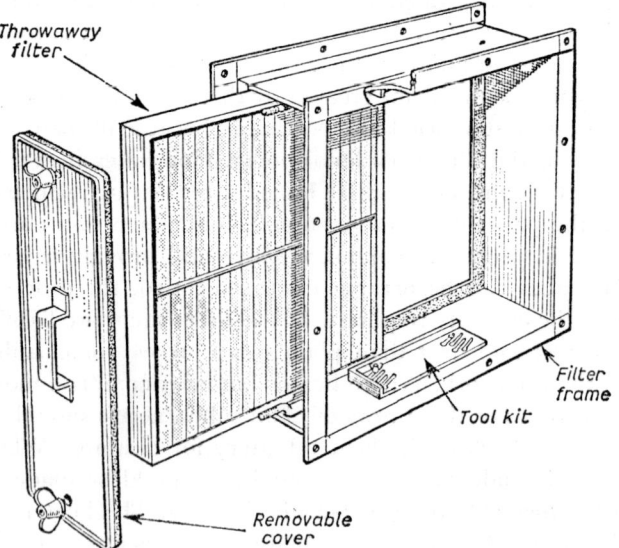

Fig. 16.8 Typical throw-away side withdrawal type air filter panel.

16.11.2 Automatic roll type filters as shown in Fig. 16.9 consist of a roll type filter that is either manually or mechanically rolled from the top roller to the bottom roller as required; the filter rolls require changing periodically. A suitable indicator should be provided to each filter to indicate when the filter is in need of change.

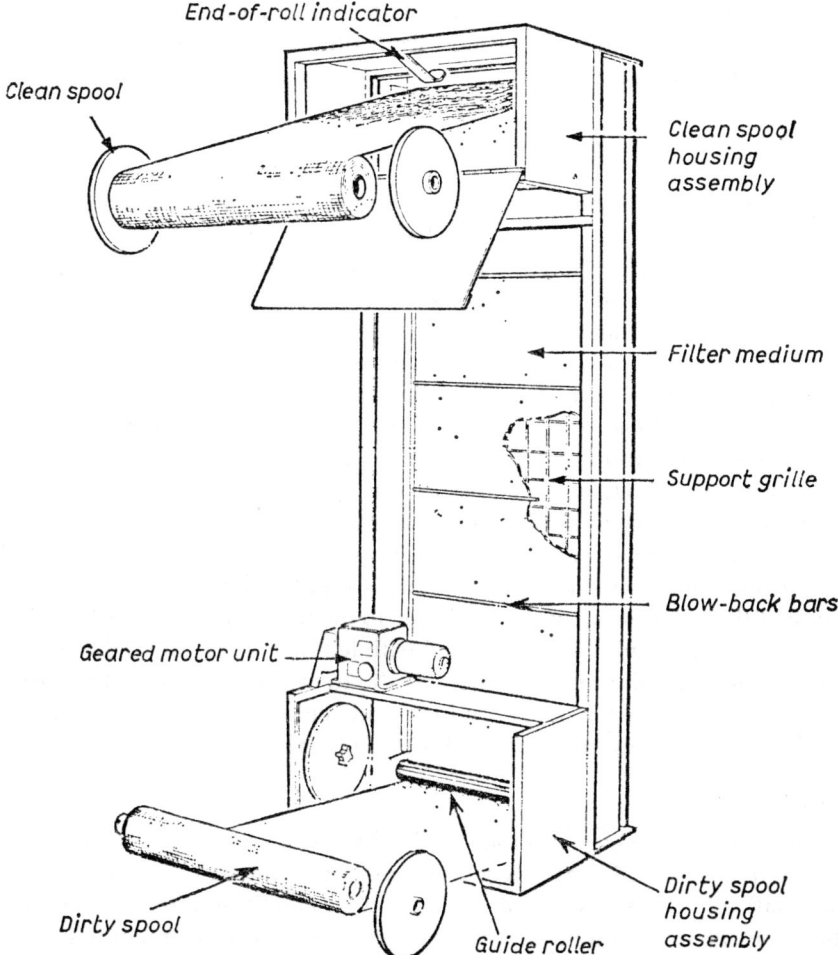

Fig. 16.9 Automatic roll type filter.

16.11.3 Viscous filters generally consist of a casing containing frames covered with, or filled with, fibreglass or some similar material, coated with a viscous fluid such as oil on which dust and dirt is retained. An alternative design consists of metal plates or coils coated with a viscous fluid. Filters of this type can be cleaned by rinsing in hot soda water and recoated with viscous fluid before

152 THE MEASUREMENT OF ENGINEERING SERVICES

being replaced. Self cleaning filters are obtainable, in these a tank is installed below the filter, the fluid is pumped from the tank and distributed across the top of the filter and permitted to flow back to the tank via the filter media.

16.11.4 Electrostatic filters consist of a battery of electrically charged parallel steel plates – alternate plates being charged and earthed. The former repel and the latter collect the dust particles – the earthed plates are cleared from time to time, either manually or mechanically.

16.12

Ductwork used for air handling installation is generally constructed from galvanized sheet metal (the thickness varying with the size of the duct). Other material such as asbestos or PVC is sometimes used for special purposes such as fume extract, etc. Ductwork can be either circular or rectangular in section. Circular ducts require less metal for a given cross sectional area than rectangular ducts, however, where space in false ceilings and the like is restricted, it is very often impracticable to use circular ducts. In rectangular and circular ducts longitudinal joints can be made by riveted or folded seams and transverse joints can be similarly made and riveted, bolted or fixed with self tapping screws or angle iron flanges. Transverse joints in spirally wound ducts are made with special locked seams. In large ducts drumming may occur as the air passes through, this can be overcome by stiffening internally or externally by mild steel angles or by ribs formed in the duct walls. On high velocity systems it is usual to use circular ducts – because of their rigidity they are less liable to drum. Supports for ductwork are generally of the cradle type and lined with felt or similar material to prevent transmission of noise and vibration. If the ductwork is insulated externally with a vapour seal it is necessary to provide enlarged supports to allow the insulation to be continuous through the supports.

16.13

Regulating dampers are installed in the ductwork system to control the rate of flow to a selected area. Regulating dampers can be either manually or automatically controlled to suit the particular conditions, if the former then they must be in a position that is easily accessible. Most commonly used are louvred dampers that consist of a number of pivoted blades spaced across the duct so that when they are closed they overlap and completely close the duct. The blades are linked and operated by an external lever. Another design is the opposed blade damper in which adjacent blades rotate in opposite directions. If a completely airtight damper is required, the louvre blades must be felt tipped and close on to a felt lined frame. On small ducts butterfly dampers consisting of a single blade of sheet metal are used. Fig. 16.10 illustrates various damper types.

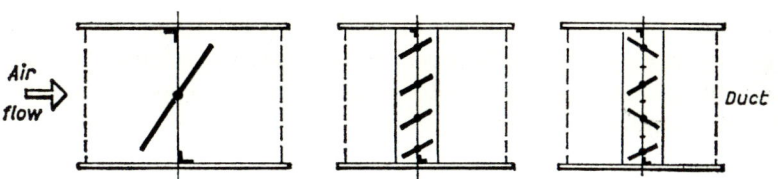

Fig. 16.10 Typical regulating dampers.
Left – single leaf-butterfly.
Centre – louvre multi-leaf.
Right – opposed louvre multi-leaf.

16.14

Fire dampers are sometimes required by fire authorities where air ducts pass through walls or floors. Fig. 16.11 shows a fire damper fixed in a heavy steel casing, the damper is kept open by a fusible link, which in the event of fire melts and the weight automatically closes the damper. Access must be provided to all dampers for inspection and resetting.

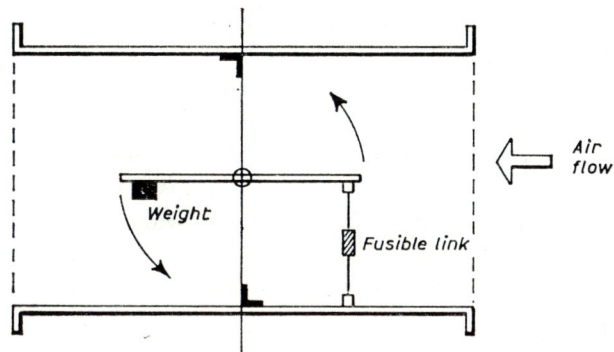

Fig. 16.11 Typical fire damper.

16.15

Inlet grilles and diffusers are designed to permit air to enter a building without causing excess draughts. Grilles have adjustable louvre blades to deflect the air to the required direction. They may also be obtained with two sets of blades one behind the other, one set vertically and the other set horizontally in order to control both planes. Extract grilles require only one set of louvre blades and their positioning is of less importance than that of inlet grilles. Diffusers comprise a series of concentric cones fitted flush with, or just below, the suspended ceiling.

16.16

Hoods or canopies are often installed in kitchens or similar areas for the removal of cooking smells and vapour. Hoods incorporate a drainage

L

channel around their perimeter to collect condensation – the channel is drained by a down pipe which can be connected to a gulley or channel. Removable grease filters are installed within the hood to protect the ductwork and extract equipment.

16.17

Full air conditioning is the ultimate air handling installation and not only permits air to be heated and filtered, but also humidified, dehumidified and cooled. Humidification becomes necessary when dry conditions prevail within a building and is achieved by passing the air through a water spray. Conversely if the relative humidity is high excess moisture is removed by means of a heat exchanger or a heat pump. Excess temperature is eliminated by the installation of refrigeration equipment or by passing the air through a cold water spray. It is beyond the bounds of this book to discuss air conditioning further.

16.18

Measurement. The Standard Method of Measurement requires ductwork to be measured linearly.

16.19

Billing – ventilation and air conditioning. The following major sub-divisions are recommended by the standard method of measurement.
16.19.1 Work in plant rooms (including tank rooms and boiler house).
16.19.2 Work outside plant rooms.
16.19.3 The suggested order of billing within these headings is as follows:

    Ducting
    Ducting fittings
    Fire dampers and special dampers
    Ducting supports
    Grilles and diffusers
    Pressure relief flaps
    Extract hoods: supports
    Roof curb: supports
    Induction units: supports
    Mixing boxes: supports
    Fans: fan ancillaries: supports
    Filters: ancillaries: supports
    Sound attenuators: supports
    Heater batteries: supports
    Cooler batteries or towers: supports
    Humidifiers: supports
    Washers: supports

Package A/H Units: supports
Drainage and overflows installation – billed in order as 'Pipework installation'
Controls and control panels: supports
Sound insulation
Thermal insulation.

16.20

Standard symbols and notations as recommended by the IHVE in respect of ductwork, section changes, grilles, dampers and equipment can be found in appendix 4.

16.21

Typical descriptions for mechanical ventilation might be as follows:

16.21.1   For electrostatic filters.

'Messrs. XYZ Model – 2134 mm × 2642 mm width to handle 7·55 m^3/s electrostatic precipitators. The filters shall be of sufficient size and capacity to clean the given air volumes to an efficiency of 85% against BS 2831 (No. 1 dust) methylene blue. The filter shall consist of an ionizing and precipitating section and a storage section, and collector elements incorporated in the agglomerating section shall be of all aluminium construction. Ionizing voltage shall be 12 kV and plate voltage 5·8 kV. The storage section shall be of heavy gauge zinc coated steel with a glass fibre blanket of continuous fibres of progressive density and diameter in the direction of the air flow. The glass fibre blanket shall be coated with an odourless flameproof adhesive, and shall have a thickness not less that 50 mm when expanded into the airstreams. The media shall be automatically fed across the airstream from a compressed clean roll at a predetermined rate by a pressure differential switch and 124·3 W motor with a separate gear reducer drive. Used media shall be compressed into a compact roll for easy removal and disposal. The filter shall be complete with external and internal agglomerator housing, agglomerating cells and storage units for assembly of the filter bank of the desired capacity, bolts and nuts and miscellaneous items for assembly, power pack suitable for 230/250 volt, 50 cycle, single phase primary wiring, 2 No. manual reset door switches, 2 No. warning lights for door switches, 2 No. combined switch and signal lights, 2 No. enamelled warning signs for doors, spare ionizing wires, high voltage cable from power pack to agglomerator, media run-out control for storage section, control panel including automatic pressure differential switch, warning signal light and manual switch. The sub-contractor shall include for one change of filter media.'

16.21.2   For dampers.

'Messrs XYZ manually controlled dampers comprising damper frames manufactured out of 51 × 3 × 3 mm welded steel channel, and damper blades of "V"-groove to gauge steel construction. Split axle shall fasten axle to blade to eliminate blade slippage. The blades shall be constructed of galvanized sheet steel and all weld points shall be coated with zinc rich primer. Blades shall have ball bearings. Corner braces shall be provided on frames for dampers exceeding 0·37 m² in area. All opposed blade dampers shall have equal percentage characteristics and so constructed that air leakage when damper blades are fully closed shall not exceed 1% of the total flow when the blades are wide open.'

16.21.3 For grilles.

'Messrs XYZ, X type – m³/s side wall grilles with opposed blade volume control. Grilles shall be constructed with a separately mounted aluminium frame and a removable steel core having a minimum free area of 85%. The core shall have adjustments to change the air pattern in the horizontal and vertical plane. The fins of the core shall be of the diffusing type to provide a rapid diffusion and high rate of aspiration. The performance of these diffusers shall be guaranteed that the air distribution will fulfil human comfort standards, the air diffusing uniformly throughout the conditioned space such that at the 1524 mm occupancy zone a velocity of air shall not exceed 9·144 m/min at a 1°C temperature differential or 15·240 m/min at a 1°C differential. Grilles to be furnished with opposed blade volume controls to provide non-directional control of the air flow, and these shall be operated from the front of the grille with a removable key. Sound power level ratings to be based on readings taken in a reverberant room, being independent in room absorption characteristics. "Deflectrol" air tuning vanes shall be installed at an angle of 12° facing the direction of air flow. Grilles shall be anodized black finish to the aluminium; and matching black finish to the steel core, and shall be tested to ASHRAE standard 36B–63 *Method of testing for rating the acoustic performance*.'

16.21.4 For centrifugal fans.

'Messrs XYZ centrifugal "slow speed multivane fans" having an air capacity not less than – cu ft/min when operating against the external static pressure. Fans to be of the forward curve blade type and the impellers shall be constructed from steel of sturdy construction and be statically and dynamically balanced at the manufacturer's works to AMCA 210–1960. Fan casing shall be of robust construction with exterior stiffeners to prevent drumming and vibration. The impellers shall be removable from the inlet side, and large fans shall have split casing. Each fan shall be provided with an inspection door in the fan scroll, drain socket with plug, common channel fan and motor base grillage, and flanged cone inlet and flanged outlet. All shafts shall have ample proportions and shall be produced from high quality ground mild steel bar. All shafts shall be mounted in self aligning type ball bearing housings. Fans shall be driven by using Fenner Taper-Lock and "V"-belt drive from a totally enclosed, squirrel cage, ball bearing, and continuously rated with class "E" insulation motor with slide rails to maintain correct belt tension. The motor shall be suitable for 415 volt, 3 phase, 50 cycle. A galvanized steel mesh guard to the fan inlet and a heavy constructed belt guard with provision to use a tachometer without removing the belt guard shall be fitted. Fans shall be tested and their performance rated in accordance with BS 848: Part 1: 1963, and test methods to BS 848: Part 2: 1966. (*Note:* Only starters, anti-vibration mountings and flexible connections are measured separately.)'

16.21.5   For roll-type filters.

'Messrs. XYZ type – 1·51 m^3/s – 1067 × 762 mm horizontal model – Roll-Kleen filters constructed of 12 gauge (2·517 mm) galvanized steel frame with 16 gauge (1·588 mm) galvanized media housing. The media shall be fed from the clean media housing via idler rollers to the dirty media housing, automatically via a direct drive geared motor unit mounted at the dirty media end. Activation of the motor shall be controlled by a differential switch with a differential of 0·125 m bars with actuation at 1·125 m bars cutting out at 1·25 m bars, giving a maximum pressure loss across the filter of 1·25 m bars with a maximum face velocity of 152·00 m/min. The clean side of the filter media shall be supported by means of a galvanized wire grid attached to both side frames and a 6 mm square mesh attached to the rear face of the media. The media shall travel down the face of the filter between side channels which shall compress it from 51 mm to 25 mm thickness. Incorporated into the clean media housing shall be a media run-out arm, which operates a warning light and isolates the motor circuit, thus preventing the filter media winding off the face of the filter. The media shall be uniformly thick glass fibre mat with a density progressively graded from front to back for maximum dirt trapping action. The media shall have an efficiency of 96% against BS 2831 (No. 2 test dust) when handling the given air quantity. The media housing covers shall be hinged. Motors shall be suitable for 230/250 single-phase 50-cycle supply. The sub-contractor shall include for one change of filter media.'

16.21.6   For axial fan.

'Messrs. XYZ axial flow fan of the aerofoil type having an air capacity not less than – m^3/s when operating against – external static pressure. Fan casing shall be hot dipped galvanized and etched to provide a key for painting. The casing shall cover the motor and impeller and be complete with access doors. The impellers shall be of the adjustable pitch design and shall be die cast in aluminium alloy or glass reinforced polyester resin. The drive motor shall be mounted in the air stream and rod mounted to the duct casing. Impellers shall be directly coupled to the motor, using a keyward shaft and a self locking securing nut to ensure positive fixing. Motors shall be totally enclosed, air stream rated, squirrel cage, ball bearing, continuously rated with class "E" insulation, suitable for 415 volt, 3 phase, 50 cycle supply. The fan shall be suitable for running with the motor shafts in any position. Attachable mounting feet shall be bolted to the casing flange so they can be fixed in any position and each fan shall be complete with a pair of matching flanges. The fans shall be tested and their performance rated in accordance with BS 848: Part 1: 1963 and test methods to BS 848: Part 2: 1966. (*Note:* Starters, flexible connections, anti-vibration mountings are measured separately.)'

16.21.7 For a ceiling diffuser.

'Messrs. XYZ, type —, size —, — m^3/s circular ceiling diffuser of the adjustable air pattern type with the inner assembly removable from the outer shell and with a full range of air patterns from horizontal to vertical. Diffusers shall be complete with opposed blade volume control. The diffuser shall pass air in accordance with the human comfort standard. Sound power levels generated by air passing through the diffuser shall be . . . Diffusers shall be finished black to match the black anodized finish on grilles, and shall be tested to ASHRAE standard 36B–63 *Method of testing for rating the acoustic performance.* Where indicated on the schedule "Deflectrol" air tuning vanes shall be fitted.'

CHAPTER 17

Supports and anchors

17.1

There are innumerable ways and means of fixing a pipe (or pipes) to walls, on soffits, in horizontal ducts, in vertical ducts, etc. Engineering sub-contractors are versatile in designing pipe supports from a conglomeration of steel angles, U-section joists, tubular steel hangers with bolted screwed ends etc. The one pipe screwed saddle band is probably the simplest form of pipe support – the multi-pipe suspended hanger is the most involved.

17.2

Fig. 17.1 shows basic examples of standard supports for fixing pipes to walls.

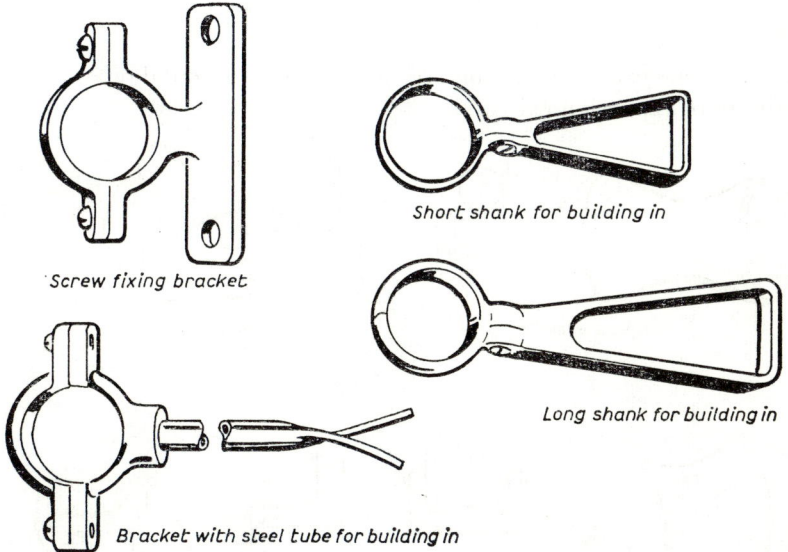

Screw fixing bracket

Short shank for building in

Long shank for building in

Bracket with steel tube for building in

Fig. 17.1   Typical standard pipe supports in malleable iron.

17.3

Fig. 17.2 shows examples of standard supports for hanging pipes from ceilings – threaded solid mild steel rod would be used to connect the flanged socket to the ring (or rings).

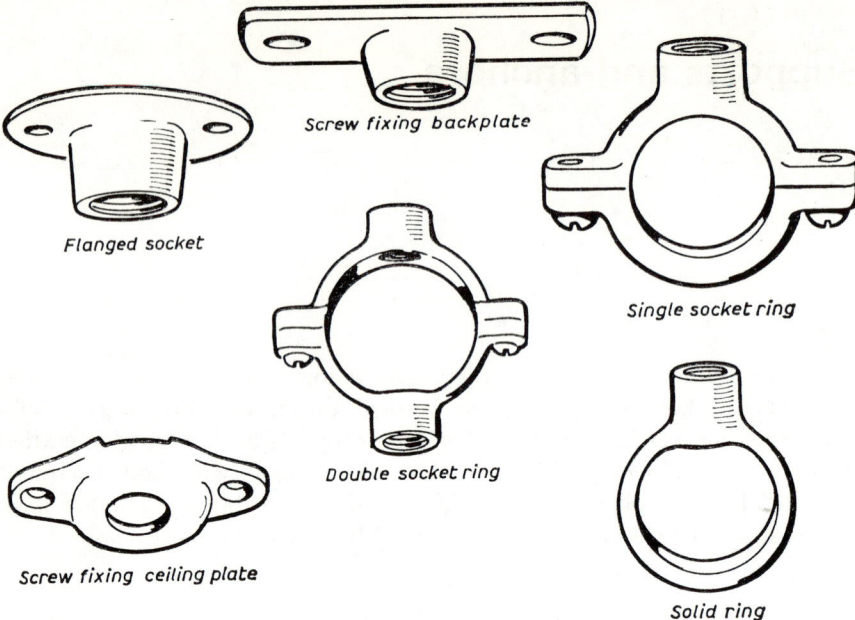

Fig. 17.2 Standard pipe supports in malleable iron.

17.4

Fig. 17.3 shows examples of standard supports for horizontal pipes where the possibility of expansion exists.

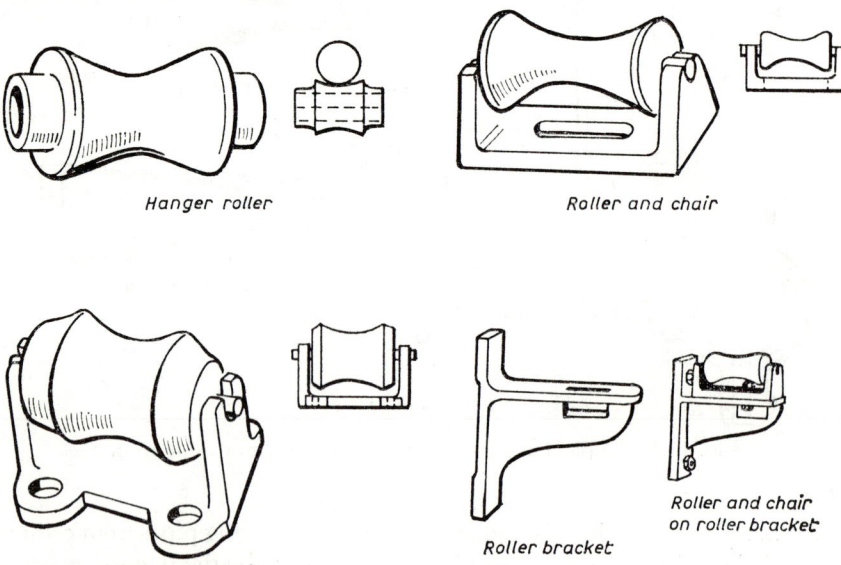

Fig. 17.3 Standard cast iron rollers and chairs.

17.5

Fig. 17.4 shows a simple purpose support for more than one pipe.

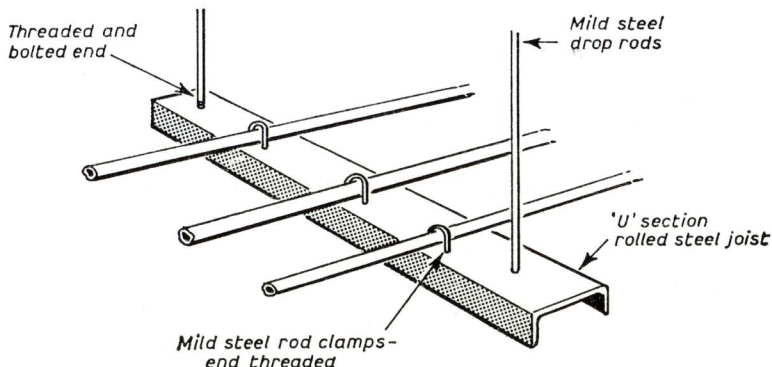

Fig. 17.4 Purpose made pipe support.

17.6

Fig. 17.5 shows an example of girder clips – it is not good practice to drill holes in the webs or flanges of joists for pipe fixings.

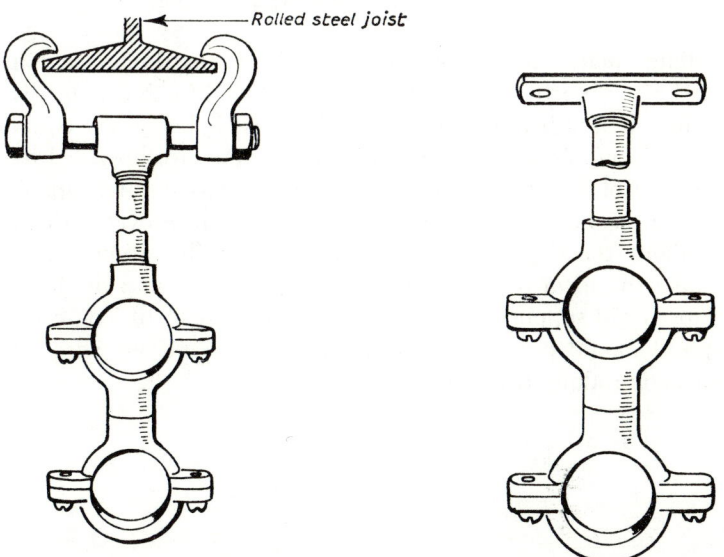

Fig. 17.5 Girder clips and hangers (unit assemblies).

17.7

Sufficient space should be left between the pipe and the wall and/or the soffit to permit insulation to be applied.

17.8

Where pipes are liable to expand and contract, pipe anchor points must be designed to cater for this. Three types of anchor supports are used – main, intermediate and directional.

Main anchors are located at the end of each straight run of pipe to contain the pipe and permit movement only towards the expansion device.

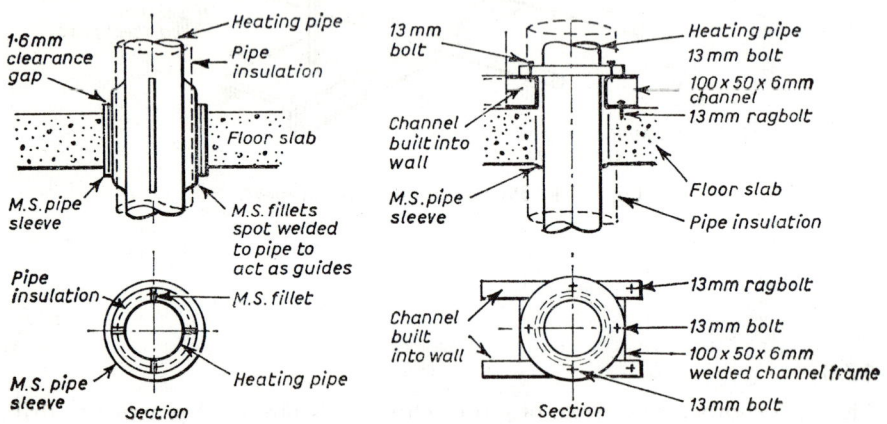

Fig. 17.6   Left – typical pipe guide.
Right – typical pipe anchor.

Intermediate anchors are subject to lighter loads than main anchors, since these need not absorb the pressure thrust. Their function is to divide the pipeline into a number of separate sections, each being self contained as regards provision of expansion. Directional anchors are provided to restrict the movement of the pipeline to one specified direction only. Pipe guides as shown in Fig. 17.6 are essential to ensure that the pipe moves in the intended manner about the expansion point and that no distortion occurs. They usually take the form of a substantially constructed strap or sleeve firmly secured to a rigid support. The guide must have sufficient length to obviate twisting and should permit the guided pipe to move freely with expansion and contraction along the axis of the pipe.

SUPPORTS AND ANCHORS 163

17.9

The recommended intervals between pipe supports are shown in Fig. 17.7 and are to be found in *Code of Practice* 341.

Wrought iron
Mild steel pipes
Heavy gauge copper pipes

Size of pipe	Intervals for vertical runs	Intervals for horizontal runs
mm	m	m
13	2·43	1·82
19	3·04	2·43
25	3·04	2·43
32	3·04	2·74
38	3·65	3·04
51	3·65	3·04
64	4·57	3·04
76	4·57	3·65
102	4·57	3·96

Light gauge copper pipes

Size of pipe	Intervals for vertical runs	Intervals for horizontal runs
mm	m	m
13	1·82	1·21
19	2·43	1·82
25	2·43	1·82
32	3·04	2·43
38	3·04	2·43
51	3·65	2·74
64	3·65	3·04
76	3·65	3·04
102	3·65	3·04

Fig. 17.7 Intervals between pipe supports

17.10

Rollers, chairs, anchors and similar items should be measured separately – preferably stating a manufacturer's catalogue number, but see SMM section S, sections 12(*c*) and (*d*).

CHAPTER 18

Pipework and fittings for internal and external installations

Water services generally

18.1

In selecting the materials to be used, much depends on the use of the building, local authority regulations and a knowledge of what materials and fittings are available and how they can best be used.

18.2

Specifications for mechanical services once written tend to be perpetuated, primarily because of the lack of time and sometimes the lack of knowledge. For example many engineers specify copper tube to BS 659 – for water services such as rising mains and hot and cold water supply, because this has always been the custom. Copper tube to BS 659 is a bendable tube and ideal for use in short connections where bends are likely to be non-standard. Since many of the pipe runs are straight, with tee branches and 90° changes in direction it is uneconomic to use copper tube to BS 659. Copper tube to BS 3931 is ideal for straight runs – this tube has been specifically designed for this purpose and is cheaper than copper tube to BS 659 – the wall thickness of tube to BS 3931 is less than tube to BS 659 – although from the performance point of view there is no difference, except in 'bendability'.

18.3

By using copper tube to BS 3931 in conjunction with manufactured fittings (as opposed to man-made pulled bends, which can only be made in copper tube to BS 659) costs can be reduced. An alternative to using manufactured bends is to introduce a short bent length of copper tube (to BS 659) into a run of copper tube to BS 3931.

18.4

Since the change to 'metric' sizes in 1971, copper tube is no longer described as 'nominal bore' since the 'outside diameter' is used. Tube to BS 3931 and BS 659 has been integrated into BS 2871, Table Z and Table X.

PIPEWORK AND FITTINGS FOR INSTALLATIONS

18.5

Copper tube to BS 3931 should be used for all straight runs up to and including 152 mm diameter with copper tube to BS 659, Table 'A' for all offsets and where non-standard bends are anticipated.

18.6

Copper fittings for use with tube to BS 3931 and BS 659 can be:

18.6.1 Capillary – (preferably of a 'non-dezincifiable' alloy) – up to 102 mm diameter. Over 102 mm diameter tees, bends and couplings are obtainable prefabricated offsite from tube to BS 659.

18.6.2 Compression – type A – non manipulative (preferably of 'non-dezincifiable' alloy) – up to 64 mm diameter. Although larger sizes are obtainable, it is often cheaper to install fabricated fittings as above.

18.6.3 Compression – type B – manipulative are available – these are more expensive than compression type A.

18.6.4 Flanges – (preferably 2 part flanges) – are used for the connection of tube of larger dimensions and for connection to plant and valves. Flanges can also be used as straight couplings in the run of pipe, but in most cases there are cheaper ways of achieving this end.

18.7

Polythene tubes to BS 1972 and BS 3284 are often used for housing where long runs are required. Polythene tube to BS 1972 is more flexible than tube to BS 3284 and requires more frequent clipping. The recommended interval for clipping is approximately 24 times the outside diameter vertically and 12–14 times horizontally. The maximum size available is 51 mm nominal for class B and C and 38 mm for class D water mains pressure. Cold bends can be made to a radius of not less than 12 times the outside diameter.

18.8

Polythene tube to BS 3284 being more rigid than tube to BS 1972 requires rather less clipping. The recommended interval for clipping is approximately 48 times the outside diameter vertically and 24 times – up to 25 mm – and 16 times over 25 mm horizontally. The maximum size available is 51 mm nominal to class B, C or D water mains pressure.

18.9

Polythene is a thermoplastic material and therefore should not be used for hot water services or installed close to hot pipes and other heat sources unless protected.

18.10

The frost resistance of polythene is good – it can therefore be used in cold situations.

18.11

Fittings for both forms of polythene tube are compression type 'A' – which are manufactured for use with polythene tube – and are supplied with a supporting sleeve which is inserted into the bore of the tube end prior to jointing. Fittings for polythene tubes are made of a 'non-dezincifiable' alloy for reasons of external and internal corrosion.

18.12

UPVC or 'unplasticized polyvinyl chloride' can be used internally providing an allowance for expansion and contraction is made. Tubes to BS 3505 with solvent welded fittings up to 203 mm diameter nominal size are manufactured.

18.13

UPVC tube installations are cheaper than most others, especially if the number of fittings is kept to a minimum. Bending on site is not practicable. Standard fittings should be used.

18.14

As UPVC is a comparatively new material, no general rules have, as yet, been made with regard to vertical or horizontal clippings – the manufacturers should be consulted. Polypropylene snap-on clips can be used.

18.15

UPVC is a thermoplastic material and therefore should not be used for hot water services or installed close to heat sources unless protected.

18.16

UPVC should be protected if used in location subject to frost.

18.17

UPVC fittings are the solvent welded type to BS 4346, Part 1 and suitable for class E working pressure.

18.18

Heavy valves, flanges and fittings should be supported directly; supports should be firm enough to avoid strain, but flexible enough to permit thermal movement.

Cold water distribution

18.19

Copper tubes and fittings – see section 18.5 and 18.6.

18.20

Polythene tubes and fittings – see sections 18.7 to 18.11. Provided adequate horizontal and vertical support is given to polythene pipe and fittings it is ideal for cold water distribution. It is not aesthetically acceptable in exposed positions and should therefore be fixed in ducts whenever possible. Exposed branch connections should be in copper since copper to polythene connectors are available.

18.21

UPVC tubes and fittings (see sections 18.12 to 18.18) the use of this material for cold water distribution is increasing due to stability of prices, resistance to corrosion and speed of jointing. UPVC has the same outside dimensions as steel tubes, therefore the 10 mm nominal size UPVC tube has a bore of 13·9 mm (mean) and can be used instead of 13 mm diameter tubes. Similarly the 13 mm nominal size UPVC tube has a bore of 16·78 mm (mean) and can be used instead of 19 mm diameter tubes. As with polythene tube, exposed branch connections should be in copper tube if the hot water installation is in copper tube – copper to UPVC connectors are available. UPVC tubes should not be used as a feed pipe from a tank to a hot water cylinder and where tubes run parallel with hot water pipes, the distance between them should be a minimum 76 mm unless the hot service is properly insulated.

18.22

Expansion and contraction of UPVC material is high in comparison with other materials – an expansion of 1·5 mm takes place in every 3·04 m of tube for every 10°C change in temperature, therefore an allowance must be made for this at corners and sleeves, etc.

Hot-water distribution and small-bore heating services

18.23

Copper tubes and fittings – see sections 18.5 and 18.6.

18.24

Polythene tubes and fittings must not be used.

18.25

UPVC tubes and fittings must not be used.

External underground water services

18.26

Generally the connecting pipe between the water main and the stopcock within a building can be manufactured from a variety of materials, those in constant use include copper, polythene or PVC. The choice of material is controlled by efficiency, availability, economics, local authority regulations and ease of handling.

18.27

Copper tube to BS 1386 is still most commonly used, for underground water services and is obtainable in size range from 13 mm to 51 mm diameter nominal bore in coils of 9·14 m, 13·71 m or 18·28 m. These coils are supplied in 'soft temper' copper to permit the coils to be unrolled with comparative ease – the tube should be stamped and marked as required by the BS and bear the BSI 'Kite Mark' symbol.

18.28

Copper tube should not be used where corrosive ground conditions exist – such as in made up ground where ash and clinker have been dumped and in clay soils which are poorly drained.

18.29

If copper tube is used where corrosive ground conditions exist – then the pipe must be protected in one of the following ways:

18.29.1 Limestone chippings placed around the pipe in a trench.
18.29.2 Wrapping with a protective pipe tape.
18.29.3 Polythene sheathed copper tube.

18.30

Copper water services are required to be laid in a trench at a depth of 762 mm or below the frost level. In some cases water services can be laid with the use of a tractor-pulled mole plough – the copper tube being unrolled from a drum and fed through the mole plough at the required depths.

18.31

Jointing of copper tube to BS 1386 is by means of fittings made of 'non-dezincifiable non-ferrous alloys or of copper' of the capillary or compression type 'B'.

18.32

Dezincification is a corrosion caused by the zinc content in certain brasses, this corrosion causes a scale to form which is detrimental to pipes and fittings. It is therefore important that fittings should be made of non-dezincifiable non-ferrous metal.

18.33

Metrication – see section 18.4.

18.34

Polythene tube is supplied in coils of between 15·24 m and 152·4 m in length, each must be stamped and marked as required by the BS and bear the BSI

'Kite Mark' symbol. Black in colour, it is normally used in the size range 13 mm to 51 mm diameter nominal size to class B, C or D water mains pressure rating.

18.35

There are two types of polythene tube – low density to BS 1972 and high density to BS 3284. The former is cheaper, more flexible and generally used for cold water services.

18.36

Polythene tube in water services is laid in a trench or by mole plough as described in section 18.30.

18.37

Jointing for polythene for both types of tube is by the use of non-manipulative compression fittings with a supporting sleeve, which is inserted into the bore of the pipe. This sleeve is made of copper and the fittings are manufactured in a non-dezincifiable alloy – such as good quality gunmetal – to BS 864. Standard compression fittings made for copper tube must not be used.

18.38

Electrical equipment should not be earthed to polythene tube.

18.39

UPVC (see sections 18.12 to 18.18) is supplied in 6·09 m straight rigid lengths to BS 3505: 1968, to class E water main pressure and in the size range 13 mm to 38 mm nominal diameter. Colours range from mid grey to dark grey. All such tube would be stamped or marked as required by the BS and should bear the BSI 'Kite Mark' symbol. The tube can be supplied with one end socketed so as to eliminate the use of straight couplings or connectors or with plain ends for use with fittings of the same material. UPVC tube is light in weight and easy to handle, simply jointed and resistant to corrosion and scale, is odourless and tasteless. Some care should be taken in the handling of tube if the temperature is near freezing point.

18.40

The UPVC tube and joints should be completed on the surface and after some hours lowered into the trench. The trench bottom should be free of sharp objects.

18.41

UPVC installations do not normally require sharp bends, but should these be necessary they can then either be a fittings bend or a purpose made bend manufactured in UPVC.

Slow bends can be created by utilizing the normal flexibility of the tube, for example a 4·57 m minimum radius bend can be obtained with a 25 mm nominal size tube.

18.42

Electrical equipment should not be earthed to UPVC tube.

18.43

Generally a 'solvent welded' type of joint would be used on tube used for UPVC installations. Solvent welding is achieved by chemically melting the surfaces to be joined.

A wide range of fittings is available and these should conform to BS 4346 Part 1 and be suitable for class E working pressure and of the same colour as the tube.

18.44

UPVC tubes, fittings, cleaning fluid and solvent cement, should all be supplied by the same manufacturer.

18.45

The manufacturer's instructions should be followed when describing a solvent welded joint. When connecting UPVC to a metal fitting it is essential to connect UPVC to metal and not vice-versa.

Stainless steel tubing

18.46

Thin wall tubing to BS 4127 is available for 13 mm – 38 mm nominal bore, with outside diameter equivalent to copper tubing and can be jointed with copper tube fittings to BS 864. As the thermal expansion of stainless steel tubing is very similar to copper tubing there is no danger of joints being weakened through unequal rates of expansion. When capillary fittings are to be used in the installation, great care must be taken to ensure that the flux that is used in jointing is not a phosphor based flux, as, over a period of time, this will attack the tube unless the installation is flushed out immediately after the joints are made. Because of this it is preferable to specify compression fittings. Providing the correct type of bending machine is used it is possible to form labour bends and offsets in this type of tubing. As there is no electrolytic reaction between stainless steel and galvanized or copper, it is possible to use a galvanized steel cold water storage tank or a copper calorifier in the same circuit. Stainless steel tube can be used in hot and cold water services or sanitary installations. When used with chromium plated fittings a high standard of finish can be obtained at a lower cost than if chromium plated copper tube is used.

CHAPTER 19

Thermal insulation

19.1

Thermal insulation of pipework and vessels is essential if heat is to be conserved. The type of insulation depends on the location of the pipes and vessels and also whether they are hidden from view or exposed.

The following forms of insulation are in general use:

19.1.1 Flexible blanket in:
- Glass fibre
- Asbestos
- Rock wool
- Slag wool
- Hair felt.

19.1.2 Preformed slabs in:
- Glass fibre
- Expanded polystyrene
- Cork
- Calcium silicate.

19.1.3 Preformed rigid sections in:
- Glass fibre
- Calcium silicate
- Expanded polystyrene
- Magnesia
- Asbestos
- Cork
- Rock wool
- Compressed paper felt.

19.2

In plant rooms the normal practice is to have a plastic insulated finish, the thickness of which depends on the temperature of water passing through the system. Plastic insulation is made from 85% magnesia in powder form and 15% asbestos fibre added to act as a binder. This compound is mixed with water to form a mortar of even consistency and applied to the pipe or vessel in layers (each layer should be dry before proceeding with the next layer) until the required thickness is obtained. A smooth protective finish is obtained by applying a 13 mm thick coat of Keene's cement. On vessels and large bore pipes it is usual to incorporate a binding of galvanized wire mesh between layers.

19.3

As this form of insulation requires heat for drying out, it is essential for the heating installation to be in operation.

19.4

In cases where the installation cannot be put into operation to permit drying out, sectional insulation (of equal efficiency), finished with Keene's cement as described, should be used.

19.5

Pipework outside plant rooms, that requires insulation and is exposed to view, should be insulated with rigid sections. These are usually supplied in standard lengths of 914 mm each in half pipe sections with the internal diameter conforming to the outside diameter of the pipe to be insulated. Sections are canvas covered and fixed with non-ferrous metal bands at approximately 457 mm intervals.

19.6

Pipework outside plant rooms (which is not on view) should be insulated with rigid sections fixed with non-ferrous metal bands or a flexible mattress secured with galvanized wire netting.

19.7

When pipes are exposed to the elements and require to be insulated it is necessary to weatherproof the insulation. This is usually achieved by covering the insulation with bituminous felt fixed with galvanized wire netting and at completion painting with two to three coats of bitumastic paint.

19.8

Internal cold water feed pipes (not on view and where condensation is likely to occur) are generally insulated with 13 mm thick hair felt secured with wire. Where pipes are on view, rigid sections covered with canvas and fixed with non-ferrous bands should be used.

19.9

The insulation of valves and flanges is generally achieved by fixing around the valve a hinged metal box or glass-fibre blankets secured with wire netting. Both methods of insulation permit easy removal should the valve become defective.

19.10

Boiler flue pipes are usually insulated with a 51 mm thick insulation fixed to metal lugs welded to boiler flue to permit a 25 mm air space between boiler flue and insulation and then finished with a layer of 13 mm thick Keene's cement.

19.11

Feed and expansion tanks, not exposed to the elements but in exposed positions, are commonly protected against frost damage by a casing of polystyrene sheet secured with wire netting or metal bands.

19.12

Descriptions. When describing insulation, it is essential to state the outside size of the pipe or vessel and the material from which it is manufactured. Calorifiers should be described as vertical or horizontal and the outside dimension of boiler flues should be given.

19.13

Air conditioning ductwork. Ductwork in many instances requires insulation not only to prevent heat loss and condensation, but also to reduce noise levels caused by vibration, etc. It is essential that the insulation used in ductwork should be as fire-proof as possible. Materials in general use include flexible lightweight fibre sheets with surface finishes of plastic or reinforced aluminium foil. These materials are light in weight and can be fixed to the surface of the ducts with adhesive, the joints covered with adhesive tapes. Rectangular and circular ducts can be insulated this way. Rigid polystyrene slabs (self-extinguishing grade) can also be used on rectangular ducts. Asbestos spray is sometimes used both internally and externally on ducts – in plant rooms a smooth protective finish of 13 mm thick Keene's cement may be called for to conform with the insulation finish of other equipment.

For ductwork located externally in buildings, it is usual to use preformed insulation securely fixed to the ductwork and covered with bituminous felt secured with wire netting and painted with bitumastic paint.

19.14

Descriptions. Some typical descriptions of various types of insulation might be:

19.14.1 For hot water service in plant rooms.
   19 mm rigid glass silk section securely fixed in position and finished with 13 mm self set cement (reinforced with scrim cloth on pipes

64 mm diameter and over) and painted one undercoat and one finishing coat of approved eggshell paint.
On 13 mm copper tube and fittings.
Ditto but 25 mm.

19.14.2 For cold water service outside plant rooms:
Expanded mould polystyrene sections set in suitable bituminous adhesive wire with 19 g galvanized wire ties and vapour sealed with 'Flint-cote' or emulsified asphalt over polystyrene with identification bands at not less than 9·144 m intervals and at all pipe junctions, suitably, and with directional arrows.
19 mm thick to 13 mm copper tube and fittings.
19 mm Ditto but to 25 mm.

19.14.3 For cold and/or hot water service outside plant rooms.
Rigid glass silk sections in 914 mm lengths finished with scrim cloth and non-ferrous metal bands (not less than 3 per 914 mm section) applied to BS 1334:1959 including identification bands and left unpainted.
13 mm thick to 13 mm copper tube and fittings.
13 mm Ditto but to 19 mm.

19.14.4 Another alternative for cold water services outside plant rooms.
Fibreglass or rocksil rigid section insulation with PVC outer sheathing to BS 476 class I with all joints PVC taped in matching colours.
25 mm thick to 13 mm copper tube and fittings.

19.14.5 For cold water services inside plant rooms.
Polystyrene sections with 13 mm self set finish reinforced with open mesh scrim cloth and painted one undercoat and one top coat of eggshell. The vapour seal to be continuous and unbroken.
25 mm thick section to 38 mm copper tube and fittings.

19.14.6 For supply ventilation and air-conditioning ducts in plant rooms.
38 mm thick self extinguishing grade polystyrene secured with 25 mm mesh 20 g galvanized wire netting, and finished with 13 mm self-setting cement, reinforced with open mesh scrim cloth, and painted one undercoat and one top coat of approved eggshell finish, including insulating all fittings and flanges. (*Note:* Only fitting to access panels and inspection doors are measured separately.)
3048 × 914 mm duct and fittings.
2743 × 1829 mm ditto.

19.14.7 For a cold water tank.
51 mm thick self extinguishing grade polystyrene slabs securely fixed with metal bands around four sides and top of 914 × 914 × 610 mm tank.

CHAPTER 20

Electrical installation

20.1

The incoming electricity main is generally provided and installed by the Electricity Board. In domestic installations where the load does not exceed 100 kW (or whatever loading is considered satisfactory by the local Electricity Board) no sub-station is necessary and the incoming voltage would be three-phase 415 volt M.V., where a sub-station is required the incoming voltage would generally be 11,000 volts (11 kV).

20.2

Fig. 20.1 shows a typical layout of a sub-station within a building. The Electricity Board will provide their own incoming meter panels comprising

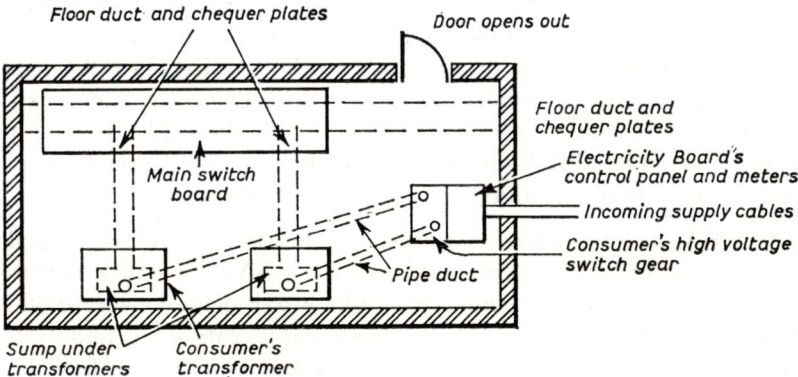

Fig. 20.1 Typical lay-out of sub-station within a building.

circuit-breakers, measuring indicators to which the electricity supply is connected. This type of installation would be found in buildings where the anticipated electrical load is high.

20.3

Adjoining the Electricity Board's equipment as described in section 20.2 is the consumer's (building owner's) high voltage switch gear and transformers (to reduce the incoming voltage) and a main switchboard for control and distribution of the electricity, the h.v. switchgear is a circuit-breaker of sufficient size to switch the load of the transformers. The h.v. switchgear would be contained in a cubicle type panel, complete with overload and earth leakage protection ammeter, voltmeter and with the necessary selection switches. In addition, the h.v. switchgear panel would have cable sealing boxes suitable for the connection of the Electricity Board's cables. The type, size and manufacturer of the h.v. switchgear panel will be specified by the engineer, the electrical sub-contractor would install the h.v. switchgear panel.

20.4

The connection between the h.v. switchgear, and the transformer is normally carried out in paper insulated lead covered steel wire armoured and sheathed cables (PILCSWA & S), or PVC insulated steel wire armoured and sheathed in PVC (PVCSWAPVC), these cables are connected to the primary side of the transformers. These cables are generally laid in floor ducts or pipe ducts that connect the h.v. switchgear and the transformers. The description of the cables should state the BS, standard voltage, grade, size and number of cores and the method of fixing.

20.5

Transformers for undercover sub-stations are generally the oil-cooled type of sufficient size to cope with the required loading. The transformers reduce the incoming 11 kV on the primary side to the required working load of 430/250 volts on the secondary side. The transformers are connected by cable (see section 20.6) to the main switchboard – the cables being laid in floor ducts or suspended from the soffit of the floor above on hangers. A typical description of a transformer might be as follows:

> '750 KVA 11,000/433 volt transformer to BS 171 and equipped to CEGBTI specification as manufactured by XYZ or other approved. Pyrochlor filled double wound type, 3 phase star/delta connected 50 Hz; with and including three pole single gland cable sealing box and inverted four pole eight gland cable sealing box, fix and connect transformer.'

20.6

The cables between the secondary side of the transformers and the main medium voltage switch panel can be single core paper insulated lead covered (PILC) cables with a copper or aluminium conductor. If the cables are fixed to the duct walls then cleats are required – if there are numerous cables then cable racks will be necessary. It is often more explicit to include the method of fixing with the description of the cable. Typical descriptions might be as follows:

600/1000 volt grade PVCSWAPVC cable as specified in Clause **X**
35 mm² two core cable lay on cable rack
70 mm² four core ditto
4 mm² two core cable with cable cleats fix to brickwork or concrete
95 mm² two core cable ditto
185 mm² four core cable ditto
300 mm² two core cable with cleats as manufactured by **XYZ** hooks, clamps, bolts, cable cleat stop and stud; fix to channel (channel measured separately)
Terminate and make off 600/1000 volt grade PVCSWAPVC cable with aluminium conductors with and including compression type cable gland and including all necessary drilling, lock nuts etc.
Termination to 4 mm² two core cable
Ditto but for 35 mm²
Termination to 70 mm² four core cable

20.7

The main switchboard panel consists of a busbar chamber that is connected to the transformers by cable (see section 20.6). An incoming switch fuse or circuit breaker controls this supply. A busbar consists of an uninsulated copper rod that permits the electricity to be received and distributed. From the busbars are the necessary outgoing switch fuses or circuit breakers. To each switch fuse or circuit breaker ammeters are fitted in order that the incoming and outgoing current can be checked. Voltmeters, phase selector switches, various meters to register electricity supplied to particular sections of a building and other pieces of apparatus as required are all housed in the prefabricated main switch panel. The description of the main switch panel should include size, manufacturer's name (or other approved) the performance required, the cable glands and sealing boxes, fuses, labels to fascia panel, circuit charts etc., and any necessary supports and fixings. A typical description might be as follows:

'Main Switch Board. Cubicle type main switch board as manufactured by **XYZ** designed for rear access operating at 415 volts 3 phase four wire 50 Hz with top and bottom entry and exit for cables comprising:

1	1000 amp four pole busbar
1	1000 amp air circuit-breaker
1	30 amp TP & N switch fuse
2	60 amp TP & N switch fuse
5	100 amp TP & N switch fuse
1	150 amp TP & N switch fuse
3	200 amp TP & N switch fuse
1	250 amp TP & N switch fuse
1	400 amp TP & N switch fuse

2 Sixteen-way 15 amp SP & N distribution board
1 Thirty-way ditto including all necessary supports, earthing, spare fuses, cable glands, sealing boxes, internal wiring, interconnections, labels, metering and instrumentation, fix to brickwork or concrete and connect.'

20.8

The sub-main distribution cables are connected to the outgoing switch fuses or circuit breakers in the main switch panels and from there are connected to the various sub-main distribution boards, boiler house and other plant rooms, lift control panels etc.

20.9

Earthing all metal work and the transformer neutrals within the sub-station must be connected to earth by copper tapes. The tapes are fixed to walls with saddles and the ends of the tape are bolted or welded to the piece of equipment that is to be earthed. The earthing terminal may be that provided by the Electricity Board or alternatively earth rods or plates are buried in the ground adjoining the sub-station. An earth test point must be provided outside the sub-station that will permit the earthing of the installation to be tested.

20.10

Fire precautions within a sub-station include the provision of sumps below the transformers. The sumps must be large enough to receive the entire oil capacity of the transformers should they leak. In addition the fire regulations require the installation of automatic fire extinguishers of the foam or CO_2 type.

20.11

Sub-main switchboards are sometimes required in large installations where it is necessary to break down the electrical distribution into smaller units. By introducing a sub-main switchboard the necessity to have numerous cables from the main switchboard is obviated. A sub-main switchboard is a miniature main switchboard and would generally include those items described in section 20.7. A typical description might be as follows:

'Sub-main switch board as manufactured by XYZ for operation at 415 volts three phase four wire 50 cycles comprising:

1 500 amp four pole busbar
1 500 amp TP & N isolator
2 160 amp TP & N fused switches
2 160 amp SP & N fused switches

ELECTRICAL INSTALLATION 179

1 Twenty-four-way SP & N distribution board with miniature circuit breakers including all necessary supports and fixings, earthing, cable glands and sealing boxes, internal wiring, interconnections and labels; fix to brickwork or concrete and connect.'

20.12

Sub-main distribution cables are normally one of the following types:

20.12.1 Paper insulated cables, lead covered and steel wire armoured and served (PILCSWA & S). These cables are mainly used where large electrical loadings are anticipated, or where there is a considerable distance from main switchboard to the point of termination. These cables are normally laid in the ground, covered with cover tiles, sifted earth or sand – if laid internally, sleeves should be measured when the cables pass through walls. With the distribution of the cable should be the method of fixing, such as cable cleats or whether or not laid in cable trays (the latter should be measured separately). A typical description might be as follows:

'600/1000 volt grade 150 mm^2 four core PILCSWA & S cable as specified complete with cable cleats – fix to brickwork or concrete in surface work.'

20.12.2 PVC covered steel wire armoured and PVC sheathed (PVC-SWAPVC). These are multi-cored cables with either copper or aluminium conductors and are used extensively for internal sub-mains distribution. A typical description might be as follows:

'600/1000 volt grade 150 mm^2 four core PVCSWAPVC cable as specified complete with cable cleats and hangers; fix to brickwork or concrete in surface work.'

20.12.3 Mineral insulated copper covered (MICC). These cables are either single or multi-cored cables and generally speaking have copper conductors and copper coverings externally. Also available are cables similar to MICC but with aluminium conductors and aluminium covering. MICC cables are used extensively for internal sub-mains distribution. Other advantages being that they are aesthetically acceptable because they can be fixed to surfaces without the use of conduit. They are also able to be buried in the ground providing the PVC covered MICC cable is used.
Typical descriptions might be as follows:

'4 mm^2 four core light duty 600 volt grade MICC cable with copper saddles; fix to cable tray.

'50 mm^2 three core heavy duty 1000 volt grade MICC cable, PVC sheathed with PVC sheathed copper saddles; fix to brickwork or concrete in surface work.'

20.13

Termination for sub-main cables are as follows:

20.13.1 PILCSWA & S.

A typical description for the termination of the above cable at a distribution board, to plant etc. might be as follows:

'Terminate and make off 150 mm^2 four core 600/1000 volt grade PILCSWA & S cable with and including cable sealing box, armour clamp earth bond; all necessary drilling, etc.'

20.13.2 PVCSWAPVC.

A typical description for the termination of the above cable might be as follows:

'Terminate and make off 150 mm^2 four core 600/1000 volt grade PVCSWAPVC cable with and including compression type cable gland and all necessary drilling, lock-nuts, etc.'

20.13.3 Mineral insulated (MICC).

A typical description for the termination of the above cable might be as follows:

'Terminate and make off 4 mm^2 four core light duty 600 volt grade MICC cable with and including cold screw on pot type seal, neoprene sleeves, ring type gland, mechanical cone grip socket; including all necessary drilling lock-nuts, etc.'

20.14

Vertical rising main busbars are used in multi-storey buildings; they consist of four copper bars (three phases and neutral) fixed vertically within a sheet metal case. They are obtainable in different lengths – 1·829 m, 2·438 m and 3·658 m lengths being common.

At each floor level there is a tap-off unit to which the sub-mains distribution board is connected. The vertical rising main busbar is connected to the main switchboard via one of the cables described in section 20.11 and controlled by an isolator switch that is mounted by the base of the vertical busbar duct which runs from the lowest level to about 1·829 m above the level of the uppermost floor.

A typical description might be as follows:

'Vertical rising main busbar
200 amp TP & N rising main busbar (approximate length 15·24 m) complete as specified manufactured by XYZ including all necessary supports and brackets, connectors, tap-off units, fire proof barriers, earth bonding links, main isolator and cable glands, fix to brickwork or concrete and connect.'

20.15

Tap-off units for vertical busbars (see section 20.14).

A typical description might be as follows:

'100 amp TP & N fused tap-off unit complete with HRC fuses; fix to rising main busbar and connect.'

20.16

Distribution boards are the means by which the final sub-circuits are controlled. The distribution board is connected to the main switchboard by cable or via the tap-off units from the vertical rising main busbars. Distribution boards are obtainable in a variety of sizes and are a standard manufactured unit – the smallest being a two-way. The control of the electrical distribution is via the fuse ways whose primary function is to prevent overloading of the particular circuit, whether it be light or power. There are three types of fuse ways available:

- (*a*) Re-wirable fuses
- (*b*) Cartridge fuses (HRC or HBC)
- (*c*) Miniature circuit breakers (MCB).

Distribution boards are manufactured in the following categories:

- (*i*) Single pole and neutral (SPN)
- (*ii*) Double pole (DP)
- (*iii*) Triple pole (TP)
- (*iv*) Triple pole and neutral (TPN).

A typical description might be as follows:

'Eight way 30 amp SP & N surface type distribution board as specified with miniature circuit breakers, shields, barriers, labels all necessary supports and fixings; fix to brickwork or concrete and connect.'

20.17

Isolated items of plant, lifts, fire alarm systems, emergency lighting, batteries, etc., are generally connected by cable direct to the main switchboard and are controlled by means of an isolator switch or switch-fuse.

20.18

The mechanical services control panels (to boiler houses etc.) are generally supplied and installed by the mechanical engineering services sub-contractor, but the mains cable from the main switchboard to this control panel is normally part of the electrical subcontract.

20.19

Cable trunking is used to enclose the final sub-circuit wiring which consists of lighting, power, fire alarm, telephone etc. there are numerous types of cable trunking available and these include:

20.19.1 Pressed metal cable trunking.

This can be single or multi-compartment. Single trunking would be used for a single service such as lighting – however, if there were several services to be distributed such as lighting, power, telephones emergency lighting, T.V. and radio, then these would be used in multi-compartment trunking (See *IEE Regulations* B45 to B50).

Typical descriptions might be as follows:

'102×51 mm single compartment steel cable trunking as manufactured by XYZ complete with overlapping lid with turn buckle fixings, cable supports, connector pieces, earth links, all necessary supports and fixings; fix to brickwork or concrete.
Extra over for:
102×51 mm Bend
102×51 mm Tee.'

20.19.2 Pressed metal floor trunking.

There are three main types in use, they can be single or multi-compartment:

(a) Continuous trunking that is buried beneath the floor screed and is accessible by means of junction boxes.
(b) Continuous trunking that has a removable recessed cover in which the appropriate floor finish is laid.

Typical descriptions might be as follows:

'102×51 mm two compartment underfloor trunking as specified complete with tray type cover, gaskets and earth links fix to concrete slab.
Extra over for:
$229 \times 229 \times 76$ mm underfloor tee junction box.'

(c) This is similar to (b) above except that the removable cover is fixed flush with the screed and the floor covering passes over the top.

20.19.3 Pressed metal or plastic skirting trunking.

There are several designs available; they all permit the housing of power and telephone circuits. They also give the facility (where a ring main system of power installation is installed) for connecting power outlets at whatever interval is required, also the connection of telephone services, if they are housed in the skirting trunking.

Typical descriptions might be as follows:

'152×51 mm two compartment skirting trunking as specified complete with connector pieces and socket outlet panels fix to brickwork or concrete.

Extra over for:

152 × 51 mm end caps.'

20.19.4 Pressed metal lighting trunking.

This is used for industrial installations and gives the facility for light fittings to be connected to and supported by the trunking. The trunking is usually accessible from the side or bottom.

20.19.5 Overhead busbar trunking.

This is used in industrial installations and protects overhead busbars. This enables pieces of plant and equipment to be moved about the factory floor and easily connected to the overhead busbars.

Measurement of trunking is dealt with in SMM/T7. In this section there is no specific mention of supporting drop rods that are necessary for suspended trunking busbars.

20.20

Lighting final sub-circuits fall generally into four categories:

20.20.1 Domestic.

On the consumer side of the meter a consumer control unit is installed to control the whole of the electrical installation for the house.

A typical description might be as follows:

'Surface type six-way consumer control unit as specified with two 5 amp, one 15 amp two 30 amp and one 45 amp miniature circuit breaker and one 60 amp DP main switch with all internal wiring and space for meter and cut-out; fix to brickwork or concrete and connect.'

The lighting circuits from the consumer control unit would be carried out in PVC insulated PVC sheathed cables (PVC/PVC) two core with earth continuity conductor (ECC). These cables are generally surface mounted, conduit only being used when the cables are required to be chased into the wall. They are generally run in floor and ceiling spaces and drop down to lighting points and switches.

20.20.2 Flats.

From the sub-distribution board the sub-circuits would be single core PVC insulated cable run in heavy gauge screwed conduit; black enamel is the most common although galvanized is used externally and various varieties of plastic conduits are available. These conduits would be chased into the walls or built in to the reinforced concrete floors, or alternatively laid on the surface of the concrete floor and covered with floor screed.

20.20.3 Offices, schools, hospitals, etc.

From the sub-distribution board final sub-circuits would be single core PVC insulated cable run vertically from the distribution board in trunking and horizontally in trunking within the space between the soffit of the concrete floor and a false ceiling, that is more often than not to be found over corridors and open areas. The distribution from the trunking to the lighting points and switches is single core PVC insulated cable run in heavy gauge screwed conduit.

20.20.4 Industrial.

This is similar to the distribution described in section 20.20.3. except that the horizontal trunking would not be over the suspended ceiling, but would be visible and supported by hangers etc. from roof trusses and the like.

In the three preceding sub-paragraphs – 20.20.2, 3 and 4 – the final sub-circuits have been described as PVC covered cable, protected by either trunking or conduit – it is equally acceptable for these installations to be in mineral insulated copper covered cable (MICC). This would be used for the entire lighting installation from the distribution board to the light fittings and switches. Where MICC cable is chased into walls it should be PVC covered.

20.21

Conduit (see Fig. 20.5).

The following are the types of conduit in common use:

20.21.1 Close joined.

This is manufactured from light gauge steel, shaped to make a perfectly round and regular tube with the edges of the seam in contact, but not joined. This type of conduit is used in isolated lengths in domestic installations and where wiring is concealed in walls – in the case of the latter, rubber bushes are used at either end to prevent the sharp end of the conduit cutting the insulation to the electric wiring.

20.21.2 Welded.

This is similar to the above, but manufactured from heavy gauge steel with the longitudinal joint welded and is either galvanized or black enamel painted. This conduit is assembled with screwed joints into elbows, tees, junction boxes etc. and is generally used for the protection of cables.

20.21.3 Solid drawn.

As the name implies this is seamless and is generally manufactured from mild steel which is then galvanized. It is put together using screwed end fittings of various types, depending on the proposed use, which includes flame proof and waterproof installations.

20.21.4 Plastic.

This consists of a plastic, seamless tube, various types of fittings are available. This conduit is assembled with patent 'push in' type joints into plastic elbows, tees, junction boxes etc. It is used extensively on domestic installations.

Typical descriptions of the various conduits described above might be as follows:

'Heavy gauge welded conduit with screwed joints in accordance with specification Clause X including associated couplings, bends, fittings, small pattern malleable iron conduit boxes with steel covers and screws; fix to brickwork or concrete
Black enamelled finish
19 mm conduit with crampets in concealed work
19 mm conduit with distance saddles in surface work
25 mm ditto
Extra over black enamel conduit for
$102 \times 102 \times 51$ mm adaptable box
Galvanized finish
19 mm conduit with distance saddles in surface work
19 mm solid drawn conduit with flameproof conduit boxes, gaskets, fittings and distance saddles in surface work
PVC
19 mm heavy gauge high impact PVC conduit as specified including associated spacer bar saddles, couplings, bends, fittings, small pattern PVC conduit boxes with covers and screws; fix to brickwork or concrete in surface work.'

20.21.5 The measurement of conduit is dealt with in SMM/T6. Generally engineers do not show the exact location of vertical or horizontal conduit on their drawings and it is therefore up to the measurer to ascertain from the engineer or his specifications where it is required.

20.22

Lighting cables (see 20.41).

The cable that is in general use for this installation is PVC covered which has a copper conductor with a sectional area of 1·5 mm^2. Although there are several methods of installing the final lighting sub-circuit, Fig. 20.2 shows the 'loop-in' method of wiring the lighting circuits. The lamp is connected between the switchline from the switch and the neutral (c.b.).

Typical descriptions might be as follows:

'600/1000 volt grade single core PVC insulated cable as specified
1·5 mm^2 cable drawn into conduit
1·5 mm^2 cable lay in trunking including taping or binding.'

Reference to *The Institution of Electrical Engineers' (IEE) Regulations for the Electrical Equipment of Buildings* indicates the cable-carrying capacity of various sizes of conduits.

Measurement of lighting installations is dealt with in SMM/T10–15 inclusive – the allowances mentioned in T10 should be especially noted.

The 'loop-in' system of wiring is generally used for lighting circuits. Before measuring lighting cables it is advisable to discuss the routing of these

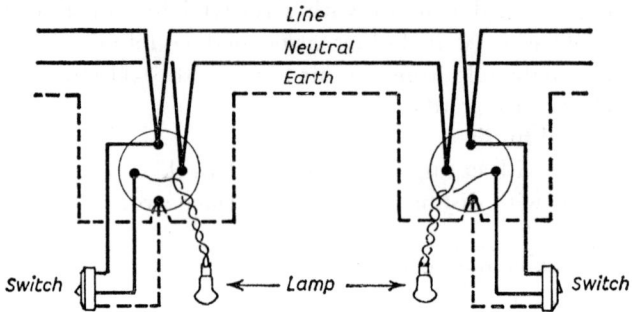

Fig. 20.2 The loop-in method of wiring lighting circuits.

with the engineer – as their exact routing will not always be readily apparent from the drawings. It should be borne in mind that the cost of final sub-circuit cabling is a small proportion of the total cost of the electrical installation.

20.23

Lighting switches.

There are numerous types of lighting switches available. When drafting a description the manufacturers catalogue references must be given, together with the voltage, the number of gangs (i.e. switches), the amperage etc.

Typical descriptions might be as follows:

'250 volt grade flush type switch as specified with rocker type switch, matt chrome finished face plate and steel box; fix to brickwork or concrete and connect.
5 amp one gang one-way switch
5 amp two gang ditto
5 amp one gang two-way switch
5 amp one gang intermediate switch
15 amp one gang one-way switch
15 amp two gang switch, one gang one-way and one gang two-way.'

Alternative two-way switching is shown in Fig. 20.3. In addition there are time-lag switches, key switches, and externally there are various waterproof 'rotary' switches.

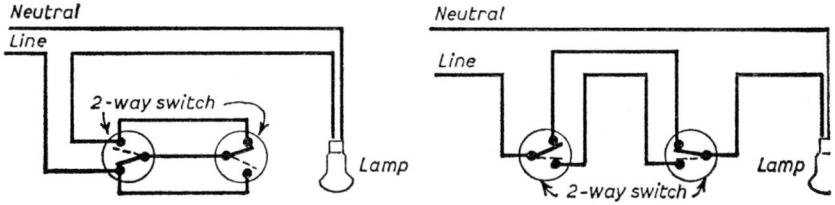

Fig. 20.3 Left – wiring for two-way switching in PVC cables.
Right – wiring for two-way switching in conduit.

20.24

Light fittings.

There are innumerable types of light fitting available. When drafting a description the manufacturer's catalogue references must be given, together with the method of termination of the conduit and cable wiring to the flexible cables which form part of the fitting, the necessary connector blocks and any other fixings and supports and the provision of all the appropriate fluorescent or tungsten lamps.

Typical descriptions might be as follows:

> 'Fluorescent lighting fittings complete as specified, including fittings wire, connector blocks, control gear, all necessary supports, suspension units and fixings; fix to small conduit boxes, connect and fit tubes (conduit boxes measured separately)
> Type A 1·219 m single tube fitting to soffit
> Type B 1·524 m twin tube fitting fixed in suspended ceiling
> Tungsten lighting fitting complete as specified including fitting wire connector blocks, all necessary supports and fixings; fix to small conduit box, connect and fit lamps (conduit box measured separately)
> Type C 60 watt fitting to soffit
> Type D 60 watt downlighter fixed in suspended ceiling
> Type E 100 watt bulkhead; wall mounted.'

20.25

Emergency lighting is to be found in most large buildings used by the general public e.g. staircases to flats, offices, etc. In these cases emergency lighting is often from batteries which are kept permanently charged by a 'trickle charger'.

These batteries are low voltage d.c. and the emergency lighting and fittings have therefore to be designed to cater for this supply. Light fittings would be designed so that a tungsten lamp could operate on low voltage d.c. current. If it is desired to convert the low voltage d.c. current (that is supplied by the battery system) to 240 volt a.c. supply in order to permit the use of standard light fittings for use as emergency lighting, then an inverter is used – this equipment is often to be found in factories and similar situations where a continuing manufacturing process has to be maintained during periods when there is a power failure.

A typical description of an emergency lighting battery-operated system might be as follows:

'Emergency lighting battery and charge control cubicle as specified manufactured by XYZ – type ABC incorporating (describe type of cells) cells complete with crates, connectors, electrolyte and mounted on two double tier wooden insulating stands, capable of maintaining a load of 20·6 kW for 3 hours with folded sheet steel charge control cubicle incorporating non-maintained emergency lighting contactor and centre zero ammeter, including all connections and interconnections; fix to brickwork or concrete and connect.'

A more sophisticated system will be by means of a diesel engine and generator which is coupled directly to the emergency lighting system without the need for storage batteries.

A typical description might be as follows:

'Diesel generator set complete as specified comprising prime mover with direct flexible coupling to 36·5 kW 415/240 volts 3 phase four wire 50 cycle alternator to provide 45·6 kvA at 0·8 power factor, mounted upon combined welded steel base-plate arranged for plinth mounting and having anti-vibration mountings; flexible fuel and exhaust connections, automatic 12 volt axial type starting and automatic mains failure control equipment; 12 volt 0·5 amp trickle charger for use as and when required; oil pressure failure switch; absorption type exhaust silencer; 273 litres capacity fuel tank, instruction manual and wiring diagrams; fix to brickwork or concrete, make all joints and connections.'

Both battery operated and diesel generator operated lighting is actuated by means of a power failure relay which is connected to the main supply to the building.

The distribution system for emergency lighting is similar to a normal lighting installation as was described in section 20.20 consisting of cables, conduit and distribution boards but without switches.

20.26

Maintained lighting is to be found in most large buildings used by the general public, e.g. multi-storey car parks, cinemas, theatres, swimming pools, hospitals, etc. In these buildings it is normal to find continuously lit 'Exit' signs and maintained lighting that is permanently in use when the main lighting system of the building is turned on. Maintained lighting is independent of the switching of the main lighting even though the maintained lighting uses the same lighting circuit – it being only the switching side that is separate.

The power supply for the maintained lighting is the normal mains supply, if this fails then emergency supply which is described in section 20.25 automatically comes into operation.

Typical descriptions for 'Exit' signs might be as follows:

'Single-face exit sign complete as specified with fittings wire, connector blocks and EXIT lettering; fix to brickwork or concrete, connect and fit lamps.

Double-face exit sign complete as specified with fittings wire, connector blocks, suspension units supports and EXIT lettering both sides; fix to brickwork or concrete, connect and fit lamps.'

20.27

Power final sub-circuits fall generally into four categories:

20.27.1   Domestic.

From the consumer control unit described in section 20.20.1 power circuits would be carried out in PVC/PVC cables. These cables when rising vertically in walls are normally protected in conduit – they are not in conduit when laid horizontally in hollow floors and in ceiling spaces.

20.27.2   Flats.

From the sub-distribution board the power sub-circuit would be PVC insulated cable run in heavy gauge conduit. These conduits would be chased into the walls and built into the reinforced concrete floors or alternatively laid on the surface of the floor and covered in floor screed.

20.27.3   Offices, schools, hospitals, etc.

From the sub-distribution board final power sub-circuits would be single core PVC insulated cable which would drop vertically in conduit or trunking from the distribution board into conduit or floor trunking which is either cast in the concrete floor or laid on the surface of the concrete floor if a floor screed is envisaged. Power distribution to power points can then be via the floor trunking. If the open office plan is required, floor mounted power plugs would give the necessary flexibility.

In the more traditional office and also in schools and hospitals, skirting trunking could be used – the skirting trunking being connected to the floor trunking both of which are designed to accommodate telephone cables and other electrical services. If trunking is not used, then power outlets on the perimeter and on partitioned walls would be connected to the main distribution board via conduit laid on the surface of the concrete floors and covered with a screed etc.

20.27.4   Industrial.

From the sub-distribution board final power sub-circuits would be single core PVC insulated cable which would rise vertically in trunking from the distribution board into overhead trunking. The trunking would be visible and supported by hangers etc. from roof trusses and the like. From the overhead trunking the various pieces of machinery etc., would be connected via conduit. An alternative method would be to install an overhead system of busbars as previously described in section 20.14.

If it was not practical to have either of the two overhead systems then a conduit distribution system mounted on the surface of the walls could be installed – the conduit laid in the floor screed if a connection to an island position was necessary.

In sections 20.27.2, 3 and 4 the final power sub-circuits have been described as PVC-covered cable protected by either trunking or conduit – it is equally acceptable for these installations to be in MICC. This would be used for the entire power installation from the distribution board to the power outlet. Generally MICC cable would be fixed to the surface of the wall or on cable trays. If it is required to be in floor screeds or chased into walls, then the MICC would normally be PVC covered.

20.28

Conduit.

The various types of conduit in common use as described in sub-sections 20.21.1 to 3 are applicable to power installations.

20.29

Power cables.

The cable that is in general use for power installations is PVC covered and has a copper conductor with a sectional area depending upon the power requirement. The normal system of power distribution from the distribution board is either by a direct connection to a particular piece of plant or by means of a ring main system for socket outlets.

Fig. 20.4 shows a typical ring main circuit wherein two cables with an earth (this can be the conduit or trunking) is taken from a 30 amp fuse-way or circuit-breaker on a distribution board, (or consumer control unit) to the first socket outlet and then on to the second socket outlet and so on, until the circuit is completed by returning to the fuse-way from the last socket outlet. By reference to the IEE regulations the number of socket outlets that can be installed on a ring main can be ascertained. The size of cable that is used for a ring main is 2·5 mm^2.

From a ring main circuit a fuse spur box can be connected exactly as if they were socket outlets – a switched fused spur box is generally used for an appliance without its own switch, such as an incinerator, water heater, inset wall fire etc. From a socket outlet in a ring main circuit it is possible to take off spurs which can feed one or two power outlets.

If it was required to serve up to six socket outlets without resorting to the

ELECTRICAL INSTALLATION

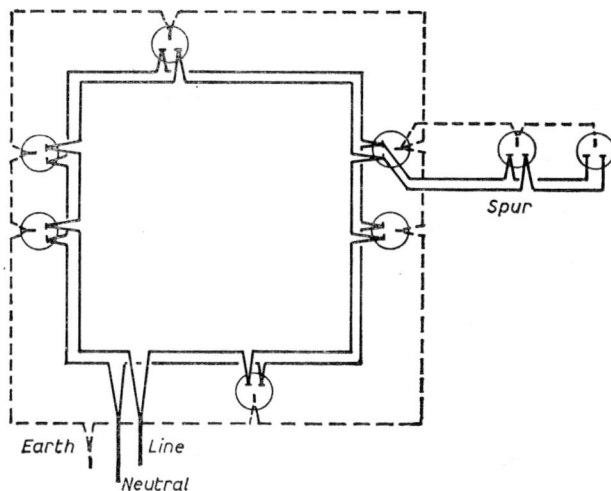

Fig. 20.4 Ring main circuit wiring for socket outlets.

installation of a ring main this could be achieved by installing a radial circuit direct from the distribution board to the various power outlets: this cable would be 4·0 mm².

20.30

Socket outlets and spur units.

There are numerous types of socket outlets and spur units available. When drafting a description the manufacturer's catalogue references must be given, together with the voltage grade.

A typical description of a 13 amp socket outlet might be as follows:

'13 amp 250 volt grade flush type single gang switch socket outlet as specified with matt chrome finished face plate, steel box and fused plug top; fix to brickwork or concrete and connect.'

A typical description of a switch fused spur box might be as follows:

'13 amp 250 volt grade flush type switched fuse spur unit as specified with matt chrome finished face plate and steel box; fix to brickwork or concrete and connect.'

20.31

A cooker control box normally consists of a switch to control the power supply to the cooker plus a 13 amp socket outlet, each of which has a neon light indicator.

A typical description might be as follows:

'30 amp 250 volt grade flush type cooker control unit as specified complete with ivory finished metal face plate, 13 amp switched socket outlet, neon indicator lights and steel box; fix to brickwork or concrete and connect.'

20.32

Domestic equipment such as refrigerators, kettles, toasters, etc., are normally connected to a power outlet by means of a 13 amp plug.

20.33

Connection to mechanical services in plant rooms, etc.

These installations would include connections to motors, valves that control water distribution in heating systems and any electrical work that is required to and from central control panels installed to control heating and air-conditioning systems.

These various pieces of mechanical plant, etc., are normally connected directly to the main switchboard or from a local distribution board, the cable being run in conduit to within about three feet of the piece of equipment, the final three feet of cable being protected by flexible conduit.

A typical description might be as follows:

'Flexible conduit
19 mm flexible conduit as specified not exceeding one metre long, with heavy brass adaptors at both ends and external bare copper earthwire and connect.'

If the connection is by means of MICC cable then a loop must be allowed in this cable to take up vibration. Generally the various pieces of mechanical plant are supplied under the mechanical services sub-contract. However, the electrical sub-contractor is often required to fix only starters, room thermostats etc., and connect only fans, pumps, motorized valves, control panels. In the case of pieces of isolated plant connected directly to the nearest distribution board or control panel, then an isolator switch should be installed.

20.34

Telephones.

The main telephone cable connecting the building would be supplied and installed by the GPO through a duct to the telephone room where the main telephone switchboards are located. Within the electrical sub-contract a prime cost sum would be provided for the telephone connection. From the entry duct it may be necessary to provide a cable tray or cable supports.

Typical descriptions might be as follows:

'Cable tray
76 mm galvanized cable tray as specified, complete with connector pieces, earthing straps, all necessary supports, hangers, distance pieces and fixings; fix to brickwork or concrete.
Extra over for:
76 mm bend piece
76 mm tee piece.'

From the main telephone switchboard, horizontal or vertical cable trays would be provided for telephone cables – in the case of tall buildings there would be provision for a vertical services duct. Distribution at each floor level from the vertical services duct would be by conduit or trunking, laid on, or cast in the concrete floors; or alternatively distributed around the perimeter in skirting trunking.

The telephone wiring and instruments are hired by the building owner from the GPO and do not, therefore, form part of the electrical sub-contract. The only wiring that the electrical sub-contractor should be responsible for consists of draw wires that are threaded through the trunking and conduit to facilitate the drawing in of the telephone cables.

20.35

Clocks.

There are two types of installations in general use:

- 20.35.1 Synchronous: This is the more common form of installation, individual clocks being wired to the adjacent lighting circuit. The wiring consisting of a connection into the nearest lighting point and a termination (prior to connection to the clock) in a fused clock connector. The description of the clock should quote the manufacturer's catalogue number, the diameter of the face and the method of fixing to the wall.
- 20.35.2 Impulse: This sort of installation is used where time accuracy is of importance such as in schools, etc., the installation consists of a master clock which is battery operated and from this master clock connections are made in parallel to slave clocks. These connections would be in cable and conduit.

20.36

Fire alarms.

There are two types of installation in general use:

- 20.36.1 Open circuit: In this installation, the alarm points from the bells are connected in parallel so that when an alarm contact is operated all the bells ring in order to warn the occupants of a building that a fire is in being. At the same time a visual signal on the main indicator panel shows which zone has been operated – thus locating the fire.
- 20.35.2 Closed circuit: In this installation the alarm points or bells are connected in series and when a contact is operated the bells ring and give warning etc., as with an open circuit.

In both types of installation the fire alarm contacts and bells are connected to the indicator panel with cable protected by heavy gauge conduit.

A flush or surface type fire alarm contact is actuated by breaking the glass, which permits the central button to spring out, thus setting off the alarms etc.

The indicator panel should be located by the main entrance of the building in order that the fire brigade can determine where the fire is situated. Indicator panels can be either luminous or drop flag.

Fire alarm systems may be connected direct to the mains via a convenient distribution board or alternatively they may be low voltage a.c. or d.c.

In the former all the equipment must be rated for 240 volts a.c. and in the latter, batteries are required and these should be connected to a battery charger which in turn is connected to a distribution board.

Typical descriptions of contacts, bells and indicator panels might be as follows:

'Fire alarm equipment as specified fix to brickwork or concrete and connect
Surface type 24/48 volts d.c. fire alarm contact reference . . .
Flush type 24/48 volts d.c. fire alarm contact reference . . . with flush fixing plate reference . . .
6 in. surface type 24/48 volts d.c. tangent bell reference . . .
Flush type twelve way 24/48 volt d.c. luminous type indicator board reference . . . complete with alarm reset button, supervisory button and appropriate lettering
Trickle charger in sheet steel cabinet reference . . . 48 volt battery reference . . . comprising twenty-four 2 volt cells complete with wood stand and all interconnections.'

20.37

A call system installation is often required in hospitals, nursing homes and old peoples' homes and is similar in operation to a fire alarm installation.

To actuate the alarm system a switch is either pushed, or pulled causing a visual indicator light up and at the same time a central indicator to operate.

Typical descriptions might be as follows:

'Call system equipment; fix to brickwork or concrete and connect
Flush type corridor indicator light as specification clause
Ditto, but including re-set push button and relay
Ceiling mounted pull cord call switch as specification clause . . . with reassurance light
Flush type call push button as specification clause . . . including reassurance light, re-set push button and relay grouped on one plate with connector blocks and flexible cable; fix to bed head unit and connect
Flush type twelve way indicator panel including control equipment, indicator lights, call buzzer, muting buttons and transformer.'

20.38

Burglar alarms.

The installation of the burglar alarm devices and the cabling etc. thereto is normally carried out by specialist firms and would therefore be covered by a prime cost sum. Within the electrical sub-contract should be provision for conduit withdraw wires as described for telephones in section 20.34.

20.39

A public address system consists of a microphone connected to a control panel and from there to loud speakers. If this was to form part of the electrical sub-contract this installation would be carried out in cables and conduit, but often this type of installation is carried out by a specialist firm and should therefore be covered by a prime cost sum – again conduit and draw wires should be provided by the electrical sub-contractor where required.

20.40

Lightning protection.

A lightning protection installation is normally carried out in copper tape, the primary object of which is to conduct electricity, generated by lightning, from a point above the roof line to earth by the shortest possible route. This is achieved by installing an air termination point (or points) at the highest point (or points) and a network of copper tape fixed at the highest levels – the tape being fixed to parapets and such like by means of saddles. The tape network at high level is connected to earth by one or more down conductors, consisting of copper tape fixed with saddles to the outside face of the building. These down conductors are terminated with either an earth plate or copper rods. The former are buried about three feet into the earth and the latter are driven into the earth.

Typical descriptions might be as follows:

'19 mm diameter copper air termination electrode 610 mm long; fix to brickwork or concrete
25 × 3 mm bare copper tape fixed with and including cast brass saddles at one metre centres including bends, sets and saddles; fix to brickwork or concrete
Gunmetal earth test clamps connected to 25 × 3 mm bare copper tape; fix to brickwork or concrete
19 mm diameter copper earthrod 4877 mm long in 1219 mm lengths with steel driving point and head, driven into ground and connected to 25 × 3 mm bare copper tape
Connect only 25 × 3 mm bare copper tape to equipment
Tinned riveted and welded junction of 25 × 3 mm bare copper tape.'

Measurement of lightning protection is dealt with in SMM/T16. The SMM does not specifically mention test points, these should be numbered separately.

Office block
lighting installation

Drawing no. and Circuit Ref.	B.E. Conduit				Trunking		PVC Cable 1.5 mm² in		Flush Switches	1524 mm Fluo Flgs.
	19 mm Flush	25 mm Flush	19 mm Surf	25 mm Surf	102 × 51 mm	102 × 51 mm End Cap	Conduit	Trunking	1 gang one way	
Drawing no. 4 Cir. E.L1/1–14 E.1.1/15	5·0 30·0	5·0	200·0	10·0	50·0	4	89·0 105·0	75·0	4 2	30
Drawing no. 12 Cir. E.12/1–14 etc.	5·0	5·0	200·0	10·0	50·0	4	89·0	1200·0	4	50
Totals										

Fig. 20.5 Lighting installation measurement schedule.

20.41

Generally.

20.41.1 Provision must be made in each of the above sections for the necessary testing as required by the SMM (see section 7.3.43).

20.41.2 Scheduling of measurements.

The measurement of final sub-circuits for lighting and power installation and emergency lighting, fire alarms etc. does, on most occasions, lend itself to scheduling because of the repetitive nature of this work – a simple example of a measurement schedule for a lighting installation is given on page 196, Fig. 20.5.

CHAPTER 21

Post-contract procedures

21.1

The *Management of Building Contracts*, a guide compiled by the National Joint Consultative Committee of Architects, Quantity Surveyors and Builders in collaboration with the then Ministry of Public Building and Works, should be studied – particularly the sections dealing with financial control.

21.2

If post-contract financial control is to be properly implemented and effective then procedures should be laid down by the architect (if he is the building team leader) before work starts on site – these procedures should be understood by the consulting engineer, the quantity surveyor, the main contractor and the engineering services sub-contractors.

21.3

The following are suggested procedures in respect of architect's and/or consulting engineer's instructions, that should aid financial control.

21.3.1 All instructions should be addressed to the main contractor. No instructions should be issued direct to any sub-contractor.

21.3.2 Instructions should only be issued by the architect and consulting engineer and/or their representatives.

21.3.3 Instructions whether written or drawn, should be issued under a formal instruction order (not by letter).

21.3.4 All instructions given direct by the consulting engineer or by the clerk of works (mechanical or electrical) to the main contractor should be confirmed in writing by the architect's instructions.

21.3.5 Where instructions involve the variation of the principal contract or of a sub-contract then an architect's variation order should be issued to the main contractor.

21.3.6 The consulting engineer should not issue variation orders direct to the main contractor. All variation orders should be issued by the architect.

21.4

At the commencement of the work on site the architect (or the quantity surveyor) should remind the main contractor and the sub-contractors that:

21.4.1 The quantity surveyor is responsible for the complete financial control of both the main and the sub-contracts.

21.4.2 The bill of quantities will be used as a basis for calculating payments on account and the agreement of variations and should not be used for ordering materials or used in place of the specification.

21.4.3 It is not the quantity surveyor's intention to remeasure all the work as installed automatically, but only to measured work varied by an architect's variation order. Where extensive variations occur, the price to be paid for this work will be assessed by negotiation and/or remeasurement.

21.4.4 Variations will generally be measured from drawings and not on site and it is therefore in the sub-contractor's interest to keep detailed information, by way of properly marked drawings, covering the information required to measure the variation properly.

21.4.5 No variation order is required to cover the adjustment of provisional quantities in the bills – these are dealt with automatically by the quantity surveyor.

21.4.6 Instructions from the architect or engineer are required to cover the following:

 (*a*) Any changes in design.
 (*b*) Discrepancies between specification and bills of quantities.
 (*c*) Discrepancies between drawings and bills of quantities.
 (*d*) The adjustment of all provisional and prime cost sums in the bill of quantities.

21.4.7 Variations will, when measured, be priced at the rates included in the bill of quantities when the work is of similar character and carried out under similar conditions. Where no rate exists, a rate will be negotiated by the quantity surveyor with the sub-contractor.

21.4.8 Although variations will not be paid for on a daywork basis, unless the architect instructs, it may sometimes be in the sub-contractor's interest to keep a time/material/plant record of the particular variation, as this may assist the quantity surveyor when pricing the variations.

21.5

Post contract cost-control is only possible if the quantity surveyor is kept fully informed on all variations. Consulting engineers, when issuing variation drawings should endeavour to mark in red the particular variations and give as much additional information to the quantity surveyor and sub-contractor as possible – thus permitting the valuation of variations to be based on the maximum information available.

21.6

In preparing financial statements for post contract financial control, the co-operation of the services consultant and sub-contractors is essential, and quotations and other information should be produced by them if it will assist the quantity surveyor in pricing the variations issued to date, and adjusting the prime cost and provisional sums contained in the bill of quantities.

21.7

Variations and final account – providing the procedures set out in sections 21.3 and 21.4 above are followed there should be no difficulty in measuring and pricing variations and settling the final account. Maximum co-operation between the consulting engineer, quantity surveyor and sub-contractors should be the aim; in order that the final account can be settled well within the period of final measurement, as stated in the appendix to the Standard Form of Building Contract. If variations can be measured from drawings and priced before the work is carried out, this procedure not only speeds up the settlement of the final account, but also fosters more accurate cost control.

21.8

Daywork – can only be permitted when authorized by the architect or consulting engineer in writing. The daywork sheets should show the number of hours worked and the quantity of materials and the type of plant used. The clerk of works (M & E) should be warned that daywork is in progress in order that he can record the hours, materials and plant and thereby know that the daywork sheet he signs (before it is sent to the quantity surveyor) is a correct record.

21.9

Valuations for interim payments on account – to speed up and simplify the preparation of valuations, the bills of quantities can sometimes be broken down into sections (e.g. floor by floor) and sub-divided into services, the total value of each of these services being pre-calculated. When preparing the valuation for interim payments the quantity surveyor and the sub-contractor can then assess the percentage completion of each of these services. This procedure is considerably less time consuming than measuring the completed work. Materials on site should be assessed – the sub-contractor should produce invoices to verify the cost and the clerk of works should confirm that none of the materials included have been condemned.

APPENDIX 1

Glossary: mechanical and electrical

Mechanical

Absorption system	Heat is used as the energy source for a sealed refrigeration system.
Access	Provision for entry to ducts to facilitate installation, maintenance and renewal of the various services.
Actual capacity	(a) Volume of the contents of a tank or cylinder. (b) Quantity of water in a cistern filled to water line.
After cooler	Heat exchanger which removes heat from air discharged from compressors and assists moisture removal from the air.
Air ducts	Square or round section enclosure for conveying air – usually made from sheet metal, asbestos, glass-fibre, rigid PVC, etc.
Air entrainment	Room air which is entrained in and circulated with air streams ejected by outlets, grilles and nozzles.
Air filter	Element located in the air stream to remove airborne dust.
Air filters	Remove dust and pollen before air enters the compressor.
Air receivers	Storage vessels, usually cylindrical, for storage of air. They serve to meet a fluctuating demand and to provide a reasonably constant pressure.
Air settling chamber	Large chamber into which duct carrying dust is expanded, the air losing its velocity and dust thus being deposited. Used for industrial dust, paint spray removal.
Air washers	Chamber wherein air is brought into contact with a dense spray of water. Will remove some dust from air, but is generally used as humidifier.
Anchor point	Position where the pipework is rigidly fixed so that expansion and contraction can take place only in a determined direction.
Anemometer	Light vaned windmill, connecting with gears to dials which register air movement when air flows.
Appliance	Receptacle or apparatus in which water is heated, treated, measured or utilized before passing to waste.
Aspect ratio	Ratio of width to height of grille.
Attenuation box	Sound absorbing box used for blending cold and hot air streams in high velocity double duct systems.
Axial fan	Fan which draws and discharges air in a direction parallel to its shaft. Designed to operate normally against resistance to air flow. Generally noisier than centrifugal.
Baudelot cooler	Consists of a number of evaporator coils, mounted over a chilled water tank. The water to be cooled is pumped over the evaporator coils. Submerged coils are also used for low temperature applications and in addition agitator pumps.

Bib tap (bib cock)	Screw-down tap, normally fitted to wall.
Boiler capacity	Rated output of a boiler when steaming at full load. Ratings are often stated from and at 100°C, that is with feed water at 100°C, evaporating to steam at 100°C at 14·7 psi absolute pressure.
Blow-down	Periodic discharge from a valve at the bottom of a boiler to remove accumulated solids in suspension in the boiler water which are sludge and scale forming. Blow-down can also be continuous, and with this system it is advantageous to use blow-down to preheat the feed water.
Blow-down pit	Usually rectangular and divided into halves by an internal weir. The function of the pit is to intercept sludge and to prevent discharge of water with a temperature over 65·6°C into the drainage system. Covers should be sealed and locked on. Hot side compartment of pit should have sufficient capacity to hold water equivalent to 25·4 mm fall in level of the water in the largest shell type boiler installed in the system.
Boiler feed pumps	Vertical or horizontal pumps, steam or electrically driven, used to deliver water to boiler, against the internal boiler pressure.
Boiler feed water	Water pumped into a boiler from the hot well to be transformed into steam. Consists of condensed steam (condensate) and fresh water make up treated to remove hardness and reduce corrosive properties.
Calorifier, storage	Cylinder in which water is heated by steam or water passing through an internal coil or battery.
Capacity modulation	Mechanism to control capacity of a compressor by rendering one or more cylinders ineffective.
Capillary fittings	Fitting for light gauge copper tube, with a solder joint made by capillary action between the two surfaces.
Capillary washer	Humidifier in which air is brought into contact with a large wetted surface.

Centrifugal fan	Wheel-shaped fan which induces air on its axis and expels it through blades at the perimeter. Designed to operate against resistance. Three main types:
	    (i) straight radial blades
	    (ii) forward curved blades
	    (iii) backward curved blades.

Charge holding	Partial charge of refrigerant given to plant after dehydration and evacuation for transportation or test purposes.
Cistern	Container for water under atmospheric pressure (i.e. with open top, or cover which is not airtight).
Cock	Device used to stop or regulate the flow of gas, operated by rotation of a drilled, slotted or taper plug.
Communication pipe	That part of the service pipe for which the water undertaking is responsible.
Compression fitting	Fitting for light gauge copper or plastic tube with unions which grip the pipe.
Compressors	Single stage and multi-stage. Air or gas is compressed in each cylinder or stage from an initial intake pressure to a final discharge pressure. Compressors may be cooled by atmospheric air circulating around them or by water circulated through jackets surrounding the cylinders.
Compressor (refrigeration)	Machine designed to pump a gas from a low pressure space to a high pressure space in a sealed refrigerant system.

GLOSSARY: MECHANICAL AND ELECTRICAL

Compressor centrifugal	Compressor which imparts motion, and therefore pressure, to a gas by means of high speed impellers. Not a positive displacement machine.
Compressor reciprocating	Compressor which imparts motion and pressure to a gas by means of reciprocating pistons. A positive displacement machine.
Condensate receiver	Receptacle fitted at the lowest point of a gas pipe line to collect condensate.
Condenser	Device for removing heat from gas for the purpose of causing it to condense to a liquid.
Conditioned air	Air that has been filtered and cleaned and is introduced at a predetermined temperature and humidity content.
Consumer's control	Cock or valve controlling the supply of gas to the consumer, normally located at the inlet of the meters. In the case of larger service pipes there may be in addition a valve on the service at its junction with the gas main.
Cooling coil	Fixed tube coils positioned in air stream and containing chilled water for purpose of reducing temperature of air and moisture content.
Cooling tower	Device for cooling water by evaporation in air. The water is usually sprayed into the air stream, causing evaporation and a temperature reduction.
Cut-out, high pressure	Controller, such as a switch, to break a circuit when pressure exceeds a predetermined point.
Cut-out, low pressure	Pressure cut-out (see high pressure).
Cylinder	Cylindrical closed container for hot water storage under the pressure of water from a feed cistern.
Damper	Throttling device fixed in air stream: can be butterfly or multi-vane type.
Defrosting	Removal of frost accumulation from cooling unit.
Dehumidification	Reduction of water vapour content of air by cooling or absorbents.
Dew point temperature	Temperature to which a mixture of air and water vapour must be reduced to produce condensation of the vapour.
Diffuser	Outlet grille or appurtenance designed to guide direction of air. (Usually shaped to spread air over a wide area.)
Diffusion area	Useful room area served by an outlet: coverage.
Direct expansion cooling coil	As cooling tower (above), but coil contains expanded refrigerant which absorbs heat from the air. Care is needed in selection of refrigerant type in this case.
Distributing pipe	Any pipe in a service carrying water from a storage cistern to draw-off points.
Domestic boiler (independent boiler)	Boiler used mainly to supply hot water.
Draining tap	Screw-down tap fitted at lowest point of a system or appliance for draining off water.
Drop	Vertical distance the lower edge of an air stream drops between the time it leaves the outlet and the time it reaches the end of its given throw.
Dry bulb temperature	Temperature of the air measured by a normal mercury or alcohol thermometer.
Duct	Enclosure constructed in suitable material to accommodate

pipes, cables, conduits etc. Ducts may be divided into five categories:

Subway: Passage or duct, constructed below ground level to accommodate pipes, cables, conduits etc. and large enough for a man to walk through.

Crawlway: Duct with clear depth of 1·067 m but not large enough to walk through. It is recommended that crawling clearance be allowed through pipework.

Trench: Duct less than 1·067 m in depth, constructed below floor level to accommodate pipes, cables, conduits etc.

Chase: Recess cut or formed in wall or ceiling to receive one or more pipes.

Casing: Enclosure constructed of timber or other suitable material on the face of a wall, floor or ceiling to accommodate one or more pipes, cables etc.

Duct splitter	Vanes in ducts arranged parallel to air flow to assist flow efficiency and reduce turbulence, usually at bends.
Duct velocity	Speed of air movement in ducts expressed in m/sec. Example of limitation of normal velocities in ducts: main ducts 4·064–5·080 m/sec branch ducts 2·540–5·080 m/sec branch risers 1·524–3·048 m/sec
Electrode water heater	Electric water heater in which the current passes through the water between electrodes.
Electrostatic precipitator	Dust particles receive an electric charge when passing through an electrostatic ionizing field and are then collected on metal plates of opposite polarity.
Eliminators or scrubbers	Specially arranged baffles to prevent entrained moisture from passing into air stream.
Enthalpy	The combination energy term which represents the sum of internal air flow energy in a steady flow process. It is determined from an arbitrary datum point for the air mixture and is expressed as a Btu/lb of dry air.
Evaporator	Any device in which refrigerant is evaporated for the purpose of extracting heat from the surrounding medium.
Evaporator, direct expansion	Evaporator which cools a medium in direct contact with it.
Evaporator, flooded	Evaporator designed to contain a definite quantity of liquid refrigerant at all times. Any refrigerant evaporated, owing to load, is replaced by means of a float valve.
Expansion bay	Recess formed in the side of a duct to accommodate the loop in a hot water or steam pipe which takes up expansion and contraction in the pipe.
Exhaust hood	Canopy covering, or fixed above, fume-producing equipment to trap fumes and water vapour.
Exhaust hood or canopy	Used as a catchment for fumes and vapours
Expansion joint	Fitting designed to accommodate linear expansion of pipework.
Expansion valve	Valve designed to regulate flow of refrigerant to an evaporator. The valve can be automatic, float or thermostatically operated.
Fan	Rotary machine which propels air or gas continuously by aerodynamic action.

Fan duty (static)	Volume of air per unit of time dealt with by a fan at a stated fan static pressure.
Fan duty (total pressure)	Volume of air per unit of time dealt with by a fan at a stated total fan pressure.
Feed cistern	Cistern for supplying cold water to hot water apparatus.
Fitting	Anything fitted to a pipe for jointing, conveying or regulating the flow of water.
Free or daylight area	Area of openings in a grille.
Fresh air	External air (reasonably free from pollution) introduced into a room or space. Pure air is composed approximately of 21% oxygen and 79% nitrogen by volume and small proportions of carbon dioxide, argon, neon and helium.
Gas	Used to denote town gas as normally manufactured and distributed through the mains of a gas undertaking.
Gas, bottled	Hydrocarbon gases, such as butane or propane, stored in portable containers and used as a substitute for town gas. Now also commonly known as liquefied petroleum gas LPG.
Gas, liquid	Condensible gas reduced to a liquid by compression and expansion, often assisted by refrigeration. Oxygen, hydrogen, helium and nitrogen are examples of gases produced in a liquid form.
Gas point	Termination of a gas installation pipe.
Governor (service)	Regulating device for maintaining a constant pressure, preferably fitted between consumer's control and meter. Service governors are rarely required and should be fitted only on the recommendation of the gas board. Many gas appliances include a governor as part of their control system. Where this is not so an appliance governor should be fitted when recommended by the gas board.
Grille	Functional or decorative covering for an outlet or intake: perforated or vane type.
Grit arrestor	Usually fitted to plants having a steam load in excess of 15,000 lb/h to trap fine grit and dust entrained in the flue gases. A common variety of arrestor is the cyclone type.
Hardness of water	The presence of salts in water which prevent lather formation and which cause formation of hard scale deposits in apparatus.
Heater battery	Element or coil located in an air stream which is heated by either steam, hot water or electricity.
Heat pump	Refrigerating plant in which condenser waste heat is used for utility service. The heat pump can be used to heat or cool with the same equipment.
High velocity ventilation system	Ducted air system from a central plant where the main duct velocities range from 15·240–25·300 m/sec. Special provision required to avoid duct leakage, noise and uneven primary air distribution.
Hot well	Covered and lagged rectangular tank which acts as a receiver for returned condensate and the make up water. Water capacity of a minimum of one hour's full boiler evaporative capacity is necessary.
Humidification	Addition of water vapour to air (increase in relative humidity).
Humidistat or hygrostat	Responds to change in air humidity content, actuating quantity and temperature of water spray at main plant etc.
Impingement or dry type filters	Usually made of fabric or glass fibres. Efficiency is related to diameter of fibre used and density of media: higher filtration can

	be obtained than by viscous impingement. Can be cleanable (vibration or vacuum) or throw away type.
Indirect cylinder	Storage calorifier, usually of small domestic type, with an internal annular heater.
Induced secondary circulation	Room air entrained and set in motion by air discharge from an outlet.
Induction unit	Cabinet type of air inlet unit which supplies primary air at high velocity through a row of nozzles. The primary air stream induces and mixes with the room air, giving an increased air distribution.
Intake	Opening through which air is returned or exhausted from a space.
Inter cooler	Heat exchanger which removes heat between compression stages.
Internal installation	The whole installation from consumer's control up to appliances.
Isolating valve	Valve positioned to isolate part of a system.
Latent heat	Heat that does not affect temperature but changes the state of the substance when added to or subtracted from it.
Louvred shutter	Hinged metal shutter opening on fan discharge side by air velocity, closed when fan not working to prevent back-draughts.
Low temperature cut-out	Thermostatic cut-out actuated by the temperature of the liquid being cooled by the temperature of the refrigerant. It also operates by stopping the prime mover (driving motor).
Low velocity ventilation system	Ducted air system from a central plant where main duct velocities are restricted to 5·080–10·160 m/sec.
Main	Pipe for general conveyance of water, normally under control of water undertakers.
Manipulative compression fitting	Compression fitting requiring shaping of the pipe ends.
Meter	Apparatus for measuring the volume of gas passed through it.
Meter compartment	(*a*) A ventilated compartment of fire resisting material provided to accommodate the meter in a position accessible to both consumer and gas undertaking. (*b*) In large premises, a separate enclosure, room or outbuilding specially constructed to accommodate a meter or meters.
Meter, primary	Meter connected to the service pipe. The index reading of this meter constitutes the basis of charge by the gas undertaking for gas used on the premises where there may, or may not, be a secondary or subsidiary meter. Meters may also be coin operated.
Meter, secondary (or check meter)	Subsidiary meter for measuring gas used in separate parts of premises, or by separate appliances after the whole supply has passed through a primary meter.
Mixing spray tap	Screw-down tap for mixing hot and cold water and discharging it through a spray nozzle.
Mixing tap	Tap arranged to mix hot and cold water on delivery.
Mixing valve	Valve arranged to mix hot and cold water, giving a controlled water temperature at the common outlet.
Multi-flue system	For varying flue gas conditions. One flue is provided for winter maximum load: one flue for summer light load conditions; sometimes a flue is also provided for an incinerator. Differential temperatures set up stresses which must be allowed for in design.

Nominal capacity	Theoretical capacity of a cistern, tank or cylinder as obtained from overall dimensions.
Non-concussive tap	Spring-loaded tap controlled by pressure of a lever or knob (as opposed to a screw-down type), but the return of the lever is retarded to avoid concussion or water hammer.
Non-return valve (check valve)	Valve arranged to permit flow of water in one direction only.
Oil separator	Device for separating out oil entrained in the discharge gas from a compressor, and returning it to the compressor crank case.
Outlet	Opening through which air is supplied to space.
Outlet velocity	Average air velocity emerging from outlet.
Overflow pipe (warning pipe)	Pipe connected to a cistern, above water line, to carry away excess water and give warning of the condition.
Packaged boiler	Self-contained shell or water tube, complete with automatic firing controls and alarms. The boilers are usually oil fired but shell type can be coal fired.
Packaged unit	Self-contained and free standing. No interconnecting pipework has to be supported from floor or ceiling.
Perforated ceiling	Used to introduce air all over a space. Accomplishes complete diffusion rapidly; can be used for high or low air changes.
pH value	Index of the hydrogen ion content of water, indicating acidity or alkalinity.
Pillar tap	Screw-down tap fixed to bath top, lavatory basin or sink.
Pipework	Any installation of piping, including supports and fittings.
Plug cock	Fitting designed to regulate or stop flow of water through a pipe by means of a drilled or slotted plug rotating in a seating.
Pressure reducing valve	Valve arranged to reduce pressure of water on the outlet side.
Pressurestats	Control which responds to pressure changes of bellow, diaphragm or bourdon tube type. Actuates dampers to control static pressure in ducts, etc.
Primary air	Air introduced into a room or space by ductwork.
Primary circuit	The flow and return circulating pipes between boiler (or other water heater) and storage cylinder.
Pounds square inch	Gauge pressure in pounds per square inch. The pressure is normally read from a Bourdon-type pressure gauge.
Propeller fan	Fan which draws and discharges air in an axial direction approximately parallel to shaft and is designed to operate normally under free inlet and outlet conditions.
Psychrometrics	Investigation of the thermal properties of moist air, measurement and control of the moisture content and its effects on material and human comfort.
Psychrometry	Measurement of moisture content of air.
Recirculated air	Air extracted from and reintroduced into a ventilated space.
Refrigeration plant	Mechanical pump used to abstract heat at one temperature level and to discharge it at a higher temperature level. See *Element Design Guide SfB (54)*.
Register	Grille provided with a damper.
Relative humidity	Ratio of the vapour pressure in a given air volume compared with the vapour pressure at saturation (dew point) expressed as a percentage, temperature of the air being the same in both cases.

Relief doors and draught stabilizer	Fitted to combustion chambers or flues to relieve excessive pressure conditions caused by faulty combustion conditions, e.g. late ignition with heavy gas or oil concentration.
Rise	Converse of drop (see above).
Rising pipe	That part of a service which is inside a building.
Roof extract unit	Unit incorporating fan, complete with weathering apron arranged for easy roof mounting. Gives positive extract; can incorporate draught shutters.
Safety valve	Boiler relief pressure valve. The valve vent pipes should be arranged to discharge above roof level, and be fitted with exhaust or cowls. Discharge pipes from safety valves should be carried clear of the working area of operating staff.
Secondary air	Air from a ventilated space introduced into primary air supply and reintroduced into the room space.
Secondary circuit	The flow and return pipes through which hot water is circulated between cylinder and draw-off points.
Sensible heat	Heat that changes the temperature of a substance when added to or subtracted from it.
Service	System of pipes and fittings for supply and distribution of water in any individual premises.
Service pipe	Pipe in a service directly subject to mains water pressure.
Shell type boiler	Boiler consisting of a cylinder containing water and steam in contact, in which is arranged a fire box, fire tubes and/or tubes for water, e.g. Cornish, Lancashire, economic, or locomotive or vertical types.
Sight glass	Pipe fitting for viewing passage of condensate after the steam trap.
Silica-gel dehumidifier	Chemical type of apparatus for removing moisture from air.
Sleeve	Tube inserted in a prepared hole in a structure to receive a service pipe.
Sling psychrometer	Instrument for measuring both dry and wet bulb temperatures.
Soot blowers	Either steam or air operated system of automatic or hand lance type, designed to remove soot from heating surfaces of boiler on the fire side.
Spray tap	Screw-down tap with a spray nozzle giving reduced rate of flow of water.
Spread	Divergence (in degrees) or air steam after leaving outlet.
Static pressure	Pressure created by resistance to air movement (duct friction) which is exerted equally in all directions.
Static regain	Regain of static air pressure, used in duct sizing, so that velocity reduction exactly offsets loss in friction.
Steam trap	Mechanical device fitted to a condense receiver which ideally permits the passage of water and air, but does not allow steam to pass.
Stopcock	Fitting designed to shut off completely the flow of water through a pipe, by means of a rotating disc closing against a seating.
Storage cistern	Any cistern other than a flushing cistern.
Strainer	Interceptor of sieve type for collecting pipe line scale and impurities which would affect action of steam traps or controls.
Sump	Pit constructed at low level to collect water drained from adjoining sources.
Tank	Closed container for water under the pressure of water from a feed cistern.

GLOSSARY: MECHANICAL AND ELECTRICAL

Tanking	Introduction of an impervious material into the construction of a sump, subway or trench to prevent infiltration of subsoil water.
Temperature differential	Temperature difference between primary and room air.
Terminal velocity	Average air stream velocity at end of throw.
Thermostat	Instrument that responds to changes in temperature, actuating controls in ventilation system; is regulating steam or hot water to heater or air damper control.
Throw	Horizontal and vertical axial distance that an air stream travels from outlet to where the average velocity is 0·254 m/sec.
Ton refrigeration	Amount of heat extracted from one American ton of water 2000 lb at 0°C to convert it to ice at 0°C. The time for the conversion is 24 hours. Thus the heat unit expressed in Btu/h is

$$\frac{2000 \times 144}{24} = 12,000 \text{ Btu/h}$$

Note: 144 Btu/lb is the latent heat of ice.

Total air	Mixture of primary and secondary air.
Total pressure	Algebraic sum of the static pressure (or depression and velocity pressure at any particular point).
Trapping set	Steam trap with strainer and sight glass, isolating valves, check valves and unions, according to use.
Turn-down ratio	Limit to which an oil burner or automatic stoker can be adjusted to give a lower rate of combustion. Turn-down is required for variable loads, night, weekend and summer operation.
Unit conditioners	Package unit containing a complete cooling system in one casing, including compressor, condenser, evaporator, fans, filters and controls.
Vacuum pumps	(*a*) Pumps which remove air from a vessel at atmospheric pressure (usually mechanical types).
	(*b*) Pumps which begin to operate below a certain limiting pressure.
	Vacuum pumps are compressors which operate with an air intake pressure below atmospheric and a discharge pressure atmospheric or slightly higher.
Valve	Fitting designed to stop or regulate flow of water in a pipe, by means of a gate or disc closing against a seating.
Vane ratio	Ratio of depth of vane to width of shortest opening between two adjacent vanes or grille bars. (To be effective vane ratio should be greater than unity. Beyond 2·0 further improvement is slight).
Velocity	Speed of air flow in m/sec.
Velocity pressure	Pressure exerted by air through its movement and speed. This pressure is exerted in same direction as flow of air.
Velometer	Very sensitive instrument incorporating a vane for registering air flow.
Ventilation rate	Number of complete changes of air contained in a space within the period of one hour.
Volume of air supply	Quantity of air delivered – m³/sec.
Water line	The designed top water level in a cistern.
Water meter	Fitting designed to indicate and/or record the quantity of water passing through a pipe.

Water softener	Apparatus in which hardness of water is removed or reduced by chemical means.
Water tube boiler	Used for high pressure and high capacity steam production. The boiler consists of a nest of tubes with bottom water or sludge drums and a top steam drum. The combustion chamber is within the tube nest.
Water treatment plant	Plant for chemical dosing raw make up water supplied to boiler.
Water undertakers	The local authority water board or water company responsible for the supply to consumers in the area.
Wet bulb depression	Common term used for mean difference between dry bulb and wet bulb temperature from which the relative humidity is deduced.
Wet bulb temperature	Temperature of air measured by a thermometer with its bulb covered by a wetted cloth or wick.

Electrical

The following definitions are taken from the IEE regulations:

Accessory	Any device, other than a lighting fitting, associated with the wiring and current-using appliances of an installation, e.g. a switch, a fuse, a plug, a socket-outlet, a lamp-holder or a ceiling rose.
Adaptor, socket-outlet	An accessory for insertion into a socket-outlet and containing metal contacts, to which may be fitted one or more plugs for the purpose of connecting to the supply portable lighting fittings or current-using appliances.
Ambient temperature (for cables)	The temperature of the surrounding medium under normal conditions, at a situation in which cables are installed, or are to be installed, including the effect of any artificial heating used in the building and any local source of heat, but not the increase of temperature in the immediate neighbourhood of the cables due to heat arising therefrom.
Apparatus	Electrical apparatus, including all machines, equipment and fittings, in which conductors are used or of which they form a part.
Appliance	Any device which utilizes electricity for a particular purpose, excluding a lighting fitting or an independent motor.
Bonded (as applied to items of metalwork)	Connected together electrically, not normally for the purpose of carrying current, but so as to ensure a common potential.
Bunched	Cables are said to be 'bunched' when two or more are contained within a single conduit, duct, or trunking or, if not enclosed, are not separated from each other.
Channel (for cables)	A groove cut or formed in part of a building and intended to receive one or more cables, the groove having removable or hinged covers to allow cables to be laid therein.
Circuit-breaker	A mechanical device for making and breaking a circuit, both under normal conditions and under abnormal conditions, such as those of a short circuit, the circuit being broken automatically.
Circuit conductor	A current-carrying conductor forming part of a circuit or final sub-circuit, but excluding the earth-continuity conductor.
Conductor (of a core or cable)	The conducting portion, consisting of a single wire or of a group of wires in contact with each other. For earthed concentric wiring, the term may also denote the metal sheath of a cable.

Connector	A device intended for connection to a flexible cord or flexible cable, which has protected current-carrying contact tubes similar to those of a socket-outlet.
Consumer's installation	Wiring and apparatus situated upon the consumer's premises and controlled or installed by him, excluding any switchgear of the supply undertaking which the consumer may be permitted to use.
Consumer's terminals	The point in the consumer's installation at which the incoming supply of energy is delivered to that installation.
Core (of a cable)	The conductor with its insulation, but not including any outer covering for mechanical or other protection.
Damp- and dust-proof	Applied to apparatus and accessories to denote that the live and other component parts are protected by an enclosure or enclosures being so protected and/or fitted as to prevent the ready ingress of dust and/or moisture.
Damp situation	A situation in which moisture is either permanently present, or intermittently present to such an extent as to be likely to impair the effectiveness of an installation conforming to the requirements for ordinary situations.
Danger	Danger to health or danger to life or limb from shock, burn, or other injury to persons (and livestock where present), or from fire, attendant upon the use of electrical energy.
Dead	At or about earth potential and disconnected from any live system.
Distribution board	An assemblage of parts, including one or more fuses or circuit-breakers, arranged for the distribution of electrical energy to final sub-circuits or to other distribution boards.
Duct (for cables)	A closed passage-way formed underground or in a structure and intended to receive one or more cables which may be drawn in.
Earth-continuity conductor	The conductor, including any clamp, connecting to the consumer's earthing terminal, or to the frame terminal of a voltage-operated earth-leakage circuit-breaker, or to each other, those parts of an installation which are required to be earthed. It may be in whole or in part the metal conduit, trunking, or duct, or the metal sheath of a cable, or the special earth-continuity conductor of a cable or flexible cord incorporating such a conductor.
Earth electrode	A metal rod or rods, a system of underground metal pipes or other conducting object, providing an effectual connection with the general mass of the earth.
Earthed	Effectually connected to the general mass of the earth.
Earthed concentric wiring	A sheath-return wiring system in which one or more insulated conductors carrying the line current are completely surrounded throughout their length by a conductor which acts both as the neutral conductor and as the earth-continuity conductor.
Earthing lead	The final conductor by which the connection to the earth electrode, or other means of earthing, is made.
Electric discharge lamp	An electric lamp comprising a hermetically sealed bulb or tube containing gas and/or metal intended to be vapourized during operation, and fitted with electrodes between which a discharge of electricity takes place, the useful light being emitted either by the discharge through the gas or vapour or by the fluorescence of a translucent coating which may be on the inner surface of the outer tube or bulb.

Electrode boiler (or electrode water heater)	Apparatus for the electrical heating of water by the passage of an electric current between electrodes immersed in the water.
Excess-current protection, close	Excess-current protection which will operate within four hours at 1·5 times the designed load current of the circuit which it protects. *Note:* Devices affording close excess-current protection include: (i) BS 88 fuses fitted with fuse-links marked to indicate a class P or class Q1 fusing factor. (ii) Fuses fitted with fuse-links complying with BS 1361. (iii) Miniature and moulded-case circuit-breakers complying with BS 3871. (iv) Circuit-breakers set to operate at an overload not exceeding 1·5 times the designed load current of the circuit.
Excess-current protection, coarse	Excess-current protection which will not operate within four hours at 1·5 times the designed load current of the circuit which it protects. *Note:* Devices affording coarse excess-current protection include: (i) BS 88 fuses fitted with fuse-links marked to indicate a class Q2 or class R fusing factor. (ii) Semi-enclosed (rewireable) fuses complying with BS 3036.
Final sub-circuit	An outgoing circuit connected to a distribution board and intended to supply electrical energy to current-using apparatus, either directly or through socket-outlets or fused spur-boxes.
Flameproof	Applied to apparatus to denote that the containing case or other enclosure will withstand, without injury, any explosion of prescribed flammable gas that may occur within it under practical conditions of operation within the rating of the apparatus (and recognized overloads, if any, associated therewith) and will prevent the transmission of flame such as will ignite any prescribed flammable gas that may be present in the surrounding atmosphere. *Note:* Electrical apparatus should not be described as 'flameproof' unless it complies in all respects with BS 229.
Flammable	A flammable material is one capable of being easily ignited.
Flexible cord	A flexible cable in which the cross-sectional area of each conductor does not exceed 4 mm^2.
Fuse	A device for opening a circuit by means of a fuse-element designed to melt when an excessive current flows. It normally consists of a fuse-base and fuse-link. The fuse-link may take the form of a cartridge or a carrier supporting a fuse-element. For the purpose of these Regulations the current rating of a fuse is a current, less than the minimum fusing-current, stated by the maker as the current that the fuse and the fuse-link with which it is fitted will carry continuously without deterioration (see BS 88 and BS 3036).
Fuse-element	That part of a fuse which is designed to melt and thus open a circuit.
h.o.f.r. sheath (of a cable)	Heat-resisting, oil-resisting, and flame-retardant sheath complying with BS 2899, part 4.
Incombustible	An incombustible material is one which neither burns nor gives off flammable vapours in sufficient quantity to ignite at a pilot flame

	when heated in the manner described in BS 476 or in BS 738, whichever is applicable.
Insulation	Suitable non-conducting material enclosing, surrounding, or supporting a conductor.
Intrinsically safe	(1) Applied to a circuit, denotes that any electrical sparking that may occur in normal working under the conditions specified by the certifying authority, and with the prescribed components, is incapable of causing an ignition of the prescribed flammable gas or vapour.
	(2) Applied to apparatus, denotes that it is so constructed that when installed and operated under the conditions specified by the certifying authority, any electrical sparking that may occur in normal working, either in the apparatus or in the circuit associated therewith, is incapable of causing an ignition of the prescribed flammable gas or vapour.
	Note 1: The use of the term 'in normal working' is intended to cover sparking that may, in normal use, be produced by breaking line current, or a short circuit across the lines, in the circuit that is required to be intrinsically safe. It is also intended to cover sparking that may be produced under any condition of fault which, in the opinion of the certifying authority, might arise in practice.
	Note 2: For applications other than coal mining, where part of the certified equipment is to be mounted outside the hazardous area or in a flameproof enclosure, the assessment of intrinsic safety may be restricted to cover only such electrical sparking as may occur within the hazardous area or outside the flameproof enclosure. Any certificate of intrinsic safety issued by the appropriate authority will then define the circumstances to which it applies.
Isolator	A mechanical device capable of opening or closing a circuit under conditions of no load or negligible current.
Joint box	A box forming part of a wiring installation, provided to contain joints in the conductors of the cables of the installation.
Live	In relation to a conductor, means that, under working conditions: (*a*) a difference of voltage exists between the conductor and earth, or (*b*) it is connected to the middle wire, common return wire or neutral wire of a supply system in which that wire is not permanently and solidly earthed.
Neutral conductor	The neutral conductor of a 3-phase 4-wire system, the conductor of a single-phase or d.c. installation which is earthed by the supply undertaking (or otherwise at the source of the supply), or the middle wire or common return conductor of a 3-wire d.c. or 3-wire single-phase a.c. system.
Non-conducting	Presenting a barrier against risk of electric shock when interposed in series with a source of low voltage.
PCP	Polychloroprene compound complying with BS 2899, part 1 (e.g. 'Neoprene').
Plug	A device intended for connection to a flexible cord or flexible cable which can be engaged manually with a socket-outlet or connector or adaptor and which has current-carrying contact pins which may be exposed when not engaged.

Point (in wiring)	Any termination of the fixed wiring intended for the attachment of a lighting fitting or of a device for connecting to the supply a current-using appliance.
PVC (as insulation or sheath of a cable)	Polyvinyl chloride compound complying with BS 2746.
Resistance area (for an earth electrode only)	The area of ground (around an earth electrode) within which a voltage gradient measurable with ordinary commercial instruments exists when the electrode is being tested.
Rubber (as insulation or sheath of a cable)	Vulcanized general-purpose rubber compound or synthetic rubber compounds (e.g. butyl rubber, silicone rubber, PCP and HOFR sheath compounds) complying with BS 2899.
Socket-outlet	A device with protected current-carrying contacts intended to be mounted in a fixed position and permanently connected to the fixed wiring of the installation, to enable the connection to it of a flexible cord or flexible cable by means of a plug.
Space factor	The ratio (expressed as a percentage) of the sum of the effective overall cross-sectional areas of cables forming a bunch to the internal cross-sectional area of the conduit, pipe, duct, trunking, or channel in which they are installed. The effective overall cross-sectional area of a non-circular cable is taken as that of a circle of diameter equal to the major axis of the cable.
Spur	A branch cable connected to a ring circuit.
Stationary appliance	An appliance intended to be fixed to a supporting surface, or used in only one place.
Switch	A mechanical device for making and breaking, non-automatically, a circuit carrying current not greatly in excess of the rated normal current.
Switch, linked	A switch the blades of which are so arranged as to make or break all poles simultaneously or in a definite sequence.
Switchboard	An assemblage of switchgear with or without instruments; but the term does not apply to a group of local switches in a final sub-circuit where each switch has its own insulating base.
Switchgear	Apparatus for controlling the distribution of electrical energy, or for controlling or protecting electrical circuits, machines and current-using appliances.
Trench, open	A trench without covering, or covered by an open grille.
Trunking (for cables)	A fabricated casing for cables, normally of rectangular cross-section, of which one side is removable or hinged to allow cables to be laid therein.
Varnished PTP fabric (as insulation of a cable)	Varnished cloth tapes of polyethylene terephthalate fibre, e.g. 'Terylene', complying with BS 3765.

Voltage, Extra-low Low Medium High	Potential differences of the following voltages (r.m.s. values, for a.c.) subject to such variations as are permissible under the *Electricity Supply Regulations*, 1937:
	  Extra-low. Normally not exceeding 50 volts between conductors, and not exceeding 30 volts a.c. or 50 volts d.c. between any conductor and earth.
	  Low. Normally exceeding extra-low voltage but not exceeding

250 volts, whether between conductors or between any conductor and earth.

Medium. Normally exceeding 250 volts but not exceeding 650 volts, whether between conductors or between any conductor and earth.

High. Normally exceeding 650 volts, whether between conductors or between any conductor and earth.

APPENDIX 2

British Standards: mechanical and electrical

Mechanical
BS No.

10	Flanges and bolting for pipes, valves and fittings
21	Pipe threads
41	Cast iron flue or smoke pipes
61	Pt 1 Copper tubes (heavy gauge) for general purposes
61 : 1969	Threads for light gauge copper tubes and fittings
65 & 540	Clay drain and sewer pipes
66 & 99	Cast copper alloy pipe fittings
78	Cast iron spigot and socket pipes (vertically cast) and spigot and socket fittings
138	Portable fire extinguishers of the water type (soda acid)
143 & 1256	Malleable cast iron and cast copper alloy screwed pipe fittings for steam, air, water, gas and oil
217	Red lead for paints and jointing compounds
219	Soft solders
334	Chemical lead (types A and B)
336	Fire hose couplings and ancillary equipment
367	A.C. electric ceiling type fans and regulators
416	Cast iron spigot and socket soil, waste and ventilating pipes and fittings
417	Galvanized mild steel cisterns and covers, tanks and cylinders
437	Cast iron spigot and socket drain pipes and fittings
460 & 1205	Cast iron rainwater goods
476	Fire tests on building materials and structures
486	Asbestos cement pressure pipes
487	Fusion-welded steel air receivers
497	Cast manhole covers, road gully gratings and frames
504	Drawn lead traps
534	Steel pipes, fittings and specials for water, gas and sewage
567	Asbestos cement flue pipes and fittings (light quality)
569	Asbestos cement rainwater goods
602 & 1085	Lead pipes for other than chemical purposes
659	Light gauge copper tubes (light drawn)
669	Flexible tubing and connector ends for appliances burning town gas
693	General requirements for oxy-acetylene welding of mild steel
699	Copper cylinders for domestic purposes
709	Methods of testing fusion welded joints and weld metal in steel

BRITISH STANDARDS: MECHANICAL AND ELECTRICAL

BS No.	
715	Sheet metal flue pipes and accessories for gas fired appliances
740	Portable fire extinguishers of the foam type – Pt I: Chemical; Pt II: Gas pressure
746	Gas meter unions and adaptors
750	Underground fire hydrants and dimensions of surface box openings
758	Small domestic hot-water supply boilers using solid fuel – Pt I: Manually controlled; Pt II: Thermostat-controlled
759	Safety fittings for application to boilers
779	Cast iron boilers for central heating and hot water supply
799	Oil burning equipment
835	Asbestos cement flue pipes and fittings, heavy quality
843	Stationary non-instantaneous electric water-heaters
848	Methods of testing of fans for general purposes
849	Plain sheet zinc roofing
853	Calorifiers for central heating and hot water supply – Pt I: Mild steel and cast iron; Pt 2: Copper
855	Welded steel boilers for central heating and hot water supply
864	Fittings for copper tube
1010	Draw off taps and stopvalves for water services
1077	Fusion-welded joints in copper
1091	Pressed steel gutters, rainwater pipes, fittings and accessories
1123	Safety valves, gauges and other safety fittings for air receivers and compressed air installations
1125	WC flushing cisterns
1130	Schedule of cast iron drain fittings, spigot and socket type
1182	Cast brass thimbles and tailpieces
1184	Copper and copper alloy traps
1188	Ceramic wash basins and pedestals
1189	Cast iron baths for domestic purposes
1206	Fireclay sinks
1208	Semi-rotary pumps, hand operated, double acting, for water
1211	Centrifugally cast (spun) iron pressure pipes for water, gas and sewage
1212	Ballvalves (Portsmouth type)
1213	Ceramic washdown WC pans
1218	Sluice valves for waterworks purposes
1229	Fireclay washtubs and tub and sink sets
1244	Metal sinks for domestic purposes
1246	Metal skirtings, picture rails and beads
1247	Manhole step irons
1250	Domestic appliances burning town gas
1254	WC seats (plastic)
1255	Brackets and supports for lavatory basins and sinks
1291	Ferrous traps for baths
1306	Pt I: Non-ferrous pipes and piping installations for and in connection with land boilers
1329	Metal lavatory basins for domestic purposes
1334	The use of thermal insulating materials for central heating and hot and cold water supply installations
1382	Portable fire extinguishers of the water type (gas pressure)
1386	Copper tubes to be buried underground
1387	Steel tubes and tubulars suitable for screwing to BS 21 pipe threads
1390	Sheet steel baths for domestic purposes

BS No.
1394	Power driven circulators for heating plants
1415	Mixing valves (manually operated) for ablutionary and domestic purposes
1426 & 3461	Surface boxes for gas and waterworks purposes
1431	Wrought copper and wrought zinc rainwater goods
1552	Control plug cocks for low-pressure gases
1553	Pt 1: Graphical symbols for pipes and valves Pt 4: Graphical symbols for heating and ventilating installations
1563	Cast-iron sectional tanks (rectangular)
1564	Pressed steel sectional tanks (rectangular)
1565	Galvanized mild steel indirect cylinders – annular or saddle-back type
1566	Copper indirect cylinders for domestic purposes
1588	The use of thermal insulating materials in the temperature range 95°C to 230°C
1635	Graphical symbols and abbreviations for fire protection drawings
1641	Cast iron pipe fittings for sprinklers and other fire protection installations
1689	Galvanized mild steel fire buckets
1710	Identification of pipelines
1721	Portable fire extinguishers of the halogenated hydrocarbon type
1723	Brazing
1724	Bronze welding by gas
1737	Jointing materials and compounds for water, town gas and low-pressure steam installations
1740	Wrought pipe fittings iron and steel (screwed BSP thread)
1780	Bourdon tube pressure and vacuum gauges
1845	Filler metals for brazing
1846	Glossary of terms relating to solid fuel burning equipment – Pt 1: Domestic appliances; Pt. 2: Industrial water heating and steam raising installations
1856	General requirements for the metal arc-welding of mild steel
1876	Automatic flushing cisterns for urinals
1894	Electrode boilers of riveted, seamless, welded and cast iron construction for water heating and steam generating
1952	Copper alloy gate valves for general purposes
1953	Copper alloy check valves for general purposes
1965	Butt-welding pipe fittings for pressure purposes
1968	Floats for ballvalves (copper)
1972	Polythene pipe (type 32) for cold water services
2017	Copper tubes for general purposes
2035	Cast iron flanged pipes and flanged fittings
2051	Tube and pipe fittings for engineering purposes
2089	WC seats (wooden)
2456	Floats for ballvalves (plastic) for cold water
2494	Rubber joint rings for gas mains, water mains and drainage purposes
2591	Glossary for valves and valve parts (for fluids) Pt 2: Safety valves and relief valves Pt 3: Plug valves and cocks Pt 4: Butterfly valves Pt 5: Ball valves
2594	Horizontal mild steel welded storage tanks
2760	Pitch-impregnated fibre pipes and fittings for drainage below and above ground
2767	Valves and unions for radiators (LPHW)

BRITISH STANDARDS: MECHANICAL AND ELECTRICAL

BS No.	
2777	Asbestos-cement cisterns
2790:1956	Cylindrical land steam boilers of welded construction (other than water-tube boilers)
2790	Pt 1: Shell boilers of welded construction (other than water-tube boilers)
2831	Methods of test for air filters used in air conditioning and general ventilation
2852	Rating and testing room air-conditioners
2871	Schedule of copper and copper alloys. Tubes
2879	Draining taps (screw-down pattern)
2910	General recommendations for the radiographic examination of fusion welded circumferential butt joints in steel pipes
2971	Class II metal-arc welding of steel pipelines and pipe assemblies for carrying fluids
2997	Aluminium rainwater goods
3116	Pt 1: Heat sensitive detectors for automatic fire alarm systems in buildings
3165	Rubber suction hose for fire-fighting purposes
3169	Rubber reel hose for fire fighting purposes
3184	Plastics fire buckets
3198	Combination hot water storage units (copper) for domestic purposes
3284	Polythene pipe (type 50) for cold water services
3326	Portable carbon dioxide fire extinguishers
3377	Back boilers for use with domestic solid fuel appliances
3380	Wastes for sanitary appliances and overflows for baths – Pt 1: Wastes and bath overflows; Pt 2: Skeleton sink wastes
3457	Materials for water tap washers
3465	Dry powder portable fire extinguishers
3505	Unplasticized PVC pipe for cold water services
3506	Unplasticized PVC pipe for industrial purposes
3601–2	Steel pipes and tubes for pressure purposes
3656	Asbestos cement pipes and fittings for sewerage and drainage
3708	The use of thermal insulating materials between 230°C and 650°C
3709	Portable fire extinguishers of the water type (stored pressure)
3899	Refrigerated room air-conditioners
3931	Hard-drawn thin wall copper tubes
3943	Plastics waste traps
3948	Cast-iron parallel slide valves for general purposes
3952	Cast-iron butterfly valves for general purposes
3954	Asbestos cement ducting
3958	Thermal insulating materials
	Pt 1: 85 per cent magnesia preformed insulation
	Pt 2: Calcium silicate preformed insulation
	Pt 3: Metal mesh faced mineral wool mats and mattresses
	Pt 4: Bonded preformed mineral wool pipe sections
	Pt 5: Bonded mineral wool slabs (for use at temperatures above 50°C)
4090	Cast-iron check valves for general purposes
4127	Light gauge stainless steel tubes
4213	Polyolefin or olefin copolymer moulded cold water storage cisterns
4346	Joints and fittings for use with unplasticized PVC pressure pipes
4485	Water cooling towers
	Pt 1: Glossary of terms
	Pt 2: Methods of test and acceptance testing
4504	Flanges and bolting for pipes, valves and fittings, metric series

Electrical
BS No.

Transformers
- 171 Power transformers

Electric lamps
- 161 240 V tungsten filament general service electric lamps
- 555 Tungsten filament miscellaneous electric lamps
- 1050 Visual indicator lamps
- 1853 Tubular fluorescent lamps for general lighting service

Lamp-caps and lampholders
- 52 Bayonet lamp-caps, lampholders and B.C. adaptors for voltages not exceeding 250 volts
- 98 Dimensions of screw lamp-caps and lampholders (Edison – type)
- 841 Lamp-caps and lampholders for architectural lamps
- 1875 Bi-pin lamp-caps and lampholders for tubular fluorescent lamps

Lighting fittings
- 364 Neck and flange dimensions of interior lighting fittings
- 495 Lamp-caps and lampholders for double-capped tubular lamps
- 889 Flameproof electric lighting fittings
- 2818 Auxiliaries for operation of fluorescent lamps on a.c. 50 c/s supplies
- 3541 Lighting fittings for general examination purposes in hospitals
- 3820 Electric lighting fittings
- 4017 Capacitors for use in tubular fluorescent, mercury and sodium discharge lamp circuits

Street lighting and signs
- 505 Road traffic control (electrical) light signals
- 1308 Concrete street lighting columns
- 1788 Street-lighting lanterns for use with electric lamps
- 1840 Street columns for street lighting
- 3989 Aluminium street lighting columns

Cables
- 3040 Radio-frequency cables for use with domestic television and VHF receiving aerials
- 6004 PVC-insulated cables (non-armoured) for electric power and lighting
- 6007 Elastomer-insulated cables for electric power and lighting
- 6207 Mineral-insulated cables
- 6231 PVC-insulated cables for switchgear and control gear wiring
- 6346 PVC-insulated cables for electricity supply
- 6480 Impregnated paper-insulated cables for electricity supply
- 6500 Insulated flexible cords
- 6977 Braided travelling cables for electric and hydraulic lifts

Cable materials and accessories
- 1442 Galvanized mild steel wire for armouring cables
- 1858 Bitumen-base filling compounds for electrical purposes
- 2484 Cable covers, concrete and earthenware
- 6746 PVC insulation and sheath of electric cables

BRITISH STANDARDS: MECHANICAL AND ELECTRICAL

BS No.
- 6746C Colour chart for PVC insulation and sheath of electric cables
- 6791   Aluminium conductors in insulated cables
- 6360   Copper conductors in insulated cables and cords
- 4081   Fittings for mineral insulated cables

Coding and marking
- 822   Terminal markings for electrical machinery and apparatus
- 1409   Letter symbols for electronic valves

Conductor materials
- 1432   Copper for electrical purposes. Strip with drawn or rolled edges
- 1433   Copper for electrical purposes. Rod and bar
- 2897   Wrought aluminium for electrical purposes – strip with drawn or rolled edges

Domestic electrical appliances
- 3456   The testing and approval of household electrical appliances

Electrical apparatus for use in explosive gas atmosphere
- 229   Flameproof enclosure of electrical apparatus
- 279   100-ampere flameproof plugs and sockets
- 542   Cable glands and sealing boxes for association with apparatus for use at mines
- 889   Flameproof electric lighting fittings
- 1395   30-ampere flameproof plugs and sockets and cable couplers

Fuses
- 88   Cartridge fuses of voltage-ratings up to 660 volts
- 646   Cartridge fuse links (rated at up to 5 amperes) for a.c. and d.c. service
- 1361   Cartridge fuses for domestic consumers' units
- 1362   Cartridge fuse-links for use in plugs

Installation materials, accessories, components and methods
- 31   Steel conduits and fittings for electrical wiring
- 52   Bayonet lamp-caps, lampholders and BC adaptors for voltages not exceeding 250 volts
- 67   Ceiling roses
- 214   Enclosed distribution fuseboards for low and medium voltages
- 951   Earthing clamps
- 3052   Electric shaver supply units
- 4177   Cooker control units rated at 30 amperes and 45 amperes, 250 volts single-phase only

Nomenclature and symbols
- 108   Graphical symbols for general electrical purposes
- 204   Glossary of terms used in telecommunication and electronics
- 205   Glossary of terms used in electrical engineering
- 1991   Letter symbols signs and abbreviations

Overhead lines
- 125   Hard-drawn copper and copper-cadmium conductors for overhead power transmission purposes

BS No.
- 174 Hard-drawn copper and copper-cadmium wire for telegraph and telephone purposes
- 176 Copper binding and jointing wires for telegraph and telephone purposes
- 177 Copper and copper-cadmium tapes and binders for telegraph and telephone purposes
- 179 Copper jointing sleeves for telegraph and telephone purposes
- 181 Copper-cadmium jointing sleeves for telegraph and telephone purposes
- 182 to
- 184 Galvanized iron and steel wire for telegraph and telephone purposes

Plugs and sockets
- 196 Protected-type non-reversible plugs, socket-outlets, cable-couplers and appliance-couplers with earthing contacts
- 279 100-ampere flameproof plugs and sockets (restrained type)
- 546 Two-pole and earthing-pin plugs, socket-outlets and socket-outlet adaptors for circuits up to 250 volts

APPENDIX 3

Codes of practice: mechanical and electrical

Mechanical

BS *Code of Practice* No.

CP3	Chapter I (c) Ventilation.
CP3	Chapter III Sound insulation and noise reduction
CP3	Chapter IV Precautions against fire
CP3	Chapter IV Part 1: 62 Fire precautions in flats and maisonettes over 24·384 m in height
CP3	Chapter VII Engineering and utility services
CP3	Chapter VII Heating and thermal insulation
CP99	Frost precautions for water services
CP131.101	Flues for domestic appliances burning solid fuel
CP143	Sheet roof and wall coverings
CP301	Building drainage
CP303	Surface water and subsoil drainage
CP304	Sanitary pipework above ground
CP305	Sanitary appliances
CP306	The storage and collection of refuse from residential buildings
CP310	Water supply
CP331	Installation of pipes and meters for town gas
CP332	Selection and installation of town gas space heating
CP337	Flues for gas appliances up to 150,000 Btu/h rating
CP341.300–307	Central heating by LPHW
CP342	Centralized hot water supply
CP352	Mechanical ventilation and air conditioning in buildings
CP402	Fire fighting installations and equipment
CP403.101	Small boiler systems using solid fuel
CP406	Mechanical refrigeration
CP413	Design and construction of ducts for services
CP3002	Oil firing
CP3005	Thermal insulation of pipework and equipment
CP3006	Central heating for domestic premises

Electrical

CP324.202 (1951)	Domestic electric water-heating installations
CP326	The protection of structures against lightning

BS *Code of Practice* No.	
CP327	Telecommunications facilities in buildings – Part 3: Sound distribution systems
CP327.102	Telephones and telegraphs – private services
CP327.201	The reception of sound and television broadcasting, with supplement No. 1 – Reception of UHF television broadcasting
CP327.401	Bell and call systems
CP327.402	Staff location systems
CP327.403	Impulse clock and timing systems
CP327.404/ 402.501	Electrical fire alarms
CP1001	Abatement of radio interference caused by motor vehicles and internal combustion engines
CP1002	Abatement of radio interference from electro-medical and industrial radio-frequency equipment
CP1003	Electrical apparatus and associated equipment for use in explosive atmospheres of gas or vapour other than mining applications
CP1004	Street lighting
CP1005	The use of electronic valves
CP1006	General aspects of radio interference suppression
CP1007	Maintained lighting for cinemas
CP1008	Maintenance of electrical switchgear
CP1009	Maintenance of insulating oil (with special reference to transformers and switchgear)
CP1010	Guide to loading of oil-immersed transformers to BS 171
CP1011	Maintenance of electrical motor control gear
CP1012	The abatement and measurement of radio interference from electrical installations in civil aircraft
CP1013	Earthing
CP1014	The protection of electrical power equipment against climatic conditions

APPENDIX 4

Standard symbols and notations: mechanical and electrical

Mechanical – being an extract from the *IHVE Guide* Section 22

Service codes	
Service	Code
Chilled water	CHW
Cold water:	
Mains	MWS
Downservice	CWS
Drinking	DWS
Flushing	FWS
Pressurized	PWS
Condensate	C
Compressed air	CA
Cooling water	CLW
Gases:	
Towns	G
Oxygen	O
Nitrous oxide	N_2O
Heating:	
Low pressure water	LPHW
Medium pressure water	MPHW
High pressure water	HPHW
Hot (domestic) water	HWS
Refrigerants	R_0
(identified by symbol for particular gas)	
Steam	S
Vacuum	V

Piping Symbols	
Position, etc.	Symbol
In roof or above ceiling	–··–––··–
At high level	–·–––·–
Vertical drop	———•
At low level	————
Below floor	– – – –

Piping Symbols	
Position, etc.	Symbol
Direction of flow	———→
Gradient (rise)	

Pipe positions, etc.	
Position, etc.	Code
High level	HL
Low level	LL
From below	FB
To below	TB
From above	FA
To above	TA
Flow	F
Return	R

Service outlets	
Service	Symbol
Water*:	
Tap	•—
Hose union	—⋈ HU
Shower mixer	
Gas*:	
Single	—→
Two-way	<
Four-way	×
Fire:	
External hydrant	—◻H
Hose reel	
Landing valve†	•⋈⋈
Sprinkler head	—○—

* Each outlet identified by the appropriate service code and size.
† Identified as wet or dry.

226 THE MEASUREMENT OF ENGINEERING SERVICES

Vents and drains

Detail	Symbol
Open vent	
Hand vent	V
Auto air valve	AAV
Air bottle with hand vent	V
Drain cock	D

Sundry codes

Item	Code
Auto air valve	AAV
Cold feed	CF
Draw-off point	DO
Feed and expansion	F & E
Lockshield valve	LSV
Open vent	OV
Plug cock	PC
Stop cock	SC
Wheel valve	WV

Heating surfaces

Surface	Symbol
Convectors:	
Natural	
Fan	
Embedded panels:	
Floor	
Ceiling	
Pipe coils:	
High level	
Low level	
Radiant strip	
Radiator	
Radiant panels:	
Industrial, single	
Industrial, double	

Heating surfaces

Surface	Symbol
Wall mounted	
Ceiling mounted	
Towel rail	TR
Unit heaters:	
Horizontal	
Downward	

Controls and instruments

Device	Symbol

Sense:

	Instrument	Pocket
Temperature	T	TP
Pressure	P	PP
Humidity	H	HP
	Local	Remote

Mounting:
  Pipe
  Duct

Function:
  Indication
  Electric control
  Pneumatic control

Examples:
  Local pressure gauge pipe mounted
  Local humidistat, pneumatic, duct mounted
  Remove thermostat, electric, pipe mounted
  Local thermometer pocket, duct mounted

STANDARD SYMBOLS AND NOTATIONS 227

Joints, anchors and expansion points

Unit	Col. 1*	Col. 2*
Union joint		
Flanged joint		
Anchor point		
Expansion loop		
Expansion bellows: Simple		
Single, linked		
Double, linked		

Hand-operated valves

Type	Col. 1*	Col. 2*
Angle		
Gate or globe		
Plug cock		
Three-way		

Self- and power-operated valves, etc.

Type	Col. 1*	Col. 2*
Safety (Relief)		
Pressure reducing		
Weight operated		
Non-return		
Ball		

Self- and power-operated valves, etc.

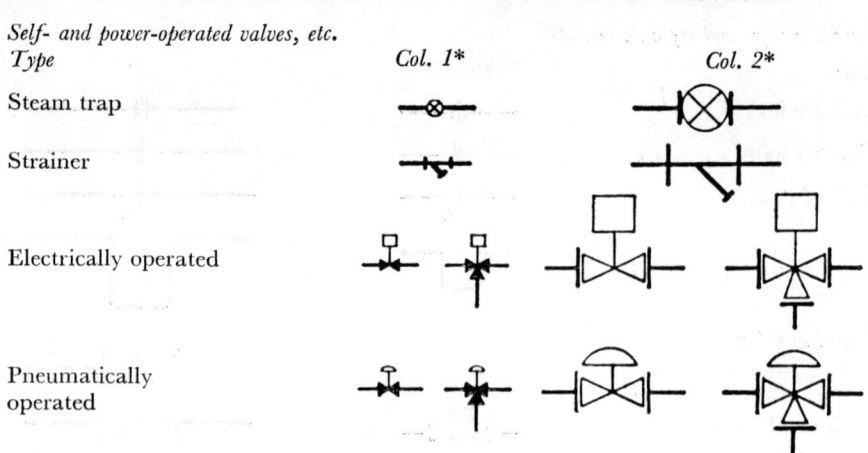

Type	Col. 1*	Col. 2*
Steam trap		
Strainer		
Electrically operated		
Pneumatically operated		

* Col. 1 gives symbol for diagrammatic or one-eighth scale representation.
Col. 2 gives stylized symbol for larger scales where leading dimensions are drawn to scale.

Ductwork, straight runs, etc.

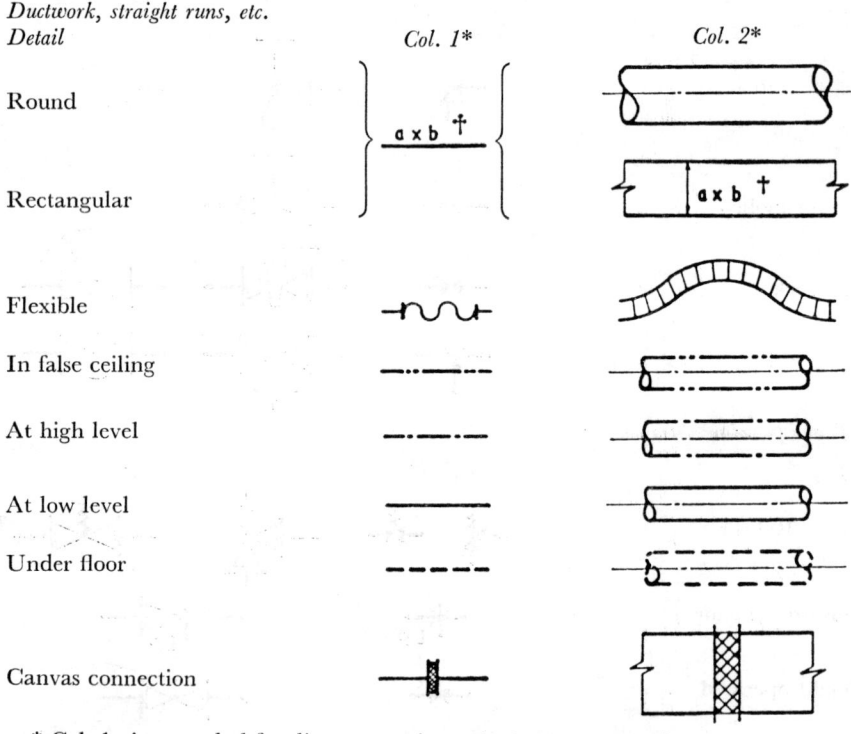

Detail	Col. 1*	Col. 2*
Round	$a \times b$ †	
Rectangular		$a \times b$ †
Flexible		
In false ceiling		
At high level		
At low level		
Under floor		
Canvas connection		

* Col. 1 gives symbol for diagrammatic or single line convention.
Col. 2 gives stylized symbol for double line convention at larger scales.

† Sizes stated as $a \times b$ where a is the dimension seen in the view drawn. 12″ × 6″ (305 × 152 mm) 6″ × 12″ (152 × 305 mm)

STANDARD SYMBOLS AND NOTATIONS

Ductwork, straight runs, etc.

Detail	Col. 1*	Col. 2*
Access door		

Ductwork, section changes, etc.

Detail	Col. 1*	Col. 2*
Change section:		
Rectangular (Drawn as seen)		
Rectangular to round		
Round		
Bend:		
Looking up		
Looking down		

Ductwork, grilles

Detail	Col. 1*	Col. 2*
Facing		

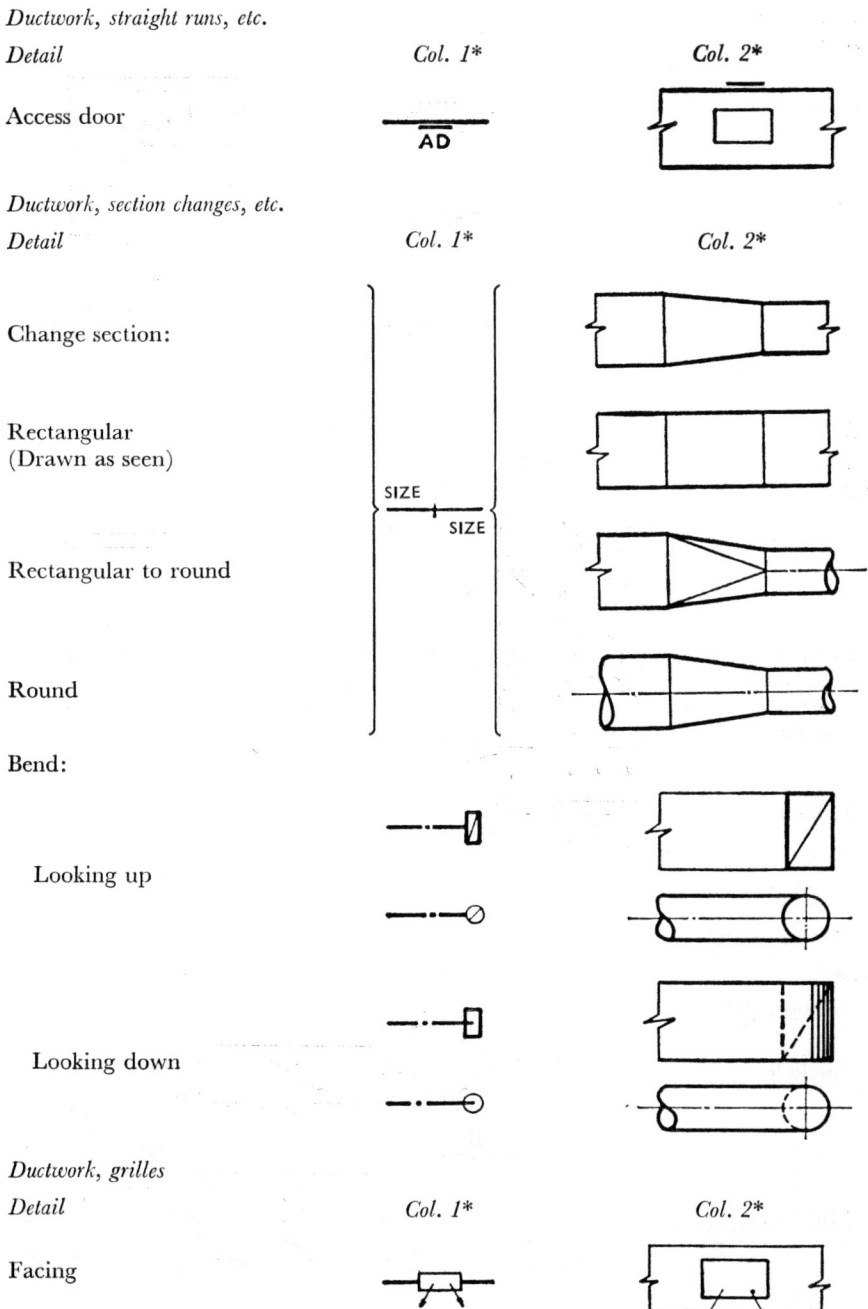

* Col. 1 gives symbol for diagrammatic or single line convention.
Col. 2 gives stylized symbol for double line convention at larger scales.

THE MEASUREMENT OF ENGINEERING SERVICES

Ductwork, grilles

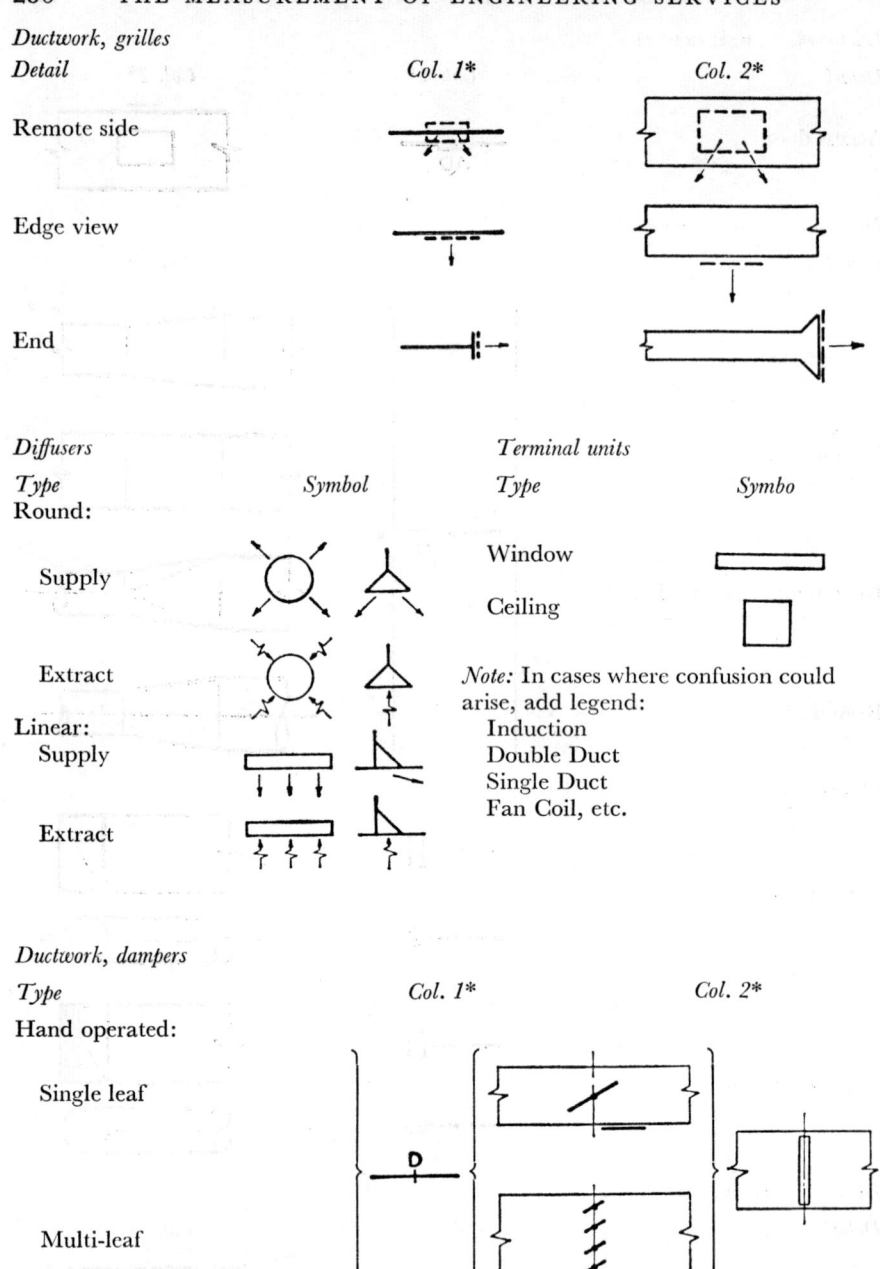

Detail	Col. 1*	Col. 2*
Remote side		
Edge view		
End		

Diffusers

Type	Symbol
Round:	
Supply	
Extract	
Linear:	
Supply	
Extract	

Terminal units

Type	Symbol
Window	
Ceiling	

Note: In cases where confusion could arise, add legend:
Induction
Double Duct
Single Duct
Fan Coil, etc.

Ductwork, dampers

Type	Col. 1*	Col. 2*
Hand operated:		
Single leaf		
Multi-leaf		

* Col. 1 gives symbol for diagrammatic or single line convention.
Col. 2 gives stylized symbol for double line convention at larger scales.

STANDARD SYMBOLS AND NOTATIONS

Ductwork, dampers
Type   Col. 1*   Col. 2*
Power operated:

Electric

Pneumatic

Fire

Equipment

Detail	Symbol	Detail	Symbol
Air compressor		Pump	
Cooling tower		Automatic stoker	
Calorifiers:		Air cooler	
Horizontal		Air heater	
Vertical		Fans:	
Indirect cylinders:		Axial	
Horizontal		Centrifugal	
Vertical		Propellor	
Oil burner		Air filter	

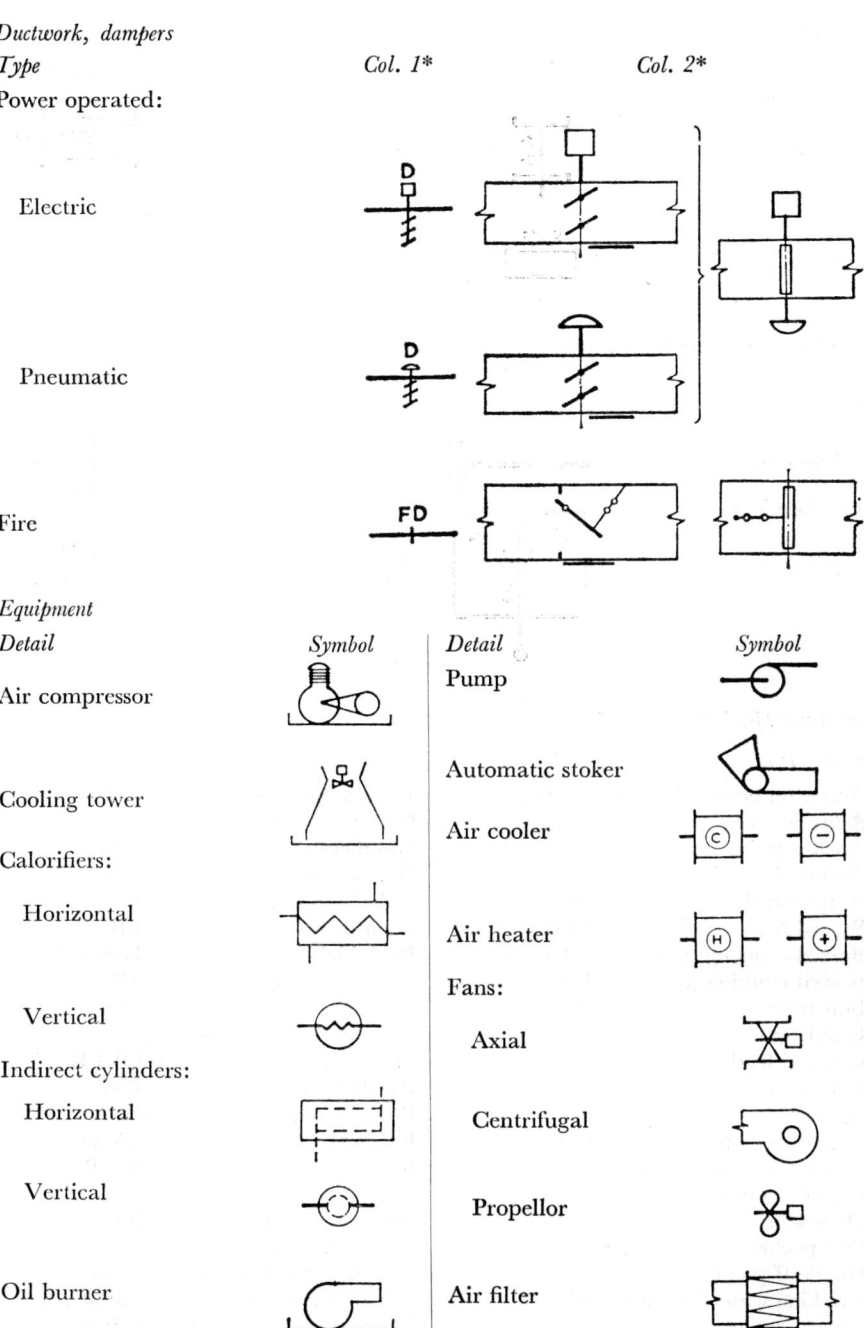

* Col. 1 gives symbol for diagrammatic or single line convention.
  Col. 2 gives stylized symbol for double line convention at larger scales.

232 THE MEASUREMENT OF ENGINEERING SERVICES

Equipment

Detail	Symbol	Detail	Symbol

Humidifiers:

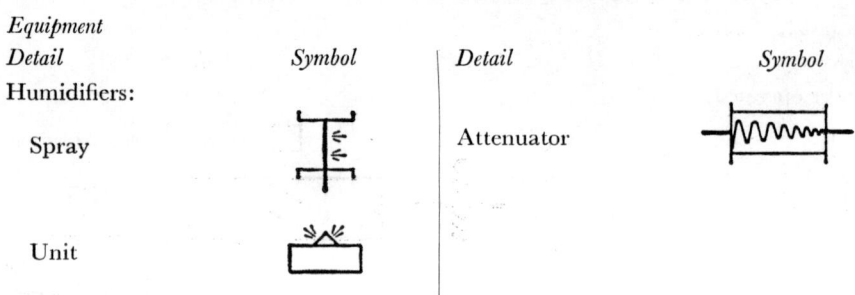

Spray

Attenuator

Unit

Symbols and notations not included in IHVE Guide, Section 22

	Symbol		Symbol

Joints:

Meters:

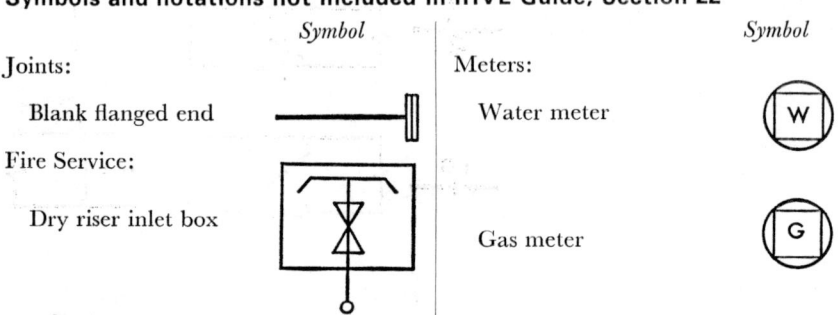

Blank flanged end

Water meter

Fire Service:

Dry riser inlet box

Gas meter

Alphabetical list of codes

Sundry items	Code or abb.	Sundry items	Code or abb.
Access on bottom length	AOBL	Fume cupboard	F/C
Altitude gauge	AG	Guide	G
Anchor point	A	Gunmetal	GM
Anti-syphon pipe	ASP	Heavy duty	HD
Anti-vibration	AV	Isolating valve	IV
Brazed branch joint	BBJ	Lavatory basin	LB
Brazed reducing joint	B Red jt	Lockshield	L/S or LS
Brazed running joint	B Rng jt	Malleable iron	MI
Butt weld	BW	Mild steel	MS
Cast iron	CI	Natural expansion point	NE
Caulked lead joint	C/L jt	Overflow	OVER
Cold feed	CF	Parallel slide valve	PSV
Copper	Cu or Cpr	Pressure gauge	PG
Copper to copper	C/C	Rainwater outlet	RWO
Copper to female iron	C/FI	Rainwater pipe	RWP
Copper to male iron	C/MI	Red lead joint	R/L jt
Deep seal	D/S	Regulating valve	RV
Dirt pocket	DP	Rigid glass silk sections	RGSS
Draw-off point	DO	School board build in	SBBI
Drinking water fountain	DWF	School board screw on	SBSO
Excess pressure relief valve	EPRV	Screwed and socketed	S & S
		Sight glass	SG
Feed and expansion	F & E	Soil and vent pipe	SVP
Floor gully	FG	Splay cut end	SCE

STANDARD SYMBOLS AND NOTATIONS

Sundry items	Code of abb.	Sundry items	Code or abb.
Supply and extract	S & E	Waste pipe	WP
Swept brazed branch joint	SBBJ	Water closet	WC
		Water waste preventor	WWP
Swept welded branch joint	SWBJ	Welded branch joint	WBJ
		Wheelhead	W/H or WH
Urinal	UR	Wrought iron	WI

Electrical (as recommended by BS 108)

Location symbols for installation

Control gear and distribution fuseboards	*Symbol*
Main control	
Main switch	
Change over switch	
Switchboard, distribution board, or fuseboard	
Contactor	
Meter	
Lighting outlets, etc.	
Ceiling outlet lighting, filament lamp	
Wall outlet lighting, filament lamp	
Ceiling outlet for discharge lamp	
Ballast unit, where installed remote from lamp fitting	
Power factor capacitor, where installed remote from lamp fitting	
Lighting outlet connected to an emergency system	
Exis box with wiring for normal and emergency systems	

Q

Lighting outlets, etc.	Symbol
Street lighting standard	⊗
Ceiling outlet for filament lamps with wiring connected to normal and emergency systems	◐
Ceiling outlet with wiring for filament and discharge lamps	⊶⊙
Ceiling outlet with wiring for discharge lamp connected to normal system, plus wiring for filament lamp connected to emergency system	⊶◐

Switch outlets

General symbol for local switch when considered applicable	●
1-way switch	⚬⟋
2-way switch	⚬⟋~
Intermediate switch	⚬⟋*
Pendant switch	⚬⟋
Pull switch	⚬⟋

Note: Combinations of the above outlets and switch symbols may be used if required
Example: Wall outlet and local switch ⊢●

Socket outlets		Alternative
Socket outlet	▷—	◉
Switch socket outlet	▷—	◉•

A reference may be given against the symbol thus:

   Current carrying capacity   ▷⑤—

   Reference as required   ◉x

STANDARD SYMBOLS AND NOTATIONS   235

Fixed heating outlets   *Symbol*

Tubular heater

   Note:
1. Length to be to scale and also to be given in schedule
2. The circle represents the position of connection to the fixed wiring
3. N equals number of tubes in bank

Fixed radiator or heating panel

   Note: Detail of equipment to be given in schedule

Convection heater

Electric unit heater

Immersion heater

Thermostat

Immersion heater with incorporated thermostat

Self contained electric water heater

Humidistat

Bells, etc.

Bell push outlet

Multi push

Bell

Buzzer

Indicator
   N equals number of ways

236 THE MEASUREMENT OF ENGINEERING SERVICES

Bells, etc. *Symbol*

Relay

Note: This general symbol is applicable to any system by the addition of an identifying symbol (appropriate to a particular system) in the upper half e.g.

Bell system relay

Where items of apparatus are combined the symbols may be combined for example:
Indicator and bell

Bell transformer
Note: May be used for any special l.v. purpose

Telephones

Telephone point, public service

Telephone board, public service

Telephone point, internal

Telephone board, internal

Clocks

Synchronous clock outlet

Impulse clock outlet

Master clock

Fire alarms

Fire push

Automatic contact

STANDARD SYMBOLS AND NOTATIONS 237

Fire alarms   *Symbol*

Bell connected to fire alarm

Fire alarm indicator
   N equals number of ways

Public address system

Amplifier

Control board

Microphone outlet

Loud speaker outlet

Radio reception outlets

Special outlet for receiver

Loud speaker outlet

Aerial

Luminous signal systems

Push

Multi push

Pilot or corridor lamp position

Indicator
   Note: Buzzer may be added if required
      N equals number of ways

Relay

Reset position

	Symbol
Special purpose signal outlets	
Special purpose push	⊗
Special purpose indicator	⊠
Special purpose bell	
Horn or hooter	
Siren	
Fixed apparatus outlets	
Fixed point (requirement unspecified, characteristics to be given in drawing or schedule)	
Outlet for motor to fixed fan	
Outlet for motor to ceiling fan	
Fan regulator	
Cooker control unit	
Earthing	
Earth (general symbol)	
Water main earth	
Tubular earth	
Strip earth	
Earth plate	
Test point for earth	
Surge diverter	

APPENDIX 5

SI units and equivalent magnitudes

SI units

Quantity	Unit	Symbol
length	metre	m
mass	kilogramme	kg
time	second	s
temperature	degree Celsius	°C or deg C*
area	square metre	m^2
volume	cubic metre	m^3
	litre	litre*
density	kilogramme per cubic metre	kg/m^3
force	newton	N
energy	joule	J
power	watt	W
pressure	newton per square metre	N/m^2
intensity of heat flow	watt per square metre	W/m^2
thermal conductivity	watt per metre degree Celsius	W/m deg C
coefficient of heat transfer	watt per square metre degree Celsius	W/m^2 deg C
thermal resistivity	metre degree Celsius per watt	m deg C/W
thermal capacity	kilojoule per kilogramme degree Celsius	kJ/kg deg C
calorific value	kilojoule per kilogramme	kJ/kg

* These units are not true SI units, but will be used in practice.

The litre is the recommended sub-multiple of the cubic metre, and can be used as a measurement of solid or liquid volume.

Equivalent magnitudes

SI Unit		Imperial Unit
1 metre	=	3·281 feet
1 kilogramme	=	2·205 pounds
1 square metre	=	10·764 square feet
1 cubic metre	=	1·308 cubic yards
1 litre	=	0·035 cubic feet
1 joule	=	$9·478 \times 10^{-4}$ Btu
1 N/m^2	=	$1·450 \times 10^{-4}$ pounds force per square inch
1 watt	=	3·412 Btu per hour

Index

Abbreviations, 36
Abortive work, 15
Access door, 55, 58, 60
  ladder, 130
  points, 77
  to site, 28
After-cooler, 137, 138
Agreement and Schedule of Conditions, of Building Contract, 22
Air bottle, 109, 116, 127
  changes, 145
  clock, 66, 109
  compressor, 64, 92
  conditioning plant, 10, 173
  drain traps, 140
  dryer, 138
  dust separators, 65
  filters, 65
  handling installation, 45
  heaters, 149
  heating or cooling batteries, 65
  high velocity units, 64
  humidifiers, 66
  purification equipment, 65
  receiver, 138
  release valve, 91, 96
  relief valve, 106
  self-contained conditioning units, 66
  silencer units, 64
Alarms, 129
  burglar, 10, 47, 194
  fire, 47
  visible, 98
All-in rates, 10, 15
Alternative systems, 7
Altitude gauge, 105, 106, 127
Amendments, 28
Ammeter, 176

Anchor points, 162
Anti-vibration, 138
  mountings, 93
  pads of cork, 60, 146
Appendix, 28
Arbitration, 28
Architect, 25, 30, 198
  instructions, 24
Asbestos to BS 486, 88
Asbestos cement cisterns, 95
As-fitted, 25, 26
Ash removal plant, 61
Attendance, 32
  general, 74
  special, 74
Automatic air eliminators, 109
  control installation, 45
  controls, 46, 70, 124
  damper, 112
  fire extinguishers, 178
  roll type fitters, 151
  stokers, 61
  vents, 116
Axial flow fans, 146

Ball valves, 93, 94, 101, 102, 114
Balloon guard, 77
  grating, 56
Basis of prices, 25, 31
Baths, 83
Bedding and pointing, 74
Bells, 10
Bidet, 84
Bills of Quantities, 24, 25, 27, 28, 29, 31, 33, 47, 199
  accuracy, 21
  approximate, 20
  ending items, 40
  errors, 17

INDEX

examination and correction of the priced, 18, 19
firm, 20
inaccuracies, 21
layout, 27
variations, 24, 25, 27, 35, 37, 198, 199, 200
Boiler, 10, 59, 111, 112
  flue pipes, 173
  flues, 112
  house, 30, 178
Booster pump control, 91
Boss pipes, 78, 79
Bottletraps, 80
Brackets and holderbats, 79, 86
Branch, 78, 85
Break tank, 89, 90, 91, 93, 97, 99, 100
Breeching, 103
British standard, 36, 115
  code of practice, 30, 36
Bronze welding, 115
Budget, 19
Builders' work, 33, 37, 74
  drawings, 37
Busbar, 181
  chamber, 177
  overhead trunking, 183
  rising main, 180

Cable-MICC, 179
  glands, 177
  PILC, 176
  PILCSWA & S, 176, 178, 179, 180
  PVC-SWAPVC, 179
  PVC-insulated steel wire armoured and sheathed, 176
  trays, 47
  trunking, 182
  UPVC, 166, 167, 169, 170
Call system, 194
Calorifier, 46, 62, 105, 106, 108, 113
  mountings, 113
Canopies, 153
Capillary, 165
  and compression fittings, 114, 115
Cash discount, 29, 40
Ceiling diffusers, 158
Central Government, 23
Centralized control station, 125
Centrifugal fans, 147, 148
  pumps, 125
Certificate, 29
  of payment, 25, 27
  valuation, 32
Check valve, 101
Chemical installation, 45
Chimneys, 56
Circuit breakers, 175, 177, 178
  charts, 177
Circulating pumps, 125
Cisterns, 95, 102
  asbestos cement, 95
  cast iron, 95
  fibreglass, 95
  flushing, 82, 83, 84
  storage, 101
Civil engineering, 23
Clerk of Works, 198, 200
Clocks, 10, 47, 193
Cocks, 69, 105
  drain off, 88, 94, 100, 105, 106, 109, 116
Code of Procedure for Selective Tendering (1969), 17, 19
  Practice, 30, 36
Cold-water feeds, 46
  feed connection, 114
  installation, 10, 44
  service, 174
  storage tank, 89, 91, 93, 94
  supply tank, 108
  tank, 174
Colour identification, 114
  coding, 42, 46
Comparitive cost studies, 15
Competitive selective tendering, 21
Completion, 24, 27
Compressed air, 10, 46
  installation, 45
Compression, 165
Compressor, 137
Condensate receiver, 136
Conduit, 184, 185, 190
Connection to mechanical services, 191, 192
Consulting engineer, 23, 25, 28, 30
  instructions, 31, 198
  specification, 31, 40
Contents gauges, 129
Contingencies, 40
Contract, 22, 23, 26, 27, 29, 30, 198
  conditions, 20, 25, 28, 31
  cost control, 15, 20
  direct, 22
  document, 31

Contract—*contd.*
  fluctuating, 31
  heading, 28
  management of building, 198
Contractor, 25, 28, 29, 30
  discount, 29
Contractual responsibilities, 24
Controls, 10, 47
  booster pump, 91
  gear, 10
  panel, 125, 178, 181
Convectional heaters, 118
Convectors, 66
Cooker, 10
  control box, 191
Cooling compressors, 139
Copper tube, 79, 114, 164, 165, 167
  BS 1386, 88
  BS 3931, 79, 88, 100, 164
  alloy check valve (non-return), 101
  alloy gate valve, 101
  alloy three-piece union, 114
  bend, 86
  heavy gauge BS 61, 88
  light gauge BS 659, 88, 100, 115, 162
  pipework, 86
Cost checking, 15
  control, 5, 199, 200
  differential, 7
  exercises, 7
  in use, 7, 9
  limit, 6, 7
  plan, 7, 10, 15
  planning, 16
Cowls, 56, 58
Critical path network, 34
Cubicle type panel, 176
Cutting away and making good, 74
  and pinning, 74
Cylinders, 107
  hot water, 62
  thermal storage, 62

Damage by fire, 27
Dampers, 55, 58, 71, 152
  fire, 59
  special, 59
Dayworks, 40, 199, 200
  prices, 25
Deduction, 28
Defects, shrinkages, 27
  liability period, 31
Definition of parties, 30

Descriptions, 36
Design attitude, 8
  work, 16
De-superheater, 60
Determination, 27
Dezincification, 168
Diagrams, 39
Diffusers, 58, 153, 158
Disconnecting and refining equipment, 73
Discrepancy, 24, 199
Distribution boards, 10, 47, 181
  SPN, 181
  DP, 181
  TP, 181
  TPN, 181
  pipework, 140
Domestic equipment, 191, 192
Doors, 55
  explosion, 60, 61, 162
Double cash columns, 42, 46
Drain off cock, 88, 94, 100, 105, 106, 109, 116
Draining and refilling, 41, 73
Draught stabilizer, 61, 112, 113
Drawings, 38
  as-fitted or record, 37, 38
  builders work, 37, 38
  co-ordinated, 37
  manufacturers, 37, 38
  master, 37
  schematic or outline, 37
  tender, 29
  working or detailed, 37, 38
  variation, 37, 38, 199
Drinking fountains, 84
Drip tray, 56, 127, 129
Dry riser inlet cabinet, 103
  installation, 96, 100
Drying out the building, 39
Ducting, 47, 56, 152
  fittings, 57
  joints, 57
  supports, 57
  turns, 58
Duplicate pump sets, 89, 90, 97, 100

Earthing systems, 47, 178
Electrical appliances, 47
  heating, 47
  power, 33
  under floor heating, 9
  work, 74

INDEX

Electricity authorities, 30
Electrode float switch, 94
  switch, 91
Electrostatic filters, 152
  precipitators, 155
Elemental analysis, 9, 16
  cost, 15
  cost balance, 15
Elements, 6
Employer, 30
  restrictions, 34
Equalizers, 58
Equipment—disconnecting and re-fixing, 41
Establishment charges, 29
Estimator, 29
Exhaust heads, 56
Expansion bellows, 117
  loops, 116
  tank, 114
Explanatory notes, 42
Extra over items, 43, 57
  work, 25
Extract grilles, 153
  hoods, 59

Facilities, 32
  hoisting, 33
Fair valuation, 25
Fall switch, 131
Fans, 10, 64, 146
  axial flow, 146
  centrifugal slow speed multivane, 156
  centrifugal, 147, 148
  forward curved, 148
Fan-assisted convector, 120
FASS, 23, 24, 27
F.B. foam inlet, 131
Feed and expansion tank, 113, 173
Ferrules, 55
Fibreglass sectional cisterns, 95
  tanks, 94
Fill pipe, 129
Filters, 150, 155
Final account, 21, 200
  cost plan, 20
  payment, 27
Financial control, 198, 199, 200
  implication, 27
  statements, 200
Fire alarms, 10, 47, 193
  brigade hydrants, 95
  damage by, 27

dampers, 153
fighting installations, 10, 44
  precaution, 131, 178
  precaution valves, 131
Fix and fixing, 29
  only, 75
Flanged joints, 115
  valves, 94
Flanges, 94, 165
  blank, 54
  mating, 49
Flashing slate, 86
Flexible bellows, 126
  connections, 93, 127, 146
Float switch, 91, 93
Flow meters, 143
Fluctuations, 26, 28, 35
  contract, 31
Foam, 131
  inlet, 131
  spreader, 131
Foreman, 26
Formal invitation to tender, 19
Format, 29
Form of contract, 22
  CCC/Wks/1, 23
  model form A, 23
  tender, 18
  warranty, 23
Forward curved fans, 148
Free fall valves, 131
Fuel conveyors, 61
  gas installation, 10, 45, 135
  hoppers, 61
  oil, 128
  oil installation, 44
  oil storage tank, 128
  supplies, 10
Full value, 57
Fuses, HRC and HBC, 177, 178, 181
Fusible links, 69

Galvanized cisterns, 95
  heavy weight mild steel tube to BS 1387, 96
  pressed steel cold water storage tanks, 102
  steel to B.S. 1387, 80, 88, 89, 100
Gas appliances, 136
  authorities, 30
  firing equipment, 60
  installation, 10
  meters, 68, 134

Gas appliances—*contd.*
  pipework, 134
  service pipes, 133
Gate valves, 101, 106
Gauges, 70, 127
General plant and facilities, 36
Glass lined cast iron, 80
Grilles, 58, 153
Guaranteed time, 32
Guide, 162
Gutters, 50
  fittings, 50
  joints, 50
  supports, 51

Hard-drawn thin wall copper tubes, 115
Heat source, 10
Heated-water installation, 44
Heaters, 10
  skirtings, 67
  unit, 67
High-level alarm, 129
  voltage cables, 46
  voltage switchgear, 46, 176
Holderbats or screw-on brackets, 94
Hoods, 153
Hopper heads, 56
Hose reels, 98, 99, 100, 102
Hot water service, 173
  pipework, 110
  storage vessel, 104, 115
Humidification, 154
Hydraulic installation, 45, 46

ICE general conditions of contract, 23
Identification plates, 42, 73
Immersion heaters, 62, 104, 105
Importing labour, 32
Inaccuracies in the bills, 21
Incentive and bonus payments, 32, 34
Incinerators, 10
Incoming electricity main, 175
  mains, 10
Indirect cylinders, 105, 107
Inlet box, 96
  breaching piece, 96
In-line pumps, 125
Inspection chambers, 74
Installation
  plans, 73
  temporarily operating, 73
  testing, 73

Instantaneous female coupling, 103
  mole coupling, 103
Instructions – operating and maintenance, 39
Insulation-backing, 67
  anti-vibration and sound, 67
  ductwork, 72
  loose insulation and cellular concrete, 72
  pipework and fittings, 71
  plant, 71
  thermal, 71
Insurance, 27, 30, 31, 33
Interim payments, 27, 32, 200
  valuations, 32
Internal drainage, 9, 44
Invitation to tender, 18
Isolator, 180

Joint Contracts Tribunal, 26, 35
Joints, 78
  branch, 85
  ducting, 57
  expansion, 80
  flanged, 53
  gutter, 50
  mastic or cement, 81, 86
  materials and compounds, 115
  pipe, 52
  plastic, 80
  soldered, 52

Keys, tools and spares, 41, 73
Kitchen equipment, 10

Labour on-costs, 32
Laundry equipment, 10
Lavatory basin, 82
Lead to BS 602, Table 1, 80, 88, 89
  BS 1085, Table 1, 88, 89
Letability, 9
Lifts, 10
  control panel, 178
Lighting cables, 185
  circuits, external, emergency, etc., 10
  emergency, 47, 187
  external, 47
  final sub-circuits, 181, 182, 183
  fittings, 187
  general, 47
  installation measurement schedule, 196
  maintained, 188

INDEX

protection and earthing, 10, 47, 195
   switches, 186
Local authority's requirements, 36
'Loop-in' system, 186
Loss or damage, 33
   or expenses by the sub-contractor, 24
Lump sum, 10
   percentage addition, 29
   preliminaries, 29

Made bends, 28, 85
Main anchors, 162
   controls, 10
   distribution, 10
   medium voltage cables, 46
   switchboard, 177
   switchgear, 46, 47
Maintenance and running costs, 7
Malleable cast iron, 114
Manufacturer, 35
Materials
   delivery, 35
   ordering, 199
   testing, 30
   unloading and storing, 35
Measured approximate quantities, 15
Measurement, 25
   domestic hot water, 110
Media, 65
Medical gas installation, 10, 45
   suction installation, 45
Mess rooms, 52
Metalwork, 75
Meter, 105
   gas, 68
   panels, 175
   water, 68
Metrication, 168
Motive power, 47
Motors, 10
Multiphase, 47

National insurance, 35
   contributions, 32
Negotiation, 19, 20, 35, 199
   reduction of tender, 18
NFBTE, 23, 24, 27
Nipples – hexagonal, 54
Nitrogen equipment, 64
Nominated sub-contractors, 20, 22, 23, 24, 25, 26, 27, 29
   sub-trader, 23
   supplier, 29

Non-productive time, 32
Non-return valves, 94, 99, 100, 101, 109
Notice prior to cover, 36
   advertisements, 34
   boards, 34
Notifying results, 18
Number of tenderers, 19

Obligations, 28
Office accommodation, 32
Off sets, 77
Oil burners, 60
   filters, 130
   heaters, 63
   intake box, 129
   storage tank, 128
   tankers, 62
Openings, 58
   tenders, 18
Open vent, 108, 116
Operating air audible alarm, 130
   and maintenance manuals, 25, 26
Order of billing preliminary clauses, 27
   cost estimate, 6, 7
   installations, 44
Orifice plates, 97
Outflow immersion heater, 130
Outline cost plan, 7, 9, 15
Overflow, 81, 84
   outlet, 83
Overload and earth leakage protection, 176
Overtime working, 34

Page signposting, 43
Painting, 75
Panels – Cubicle type, 176
   embedded, 67
   enclosed single-sided, 123
   horizontal single-sided, 123
   radiant, 67
   vertical double-sided, 123
Payments on account, 198
Pensions, 32, 35
Percentage addition, 29, 36
   deduction, 36
   total cost, 7
Period of final measurement, 25, 200
Pipeline pressure unit, 99, 100
Pipes, 51
   anti-siphonage, 44
   boss, 78, 79

Pipes—*contd.*
  capillary to B.S. 864, 79
  fittings, 53
  flow and return head, 51
  guides, 162
  insulation, 71
  joints, 52
  labourers' 53
  overflow, 44
  plates, 55
  sleeves, 55
  soil and ventilation, 44
  steel to BS 1387, 115
  threads, 114
  trenches, 74
  ventilation, 130
  warning, 94, 102
  waste, 44, 77
Pitch impregnated fibre, 80
  boss connections, 80
Plant room, 30, 42, 50
  tools, 28
Plastic, 80
Plugs, 55
Pneumatic booster sets, 89, 91
  tube installation, 45
Polythene, 165
  tube, 88, 89, 165, 168, 169
  and polypropylene cisterns, 95
Post-contract stage, 20
Power cables, 190
  final sub-circuits, 189
Practical completion, 33
Pre-contract cost control, 15
Pre-fabricated work, 43
Pre-heaters, 130
Preliminaries, 20, 32
  bill, 29, 31
  cost plan, 9, 10
  drawings, 9
Presentation, 41
Pressed steel tanks, 94, 95
Pressurizing units, 60
Priceable headings, 27
Priced bill of quantities, 18
  Bill of Variation, 25
  sub-contract Bill of Quantities, 25
  errors in priced Bill of Quantities, 18
Prime cost sums, 40, 199
  movers, 58, 63, 64, 67
Procedure, 34
Production information, 15
Profit, 29

Programme, 28
  and progress chart, 34
Protection and risk of damage, 33, 41, 43, 75
Provision for expansion, 116
  of water, 28
Provisional Quantities, 199
  sums, 199
Public address system, 195
Pull bends, 88
Pumps, 63, 93, 97, 98, 99, 100, 109, 126, 127
  circulating, 125
  in-line, 125
  traps, 64
Purchase tax, 35
PVC stacks, 78
  BS 3505, 88
Pylons and poles, 75

Qualified supervisor, 26
  surveyor, 25, 30
Quotations, 200

Radiant panels, 121, 124
Radiators, 66, 118
Rainwater heads, 55
  installation, 44
Raystrip, 124
Reading gauges, 129
Recommendations on billing, 42
Record, 199
  drawings, 25, 26
  material, plant, time, 199
Reducers – eccentric, 53
  concentric, 53
Redundancy payments, 35
Reel, 99
Refractory linings to flues, 72
Refrigerators, 10
  apparatus, 66
  installation, 45
Refuse disposal, 45
Reliability, 9
Remeasurement, 199
Removable grease filters, 154
Resaleability, 9
Resident engineer, 26
Restrictions, 28
Retention money, 25, 27
Right of access, 28
  of main and sub-contractor, 24
Rising main busbars, 180
Roll media, 65

Rollers, chairs, 163
'Roll-Kleen' filters, 157
Roof-outlets, 55
    ventilators, 58
Room thermostats, 124

Sanitary accommodation, 32
    fittings, 44, 81, 86
Scaffolding, 28, 32
Schedules, 39
    of rates, 5
Screw to wall, 94
Sealing boxes, 176, 177
Seamless steel butt welding, 115
Sectionalization, 44
Selected firms, 20
Selective employment tax, 32, 35
Service governor, 134
Set-off, 28
Setting out, 33
Shower trays, 84
Shutters, 58
Single cash column bill paper, 29
    phase, 47
Sink cleaner, 82
    fireclay, 81
    stainless steel, 82
Site, 29, 30
    adjoining premises, 33
    cleanliness, 33
    means of access, 30, 34
    police regulations, 30
    taking over date, 33
    traffic restrictions, 30
    working area, 30
Sleeve, 136
Sluice valves, 100, 101
Socket outlets and spur units, 191
Soot-blowing equipment, 61
Sound distribution, 47
Special equipment, 45
    interim payment, 27
    services, 47
Specification, 24, 27, 31, 39, 41, 199
    engineers, 40
Spun-iron to BS 1211, 88, 89
Stacks, 78
Standard Form of Building Contract, 19, 20, 22, 23, 28, 31, 32, 40, 48, 200
    building sub-contract, 29
        amendments, 24
        estimate for Nominated Sub-contractor, 19, 31, 33, 43

form of tender, 25
    method of measurement for building works, 28, 29, 32, 33, 36, 38, 39, 41, 42, 43, 48
    sliding expansion joints, 117
Steam generators, 60
    and condensate installation, 45
    traps, 70
Stopcock, 93, 100, 101
    valve, 89
Storage cisterns, 101
    of plant, 32
    tank, 89
    vessel, 104, 105
Strainers, 93
Study of cost control, 5
Sub-contract, 29, 198
    conditions, 31
    documents, 30
    works, 30
Sub-contractors' drawings, 37
    liability, 27
    staff, 35
    supervision, 26
Sub-letting, 28, 34
Sub-mains, 47
    distribution, 179
    distribution boards, 178
    distribution cables, 178, 179
    for power, light, etc., 10
    switchboards, 178
    termination of cables, 179, 180
Sub-station, 175
    equipment and control gear, 46
Supervision, 33
Supplementary rules of measurement, 41
    clauses, 28
Supply only, 76
    and fix, 76
    ventilation, 174
Supports and anchors, 45, 162, 163
Switch, 131
    fuse, 177, 178
    gear, 10
Syphon box, 133

Tanks, 61, 89, 93, 94, 107
Tap off units, 180, 181
Telephone, 47, 192
    trunking, 10
Temperature regulator, 105
Temporary offices, 35, 36
    telephone, 36

INDEX

Temporary workshops, 28
Tender, 17, 18, 21
  documents, 18, 19, 24, 28, 31, 40
  list of, 17
  list of received, 18
  lowest, 17, 18
  negotiated reduction, 18
  notifying results, 18
  opening, 18
  selected firms, 20
  standard Form, 25
Tenderers, 27
  number, 19
Tendering – competitive selective, 21
  parity of, 35
  procedure, 28
  time for, 18, 19
  two-stage procedures, 20
Terminals, 56, 58
Terms, 36
Test programme, 40
  pressures, 60
Testing, 36, 81, 136
  and commissioning, 41, 43
  facilities, 30
  of materials, 30
  water, 81
Thermal insulation, 171
Thermometers, 70, 105, 106
Thermostat, 106
Thimbles, 55
Thin wall tubing to BS 4127, 170
Time and wage sheets, 35
Time delay unit, 91
  switch, 100
Towel rails, 109
Town gas, 113
Transformers, 10, 46, 176
Traps, 55, 77, 80, 86
Travelling time, 32
Treated water installation, 44
Trunking, 47
  overhead busbar, 182
  plastic skirting, 182
  pressed metal, 182
  pressed metal cable, 182
  pressed metal floor, 182
  pressed metal lighting, 183
Tundishes, 56
Two-stage tendering procedures, 20

Unions, 54, 106
Unit cookers, 64, 120, 121

Urinals, 84
Use by local authorities, 22

Valuation, 25
  fair, 25
  interim, 32
  of variation, 25
Valves, 69, 93, 100, 116, 118
  ball, 93, 94, 101, 102, 114
  blending, 84
  check, 101
  fire, 131
  flanged, 94
  free fall, 131
  gate, 101, 106
  isolating, 94, 109
  landing, 96, 100, 103
  lockshield isolating, 105
  mixing and blenders, 69
  reducing sets, 70
  regulating, 109, 116
  release, 91, 96
  relief, 106
  safety, 105, 106
  sluice, 100, 101
  thermostatic mixing, 101
Variations, 24, 25, 27, 35, 198, 199, 200
Ventilation pipes, 130
Vibration, 126
Viscous filter, 151
Voltmeter, 176
Volume control, 156
Vouchers, 25

Wages, 28
Waste stack, 77
Water authorities, 30
  meter, 68, 93, 105
  tanks, 61
  test, 81
  treatment plant, 60
W.C. branch, 78
  pan, 82, 83
Welding, 74
Welfare facilities, 32
Wet riser installation, 96, 97
Witness inspected, 59
Working charge hand, 26
Works, 29, 30
Wrought pipe fittings, 115
  iron tubes, 115